CRYSTAL & DRAGON

CRYSTAL & DRAGON

THE COSMIC TWO-STEP

DAVID WADE

A Resurgence Book

First published in 1991 by
Green Books
Ford House, Hartland
Bideford, Devon EX39 6EE

Typeset by Neal's Yard Desktop Publishing, London
and Presentation Computer Graphics, Ross-on-Wye, Herefordshire

Printed by
Hartnolls Ltd, Victoria Square
Bodmin, Cornwall

British Library Cataloguing-in-Publication Data

Wade, David
Crystal & Dragon: The Cosmic Two-Step.
I. Title
113.093

ISBN 1 870098 07 2

CONTENTS

This book is dedicated to

Gini – for her patient support and encouragement throughout

Ann – for her work in committing the book to disc, and for her invaluable grammatical advice and criticism

Nick – for laying out and typesetting the whole thing

The author and publishers wish to acknowledge with thanks the use of the following material:

Aris & Phillips for an illustration from *Canon and Proportion in Egyptian Art* by Eric Iverson, 1975, on page 198.

The British Museum for illustrations from *Flowers in Art from East and West,* on pages 258 & 271; and for illustrations on pages 189 and 230.

The British Library for illustrations on pages 55 and 231.

Brookhaven National Laboratory, USA, for the illustration on page 47.

Curtis Brown on behalf of the Estate of Mr Lin Yutang for extracts from *A Chinese Theory of Art* by Lin Yutang (London, William Heinemann).

Munich Planetarium for the illustration on page 28.

Paul Popper Ltd for the use of a photograph of Max Planck, on page 93.

Preface

'The visible world is neither matter nor spirit but the invisible organisation of energy.' Heinz R Pagels

This book began life as a series of talks around the general subject of order and disorder, talks that were themselves inspired by an earlier preoccupation with the themes of symmetry and asymmetry in art. These topics still constitute the main subject matter of the present work, but in the process of laying out my ideas a more extensive and somewhat grander thesis emerged, namely that of a dualistic interpretation of nature. A casual glance at the contents of this book shows that it deals with both art and science subjects, but the underlying intention is to present a fresh way of looking at the world. The reader should not, however, anticipate a sustained, sequential argument of its basic propositions; in fact each chapter is fairly self-contained, in line with the original talks, and the progression, such as it is, is rather that of an elliptical tour around the central theme. As far as possible I have tried to retain the free-wheeling style of the lectures, an approach that involves a great many diversions and general meanderings. In fact the only consistency that I can claim is that each subject that is dealt with is intended finally to contribute to the central proposition, which is that of a complementary dualism of form and energy, principles for which the 'crystal' and 'dragon' of the title are metaphors.

David Wade
Llanidloes, Powys
June 1991

Introduction

Many people today are famed and respected for their ability to provide instant, one-sided opinions on any given subject. They sound off in the press or argue their cases on television, never conceding a point to their opponents or showing any sign of doubt in the rightness of whatever they are upholding. The cause of their popularity is the media convention that gladiatorial debates, where the object is to champion a particular viewpoint against others, is more entertaining than a discussion which aims towards agreement. No one expects two boxers to make peace in the middle of a bout.

A similar convention prevails in politics, to the extent that politicians claim credit for never changing their views and take pride in the consistency of their opinions over a lifetime.

These attitudes reflect those of 19th-century scientists, who assumed that the secrets of the universe were imminently within human grasp and competed fiercely to establish their own schools of thought as the orthodoxy of the future.

Since that time, the scientific world-view has changed radically. Its very founder, the god of Certainty, has fallen victim to the 'uncertainty principle', and its foundation stone, materialism, has been proved to have no substance. As science cautiously progresses, under the guidance of modern physics, towards the Pythagorean world-view and the dicta of traditional philosophy, the rest of the world is left in suspense – a kind of cosmological limbo. Science has disclaimed Certainty; so too has the Church; and it is up to individuals to make up their own minds and form opinions for themselves.

No wonder fundamentalism is flourishing! Nor is it surprising that the vain and greedy, the cheats and liars, the most stupid and implausible of con-men can become public figures and attract a respectable following. We are brought up to form and flaunt opinions, to know what is wrong and what is right and to oppose the first in the name of the second. Certainty is required, and if the bishops and professors are unable to provide it, it will be sought elsewhere – in the cheapjack market of bullies, blusterers and crackpot revivalists.

This is the background to the publication of *Crystal & Dragon*. As Certainty vanishes from view and the conventional pseudo-certainties of education seem increasingly banal, the temptations of irrationality grow stronger. This book offers the most powerful alternative. David Wade is completely unperturbed by the current process of transition. He recognises it, accepts its implications and specifies the inevitable and very major adjustments to the currently held world-view which the transition must bring about.

Obviously and by definition the universe is all-inclusive. It includes all the logical opposites, positive and negative, the limited and the unlimited, darkness and light, reason and romance, order and chaos. It is, indeed, a creature of opposites, a total paradox which can only be proved to exist by virtue of the fact that it actually does so. Science today is looking for a

Theory of Everything (TOE) which will explain in coherent mathematical terms the inter-relationship of the forces which underlie the physical universe. Yet, as David Wade points out, such a construct would explain almost nothing about everyday experience. Therein, as in the world generally, paradox reigns. As Plato showed in *Parmenides*, every statement one can make about the universe has its antithesis which is equally true. Similarly, on the mundane level, every small decision one takes is a resolution between opposite possibilities. On the one hand... on the other hand: that is the data from which we proceed; and it is the same throughout nature. Not even the humblest atomic particle deigns to be predictable. We admire modern science and are awe-struck by its achievements, and we may also admire the truth and beauty in ancient philosophy. But have these systems actually explained anything? Do we really know anything about this state of existence in which, for a limited period, we happen to find ourselves?

Well, we do and we don't. That is the sort of answer which, as David Wade reminds us, we must learn to live with. On the one hand, nothing for sure is known and we can find philosophical firm ground in universal nescience. On the other hand there are certain objective truths, available to and recognised by people of all times and cultures. They begin with number and extend into music and geometry and the harmonising of life generally. The study of number in its cosmological aspect, as a paradigm of Creation, is associated in the West with Pythagoras, but the science and philosophy which we call Pythagorean was practised long before his time, in ancient Egypt, Babylon, China and all the great civilizations of antiquity. At the root of the ancient system was a comprehensive, organic world-view which modern science, over the last 300 years or so, has totally rejected. Only a few years ago, Pythagorean notions were seen as unquestionably outmoded and were studied, if at all, as curious relics of a primitive mentality. Now we know better – or, at least, differently. As modern physicists feel their way into the forgotten world of Pythagorean perceptions, we catch the pendulum in the act of swinging and glimpse a process which, in more certain times, when the dominant world-view holds total sway over human minds and senses, is hidden from us. We see the process of transition. On one pole is scientific materialism; on the other is Pythagorean number mysticism. Surely, since these are on opposite poles and represent two opposite approaches to nature, they can not logically co-exist. One must be right and the other wrong.

That is precisely the style of logic which David Wade is most concerned to refute. As a man of his times, living in the current period of transition, he can see both sides of the divide and seems equally at home in each of them. The two poles co-exist and form, as it were, a magnetic field which represents the complete potential range of human perception. Like nature, philosophy is ruled by symmetry, every concept having its antithesis or complementary opposite. There is nothing wrong in Creation itself, only in the way we perceive and understand it. A partial, one-sided view of things is wrong, because the information it conveys is imperfect and the result is misunderstanding and strife. In principle, therefore, it is right to cultivate the wider view which recognises the two opposites.

Here, of course, as the sharp reader will have noticed, we seem to be caught upon the horns of our own philosophy. A magnetic field has been set up, with the one-sided and the comprehensive viewpoints forming its two poles. Must we then admit that one-sidedness too has its place? Yes indeed! There may be times when an extreme, partisan attitude is temporarily right and necessary. This occurs when one particular viewpoint has become exaggeratedly predominant and demands an emphatic reaction by way of corrective.

The art of navigating one's way through life is thus seen as a matter of proportion and balance. This gives a new relevance to the ancient system in which the acquisition of a sense of proportion was the chief object of education. As the best means to this, Plato recommends the study of number and the numerical science (astronomy, geometry and music). Therein lies the key to the art of balancing opposites, to refining one's instincts towards doing the right thing, and these are the abilities which distinguish great artists and great statesmen.

By reintroducing us to the Pythagorean world of number and pattern, David Wade anticipates the coming synthesis of traditional philosophy and modern science which will effectively amount to a new world order. This is surely the best that any modern writer can do. This writer is merely saying what many other people are now thinking, but he is well equipped to express it. In a modest, matter-of-fact, twentieth-century manner, David Wade highlights the few given facts of our existence, reviews them in the context of both the modern and the ancient scientific traditions and points to the inevitable, common-sense conclusions. One can not help learning from this book, and the education it provides is highly reassuring. We are shown how the present age of transition can proceed in a more or less orderly way, avoiding the much predicted horrors and cataclysms. From the doctrines of modern physics to those of the perennial philosophy is a short step; and it is an easy step for anyone to take because it is guided by nature. It requires no new system of belief, nor does it devalue present knowledge. The scientific approach not only retains its validity but gains new relevance within the comprehensive world-view which is here advocated. In the following chapters we leave behind us the world of competitiveness and reaction and are led towards the higher reality where every element in Creation enjoys its rightful place and contributes to the universal harmony.

John Michell

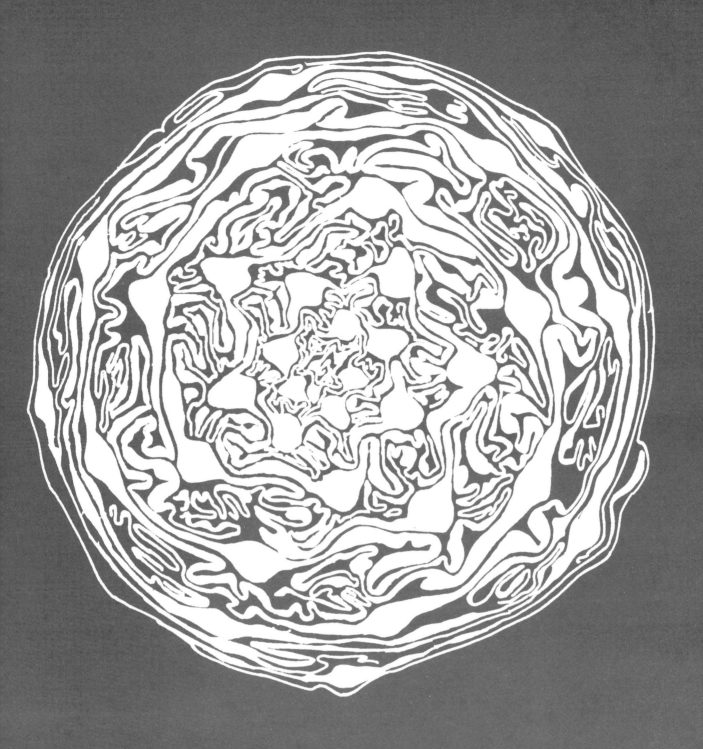

1
Things and processes

All About Everything

In the very near future it is fully expected that scientists will deliver up a Theory of Everything. When this goal is reached (and much of the theory is already in place) we will have got to the very heart of matter, to the middle of the onion as it were. The realisation of a TOE, as it has become known, will be tremendously important since it promises an explanation of the underlying physical processes involved in everything that has happened since the very beginning of time! Clearly the attainment of a TOE will be something of a milestone since it will amount to a declaration that a complete understanding has been reached of all the various kinds of particles that make up the 'stuff' of the universe and of the forces that move them around. It will represent the culminating achievement of a body of knowledge the foundation of which was laid way back in the early history of civilisation, beginning perhaps when some long forgotten group of priest-scribes managed to predict an eclipse for the first time.

But the Theory of Everything will not *really* be about *everything;* the term is itself more than a little tongue-in-cheek. A scientist armed with a fully developed TOE could not, for instance, predict whether or not I would be going to my aunt's for tea on Saturday – even if he did come up with a forecast, I could act contrarily. It is now perfectly understood that not everything can be predicted with the same degree of certainty with which it is possible to make the calculations necessary to predict an eclipse, or to work out the future movements of the planets and a great deal else. We have been very successful at finding out how nature works, but it has also been realised, though only relatively recently, that there are definite limits to prediction. It is curious that it should be more difficult to predict next week's weather than to put a man on the moon, but it appears that whilst both undertakings are extremely complicated the former is impossibly so.

The matter of complexity and the limitations of the scientific method are topics that I shall be returning to, but the point that I am trying to make here is that fundamental laws, such as the TOE, do not necessarily explain the details of phenomena; in fact they rarely do. Even when a prominent physicist assures us that at the foundational level there are 'no things, only processes', we still have to walk around furniture rather than through it. The layman, who may easily feel that he is about to be short-changed by science, might well ask: If the Theory of Everything is not about absolutely everything, what exactly is it about? The answer is that it is a sort of modern creation story. In the beginning of spacetime there was, for some reason, a very hot, very big bang. The enormous power released by this event separated out, for some reason, into four different forces, which then shaped everything that ever was and that ever will be. The latest, and possibly the final, consensus, is that there are twelve fundamental particles, in groups of quarks and leptons, and as many corresponding antiparticles. The interactions between all of these are governed by four fundamental forces: the weak and strong nuclear, the electromagnetic and the gravitational. It is expected of the TOE that it will describe in one grand theory all possible interactions between all of these particles. Now this is a somewhat sketchy account of what will undoubtedly prove to be the greatest collective intellectual accomplishment of this or any previous century, but as an outsider one could be forgiven for feeling that for all its prodigious achievement the TOE as a description of everything seems in danger of overlooking something rather important in the scheme of things, and that is the essentially creative potential of nature: it does not venture to account for the original, creative act of the Big Bang, nor does it explain what must surely be the most impressive aspect of the creative continuum, its tendency towards ever more complex forms of organisation.

I do not want to appear to be peddling a fashionably anti-science line here; in my view this is a disingenuous attitude. In terms of the acquisition of knowledge the scientific method has been enormously successful, and in many ways it already presents a complete description of the world we live in. We now know how big the universe is, how old it is, the elements that it is composed of, how these came into being and how they are distributed, how living things are different from non-living things, etc. Most importantly a systematic approach to natural phenomena has been developed which allows constant refinement of their description in ever greater detail. In spite of this many intelligent people are beginning to suspect that the universe is so constructed that there will *always* be further mysteries to be uncovered by scientific enquiry.

We can build bigger telescopes to see further across the universe, and bigger accelerators to probe ever deeper into it; we can also expect new theories to come up with entirely new ways of looking at the things with which we are already familiar. If, as seems increasingly likely, the universe is infinitely complicated, we can expect continued questioning and posing of hypotheses for a very long time to come. Since we are obviously not as complicated as the universe itself there seems no immediate danger that we will ever actually get to know all about everything, and in the meantime, the big question — of ultimate causation — is still an open one.

It is clear that the rise of science, with the sceptical and materialistic leanings of its practitioners, has presented a serious challenge to older-established beliefs in practically every part of the world. Atheistic tendencies were well established by the end of the eighteenth century, when they were epitomised by the mathematician Laplace who, when asked by Napoleon where God fitted into his universal scheme, replied 'I have no need of such a hypothesis.' This development does not appear to have diminished the basic human need for a foundational belief system, as is well testified to by the current vogue for religious revivalism and experimentation. But it has brought about a certain aetiological irresolution: although we know a great deal more about the cosmos than ever before there is probably less conviction now than at any time in the past as to its *primum mobile,* the nature of the principles which brought it into being.

Although the notion of a single, omniscient creator has been eroded by the advance of social secularisation there is something of a reluctance to adopt the atheistic alternative that paints a picture of a universe driven by blind, purposeless forces. The monotheistic argument that a grand design is inconceivable without a designer is as valid as it ever was, but so also are the traditional objections – why should a perfect creator have created such an imperfect world? There is a sense in which this dilemma is actually held in place with attitudes that are formed by an abiding cultural monotheism; it is this influence too that inclines us to discount one of the most obvious 'solutions', that of a causal duality. Which brings us to the point of the present work; insofar as it has a central theme this book sets out to re-examine the notion of a dualistic interpretation of phenomena, an outlook which though unfamiliar to the western mind is regarded in other parts of the world as being as 'natural' and established a mode of thought as that of our perception of a single, original creative principle.

Invariance and Uncertainty

The scientific approach, taking things apart to see what they are made of, is very good for developing understanding but, historically, there has always been a tendency to overlook the important integrative qualities of nature. Within scientific enquiry the impulse has always been analytical and reductionist; these methods have been rewarded with astonishing success, but they are also responsible for a persistent shortcoming, namely the failure to see that a system as a whole may have qualities over and above those that are apparent from an analysis of its respective parts. The basic laws of quantum theory, for instance, underlie most physical and all chemical interactions, including all the complexities of animate existence, even those of thought and consciousness; but these higher functions cannot, in any way, be explained by such fundamental physical laws, and certainly could not be predicted by them.

'As far as I can see all a priori *statements in physics have their origins in symmetry.'*

Hermann Weyl

There is now a movement within the scientific world itself that seriously questions these deep-seated reductionist tendencies. In fact the very term now tends to be used rather disparagingly. However, this development raises the interesting question as to why science evolved in this way in the first place. We can safely say that the study of science is a specifically human activity. Man, in common with others of the higher primates, has a natural nit-picking curiosity, but although sheer curiosity has always been a strong stimulus to the study of science there has also been a more purposeful intention. The primary function is that of pattern recognition, which is to say concern with the *invariant* aspects of nature.

Science began as an almost magical process, of the extrication of regularities from the chaotic continuum of natural phenomena. The ability to plot the wayward habits of the 'wandering' stars, the planets, is likely to have been among the first of all genuinely scientific discoveries. A process that probably began as a simple celestial accountancy rapidly became a potent predictive tool in the hands of the earliest star-watching priests. Gradually more and more of nature succumbed to this reductionist magic. Natural phenomena that had so often seemed wilful and unpredictable were found to contain mysterious and profound regularities, a fact that must have made the deepest impression on the minds of early civilised man.

Science has developed in parallel with mathematics. It is hard to imagine an advanced science without an equally well-developed maths, but from a purely objective viewpoint it does seem remarkable that nature should respond so well to number, especially if one is inclined to regard the latter as a purely abstract concept, a construct of the human mind. The precise relation of physical laws to mathematics is a matter that has continued to intrigue scientific thinkers right up to the present time. Paul Dirac, one of the founders of quantum theory, once declared that God must have used 'beautiful mathematics' to create the world. The great nineteenth-century physicist Hertz felt that mathematical formulae might have 'an independent existence and an intelligence of their own'. Can the language of mathematics ever provide a complete and definitive description of nature? Certainly one of its primary objectives is to extract what order it can from the complexity of nature, but many of the more interesting developments of recent physics seem to indicate a definite limitation to this process. As we shall see, the old deterministic attitude of science, what might be called the clockwork view of the world, has been steadily superseded throughout the course of this century, and it now seems far less likely that either nature or mathematics are orderly in any absolute sense.

Certainty and Indeterminacy

These days we are becoming increasingly familiar with the scientific view of the atomic underworld, and with the demand that our ordinary perception of 'substance' should give way to more abstruse notions of particulate 'events' when thinking about matter at this level. The past few decades have seen a revolution in scientific thought that has transformed perceptions of the nature of the physical world, but this has had surprisingly little effect on our general, day-to-day experience of reality. The world does seem much the same place in spite of our being told that it is actually made up of various aggregations of infinitesimal particles, though it must be admitted that atomist theories have been around for a very long time. However there are implications in the new physics, at work yeast-like in society, that are bound to have a profound effect on the way that all of us will see the world in the future. It is one thing to be told that everything we see consists of infinitely small components, but rather more disturbing to realise that these entities consist of little more than 'organised energy', and that ultimately the familiar phenomenal world of our sense-experience can only be explained in terms of an interaction between two equally indeterminate principles, of *form* and *energy*.

'The staggering theories of Einstein, Heisenberg, Planck, Eddington and Dirac on the structure of the atom and the universe have projected the new task for the philosophers not only of today, but of generations to come.'

Heinrich Zimmer in
Philosophies of India.

During the course of this century there has been a major shift of emphasis in physics, away from older positions that built a hard-edged structure of classical certainties, towards a more 'fuzzy' interpretation of nature, an emphasis that is more concerned with those 'patterns of probability' which have emerged from a background of restless and erratic particulate activity. Naturally this change of focus has had to be accompanied by a fairly substantial review of its philosophical base. There has been little sense of any crisis of confidence in this re-evaluation – the impressive achievements of modern science have saved it from that – but since the quantum revelations of the twenties and thirties and all the ensuing peculiarities of recent physics there has been a general feeling of the need for a new exegisis. Ever since the new theories began to question such well-established concepts as time, energy and matter itself it has been clear that any reassessment of its basic philosophical stance must be very fundamental indeed. In recent decades we have seen a re-examination of the deepest assumptions of the western scientific tradition; there has been a revival of interest in the earlier Greek philosophers and other metaphysical speculations, often mystical or religious, that are entirely outside the western tradition. Parallels have been drawn between the new interpretation of phenomena by scientists and the precepts of a whole range of eastern religious teachings, often very different to each other. It may be that many of the analogies and correspondences that have been found here have already been overstated; there are obvious dangers in forcing comparisons between the essentially technical nature of scientific observations and vaguer, often over-simplified, interpretations of 'eastern mysticism' for instance. At bottom though, this search is entirely valid since it is concerned to restore a sense of conceptual direction, an undertaking for which there is a clear need at the present time.

If there is one precept that we can extract from the history of ideas with any degree of certainty it is that nature is amenable to theories of all kinds, and any seriously held explanation can be supported – at least for a while. Only for a while because, as Heraclitus noted, nature loves to hide: the best we can do is to assemble a passable *modus operandi*. It is characteristic of the present era however that there should be a certain loss of bearing, a sort of ontological hiatus, of which the proliferation of decadent 'fundamentalisms' in various parts of the world are just one manifestation. But for all the influence that science and its technology have over our lives there is now a serious questioning of the direction in which they are leading us, and the strange and unsettling descriptions that emanate from the sharp end of contemporary physics often appear just as remote and irrelevant to everyday experience as the intricacies of some ancient cosmology. The point is that just to get around we need a firm grip on reality, and it is really of little practical use to be informed, either through science or mysticism, that matter is essentially a void, and apparent substantiality no more than the play of mysterious forces – even if it is true!

Permanence, Change and Complementarity

In speaking of the achievements of the earlier Greek philosophers Aristotle declared that 'It was wonder that first led men to philosophy; at first they wondered at the obvious puzzles, little by little they advanced to enquire into the larger problems.' *(Metaphysics)*. Aristotle's account of these early speculations conveys little of the sense of necessity that comes across in the surviving works. These thinkers were, after all, living at a time when a world view of great antiquity was under severe pressure; in fact the old gods were dying and a new interpretation of phenomena was urgently required. Although most of them were suspicious of the older, mythological explanations, those early philosophers had not yet made the distinction between religion and science. They were, however, tending to regard the gods less anthropomorphically, and rather more as the personification of natural forces.

Among the 'obvious' puzzles that faced the early Greek philosophers was the question of primal substance. What is the world made of? Remember that at this time there was no concept of matter or of the physical laws affecting it, and there was the allied problem of permanence and change. What is real and permanent in the universe? Thales of Miletus, generally recognised as the first philosopher, is thought to have identified the primal substance as water, believing all things to have been composed of water in different states. Anaximenes, on the other hand, believed that the basic raw material was air, and Heraclitus that it was fire. Since no-one had ever thought of these matters before these were, in their time, highly original speculations, and gradually led to a logical and distinctly scientific approach to problems, which of course was of great historical importance. In little more than a century after Thales, that is to say by the mid-fifth century BC, we find Empedocles propounding a system of elements, and Leucippus positing the existence of atoms! The resolution of the purely philosophical problems involved in reconciling the fixed and changing aspects of the world had an equally important role in establishing the basic outlook of western culture. In the early history of philosophy there were deep divergencies of view in these matters which, interestingly, came to be represented by a division between eastern and western schools of thought; the main protagonists being the followers of Heraclitus of Ephesus in Asia Minor, and those of Parmenides of Elea, in what is now southern Italy.

Heraclitus was the theoretician of the principle of change. His perception of the world was that of a place that was constantly and ceaselessly changing, of a universe of total flux. The only constant in this system was the principle of change itself. To illustrate his ideas on the nature of reality Heraclitus used the analogies of a flame and a river, both of which could be held to persist and yet to be in a state of constant change. It was he also who declared that it was impossible to step into the same river twice. There are interesting points of contact between this early Greek philosophy of change and that of Chinese Taoism, to which I shall be returning, noting

Change is certainly one of the more prominent features of the universe: weather pattern of the entire northern hemisphere.

in passing that this school was also fond of using the image of a flowing river as a metaphor for existence. A disciple of Heraclitus, one Cratyllus, was later to take his theory of change to extreme conclusions, as disciples are wont to do. Cratyllus came to the view that the principle of change was itself subject to change, declaring that it was impossible even to step into the same river once! Feeling the futility of any attempt to make sense of a universe in total flux, and resolving never to make a statement of whose truth he could not be *absolutely* certain, he, poor man, was reduced to simply wiggling his finger to acknowledge that he had been addressed. Any attempt to go beyond this was, in his view, bound to lead to confusion, since by the time one had finished answering any question everything would have changed, oneself, the meaning of one's words, even the questioner.

For Heraclitus permanence lay in the principle of the law of change itself rather than in any material substance.

Understandably this rather extreme hypothesis was to provoke a strong and, one might say, decisive reaction. Parmenides completely rejected the notion that change could be taken as a fundamental characteristic of the cosmos, and argued that only the permanent could be regarded as real. For him change and movement were simply unfortunate illusions; his catchphrase was 'Being is, non-being is not.' Parmenides is generally regarded as the first true logician, and in his almost exasperated response to the universal flux of the Heraclitean school one can detect the first steps towards the credo of analytical materialism that was later to become the hallmark of western scientific tradition. Parmenides also had a younger disciple who took the ideas of the master to extreme conclusions; Zeno was to achieve lasting fame for the series of paradoxes, 'Achilles and the Tortoise', ' The Arrow in Flight', etc., that he devised to demonstrate that the world of change could have nothing to do with the real and permanent world.

The impassioned debate between the respective proponents of change and permanence was of great significance to the development of western thought in two ways. From the point of view of the evolution of science it was important in that it led directly to the formation of early atomist theories. As the smallest, indivisible, constituents of the physical world, atoms themselves could be held to account for its permanent features; whilst their ceaseless movement, which created all the forms of the physical world, explained its essential impermanence. This elegant resolution, arrived at in the fifth century BC, and which seems so uncannily farsighted, is testimony to the intensity and rigour of these early speculations. The atom, which had been conjectured by pure abstract reasoning, had to wait for nearly two and a half thousand years for its validation.

There were broader implications of this dialectic: for reasons that will probably never be completely understood, the rational and logical approach of the Eleatic school came to exert a greater influence over Greek thought in general than that of the more intuitive philosophy of Heraclitus. Western science, with its impressive achievements and increasingly dominant role, traces back directly to the Parmenidean credo with its materialistic, objective and essentially reductionist attitudes towards natural phenomena. In the process though it simply buried many of the problems that were first raised by Heraclitus and these, in the late twentieth century, have come back to haunt it; now the very term 'reductionist' is one of opprobrium, and objectivity, in any absolute sense, is recognised as illusory.

As I have indicated, it was not only within the European philosophical tradition that there arose a separation between respective modes of thought that chose to emphasise either the fixed or the changing aspects of the world. At about the same time that this debate was taking place in Greece, arguments of a somewhat similar kind were being rehearsed in China. In China however the outcome was rather different, and the dialectic itself became 'institutionalised' as a dual, or complementary, system of thought. This came to be comprised of the co-existent philosophies of Confucianism and Taoism which were to hold sway for centuries in China, in spite of the fact that their ethos and world views were polarised in virtually every aspect.

The doctrines of the Confucians were characterised by a high regard for tradition, and they advocated sober and rational conduct in all matters; for them, virtue resided in principles that supported social stability. Taoism, by contrast, was essentially a philosophy of change; mystical and non-conformist, it was intensely sceptical of the value of laws of any kind as a regulating force in human affairs. It was, in fact, highly individualistic; Taoists tended to disdain human society, preferring instead to engage in the calm contemplation of nature.

This traditional division of attitudes and roles in Chinese society, which amounted to a sort of binary combination, can be seen to represent the almost archetypal differences of outlook that devolve, ultimately, to those differences between 'structuralist' and 'vitalist' views of the world. However, although it is true that each of these philosophies had its own thoroughly evolved and distinctive outlook, they were complementary rather than opposed. In fact if they are taken together, borrowing a term from contemporary physics, their views have a *complementarity*.

The notion of complementarity was one part of the strange new conception of the physical world that was necessary to bring about the quantum revolution: this was a term that virtually forced itself on the attention of the pioneer physicists as a means of accounting for the inexplicable contradictions in the behaviour of basic quanta such as electrons, which in some experiments appeared as particles and in others as waves, though never as both. It was Niels Bohr who resolved this dilemma with the proposal that there were in fact no particles or waves as such in nature, but that there existed a duality of wave-particles, or particle-waves, and that the particular aspect that was recognised depended entirely on the nature of the experiment set up to detect it. The most significant point of this discovery was that the arrangements that would be capable of detecting the existence of either particle or wave forms would, by the very terms of the new physics, be mutually exclusive. Heraclitus' assertion that there was no separate 'substance', that matter is rather a continuous 'process', finally came home to roost.

As Bohr himself quickly recognised, the notion of complementarity had philosophical implications that went far beyond the purely technical considerations of foundational physics. Indeed he was inclined to the view that the basic assumption of the notion of complementarity, that knowledge

'In order to measure space-coordinates and instants of time, rigid measuring rods and clocks are required. To measure moments and energies, arrangements with moveable parts are needed to take up and indicate the impact of the object. If quantum mechanics describes the interaction of the object and the measuring device, both arrangements are not possible.'
Max Born on the impossibility of measuring a wave-particle position and momentum simultaneously.

of one kind would naturally exclude knowledge of another, applied as a general principle, and in this of course he came very close to the position of the complementary duality of the Chinese system of two mutually interdependent creative principles, *ti* and *t'ien*.

The correspondence between the new quantum interpretation by science and certain precepts of eastern religious and philosophical traditions was first noted by the pioneering physicists themselves. It is difficult to assess what influence these older ideas may have had on the progress of science but their contribution was probably indirect and peripheral at most. Scientific enquiry had to find its own way, and its apparent convergence with more ancient perceptions of the construction of the world came essentially from its own internal development. Nevertheless there are striking analogies between the assumptions of new physics and those more spiritual insights that are concerned to transcend the 'illusion of the world of opposites'. There is a certain commonality of belief in some of the major eastern religious traditions, such as Hinduism, Buddhism and Taoism, that tends to view the cosmos as indivisible in any absolute sense, and regard it rather as a dynamic and perfectly interconnected continuum. According to such views even the best attempts to apprehend reality are destined to be partial and dualistic. In attempting to describe the world, even simply by being consciously aware of it, we run the risk of falling into the error of mistaking the description for the thing itself. This premise, which is central to many traditions of eastern thought, accords completely with the quantum contingencies of an observer-created reality. It is this notion of a universe without beginning, end or centre, and of which we can never be entirely detached observers, that really marks the separation of the new physics from traditional western thought with its preoccupation with causes and effects and the central role of a single creative principle (see Glossary).

Order and Disorder

According to Chinese dualistic cosmologies all the complexities of the phenomenal world are brought about by the play of two mutually interdependent creative principles, 'The Two Forces of Nature', but these principles themselves are perceived to be contained within a transcendent unity. This solution, it is worth pointing out, is utterly different from that of the more radical Persian dualisms which deny all possibility of reconciliation between their opposing elements. Strictly speaking the Chinese outlook is neither dualistic nor monistic according to western interpretations of these terms; its duality is in fact a harmonious unity, with neither aspect being complete in itself. Perhaps the best approach to this unaccustomed way of thinking is through the more familiar complementary dualities of order and disorder. All of us encounter ordered and disordered states as part of our everyday existence, indeed a great deal of everyone's time is devoted to imposing order of various sorts on a world that seems positively to resist it. We experience these states as manifestations of opposite tendencies and although it is clear that these are only relative conditions,

Even the model of flawless beauty, the diamond, presents the mingling of order and disorder that is found in every aspect of nature. Highly magnified detail of the surface of a diamond showing 'etch-pits'.

The 'disorderly' processes of the elements of wind, currents and tides often combine to create forms of surprising regularity.

that there is no absolute separation, we tend to feel that we can recognise order when we see it. Order is a state of regular arrangement, and disorder occurs when this arrangement is disturbed; but there is a complementarity here, because the sort of disorder that we find will depend entirely on the order that we set out to recognise in the first place. It is entirely a matter of the way we choose to slice reality: a tropical rain forest, for instance, can be seen as a totally chaotic environment or an exquisitely structured one, according to viewpoint.

When we speak of order and structure, or indeed of regularities of any kind, we are invoking the principle of symmetry. Symmetry is a *sine qua non*, an indispensable condition of existence since it is involved in the form of everything that can be held to exist, from atoms to galaxies. Symmetry as a subject has always been of interest both to the arts and to science, but in recent decades it has become an important concept in exploring the very foundation of physical being. In its essence symmetry is to do with the way that an object, or one or other aspect of an object, remains unchanged through various transformations. This is a somewhat technical matter that will be investigated in a later chapter of this book, but symmetry also has an undeniable aesthetic appeal. In fact a symmetrical regularity of appearance is perhaps one of the more identifiable aspects of beauty, which otherwise is a notoriously difficult quality to define. Most of us will have been struck, at some time or another, by the appearance of a particular example of natural symmetry. Even the most unobservant individual can be moved by the delicate precision of a sea shell, or the meticulous structure of a pine cone. When we chance on such things we are instinctively impressed, not simply by the attractive qualities of a particular example, but also by the occurrence of such regularities in nature at all.

'The universe from its very beginnings to the present may be viewed as a hierarchy of successively broken symmetries.'
Heinz Pagels

It is clear that symmetries of many kinds can convey a strong aesthetic impression, but it is not so easy to determine precisely what it is that we are responding to. How is it, for instance, that a few pieces of coloured glass can be converted by a kaleidoscope into an endless series of intriguing patterns? And what is it exactly that is so engaging about the orderly, geometric arrangements of so many plant forms? The answer, I believe, is that in contemplating the more obvious symmetries of this sort our perceptual focus is directed towards the ordering principle itself. All

Symmetry is the basis of order, however it presents itself.

symmetrical arrangements, whether in nature or art, evoke this principle and serve to remind us of its omnipresence throughout the whole fabric of existence. Nature is thoroughly permeated with the regularities of symmetry and pattern at all levels, but this sense of universal order only occasionally claims our attention; in general it is occluded by the sheer complexity of phenomena. As powerful as it is, the tendency towards order in nature seems subject to perpetual disturbance. This is the way things are; at bottom everything depends on some element of order, and therefore of symmetry, but nothing is ever *perfectly* ordered.

Order and disorder are entirely relative terms, and are not separable in any absolute sense: a decrease in order is exactly the same thing as an increase in disorder. Moreover it would appear that neither condition can ever entirely displace the other. Surprisingly though it is only in fairly recent decades that science has admitted this last observation to the higher reaches of physics: it is not long since it was believed that perfectly ordered and completely chaotic states of matter could and did exist. The present view is nothing like as simple. Evidence of disorder can be found in even that most regular of natural arrangements, the atomic array, and order in various guises seems to appear in conditions that had previously been thought of as total molecular chaos.

The gradual uncovering of this state of affairs has been of enormous significance to the development of physics and has, in the process, led to the formulation of a range of new and important laws that explain phenomena in terms of changes of degrees and modes of order. In fact the whole area of the physical transition between relatively ordered and disordered phases, such as that of solid to liquid, liquid to gas, unmagnetised to magnetised etc., has become a new focus of attention for physicists, one that has proved highly productive, not least because of its relevance to many advanced technological processes. Some molecular transformations can, of course, be quite dramatic, such as when water freezes into ice (especially if it bursts one's pipes!), but the overview that is emerging from contemporary physics is predominantly that of a whole spectrum of conditions that are able to establish an equilibrium between a formalising, ordering tendency on the one hand and a disruptive or energising principle on the other. Moreover it appears that things have always been this way: the picture we are getting from modern cosmologists is one of a world that has from its very beginning presented all the features of a disturbed pattern of events, with time, space and matter itself now being seen as a magnificent succession of broken symmetries.

'A truly elementary particle, one completely devoid of internal structure, could not be subject to any forces that would allow us to detect its existence. The mere knowledge of a particle's existence, that is to say, implies that the particle possesses internal structure.'
Geoffrey Chew

In most phenomena one may observe a compromise between two opposing tendencies: that towards the achievement of a stable equilibrium, i.e. towards order; and another towards the most probable distribution characteristics of particles in thermal motion, i.e. towards disorder.

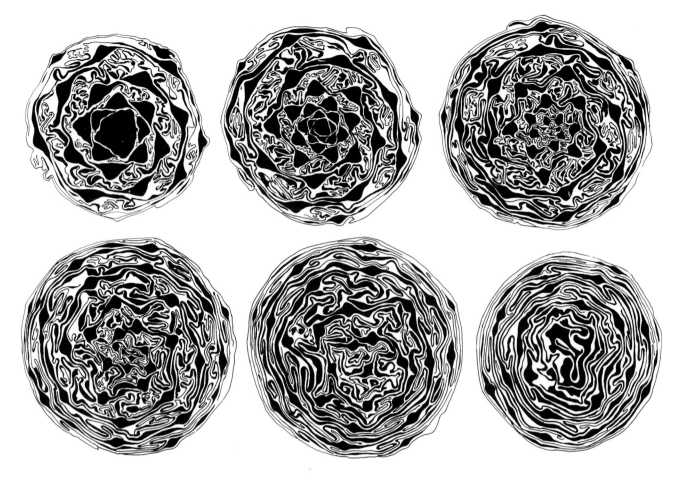

Successive slices through a cabbage reveal a gradual transition through a spectrum of order/disorder.

Pattern and Dissolution

The terms of this book, of a manifest duality of form and energy, should, I hope, be emerging by now. We have seen that order and disorder are not absolute but entirely relative expressions, and that the same criteria apply to the notions of symmetry and asymmetry. For a thing to exist at all, or at least for us to experience its existence, which amounts to the same thing, it must have a structure and therefore a symmetry or, more likely, a compound of symmetrical relations. We would also expect this symmetry, however it is presented, to be disturbed. These are the conditions of existence to be found at whatever level we choose to slice reality, whether we disect an atomic nucleus in a physics laboratory or a cabbage on the kitchen table. So let us turn, for the moment, to the latter, more homely example. We are all familiar with the structure of the common cabbage with its large outer leaves enclosing the inner in a tightly packed succession; the form, in fact, is that of a greatly enlarged terminal bud. If we gradually section the vegetable from the bottom, thin slice by thin slice, a gradual transition is revealed, from an ordered, almost geometrical arrangement at the base, through graduations of increasing intricacy and complexity to a sort of swirling confusion at the top. It is not too fanciful to imagine that this progression might make a short but interesting piece of movie footage. The ordered end of this sequence derives from the inherent geometrical regularities of the leaf distribution pattern of the plant, its *phyllotaxy*. As we progress through the sections this orderly arrangement is gradually overthrown by the jostling, space-seeking action of individual leaves. By the time we reach the top there is little trace of the neat spiral arrangement that we had at the beginning, or indeed of any sign of order at all, other than a vague concentric configuration.

Naturally all cabbages will show the same sort of progression, though each will have individual variations. This is just what we would expect from plants: minute differences of soil and weather conditions contribute to an essentially unpredictable process of individuation. Every section of every cabbage will present a profile that is as unique as a fingerprint, and one could not predict with any degree of certainty the configuration of any one section. The point of this botanical digression is that just about everything is like this; there is an infinite variety of ordered conditions, but no perfect order. By the same token, in all the states of disorder in the universe there is not one that is utterly devoid of form; there will always be some trace of order in a given condition, however tenuous.

The universe is perfectly differentiated in all its parts, down to the most minute detail, but it is not, by most objective criteria, perfect in any other way. However, it is certainly complicated. Not only does the cosmos manifest all manner of forms, and every degree of dissolution of those forms, but it seems that these ordered and disordered conditions are constantly and freely transposing, one to the other. As confident as we might be that we can recognise certain organised features in the world, we can be sure that even its most abiding aspects will ultimately pass away; even the mountains will pass like clouds. However decay and disintegration are not the only, or even the dominant, forces in nature; it is as often the case that regular forms are the product of random forces as the other way round, and of course a 'formation' of one kind may be a 'dissolution' of another – this is what happens every time we eat a meal.

Though all conditioned things seem to occupy a place somewhere between the absolutes of order and chaos we have to remind ourselves again that in the real world these terms are complementary, that the very notion of disorder relies on that of order, and vice versa. The terms are relative, but it is entirely natural for us to try to impose a pattern on events, to seek for explanations in the world of appearances. The term 'pattern' itself crops up fairly often in ordinary speech; we talk of weather patterns, of behavioural patterns, patterns of events, of speech etc. In all of these usages there is the implication of a recognisable, orderly array, a repetitious

Every part of the universe, in its most minute detail, is differentiated. This dragonfly wing has the vein structure characteristic of its species, but it is also bound to have features that are unique to itself.

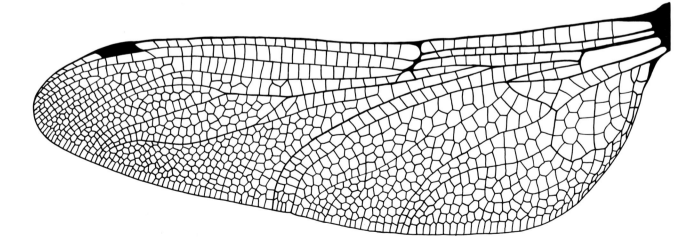

structure in other words. The common factor in a pattern, of whatever kind, is this recurrence, which in itself implies a certain predictability. All enduring conditions are structured in one sense or another. Just as a cultural style is sustained by the collective observation of social customs and laws, and language by deference to the constraints of grammar, so even elementary particles have their delimiting symmetries. An entity without structure and without symmetry is inconceivable.

Planetary symmetries: The paths of the planets as viewed from Earth
Illustration: Munich Planetarium.

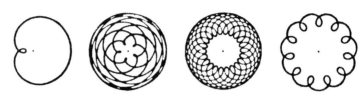

It is this universal structuring and formative tendency that binds atoms together and, under certain conditions, orders them into greater cohesion to form solid matter; that is responsible for building up the great hierarchies of structure which culminate in all the complexities of living organisms; that regulates the grand, orderly progression of the stars and their planets within the galaxies. However all structures are vulnerable to change, and against any order there are arrayed all the forces of disintegration, dissolution, erosion and decay. Quite understandably the contemplation of this cosmic hustle and bustle has preoccupied man ever since he has been capable of formulating abstract thought. As we have seen, the problem of reconciling the apparently fixed with the obviously changing aspect of nature was a matter of the greatest concern to the earlier philosophers, not only of our own but of other traditions. How could anything be thought of as existing, in the sense that we ordinarily experience things, when all things manifest such obviously conflicting features?

'A rhythm involves a pattern, and, to that extent is always self-identical. But no rhythm can be a mere pattern, for the rhythmic quality depends equally upon the differences involved in each exhibition of the pattern. The essence of rhythm is the fusion of sameness and novelty, so that the whole never loses the essential unity of the pattern, while the parts exhibit the contrast arising from the novelty of their detail.'
Alfred North Whitehead

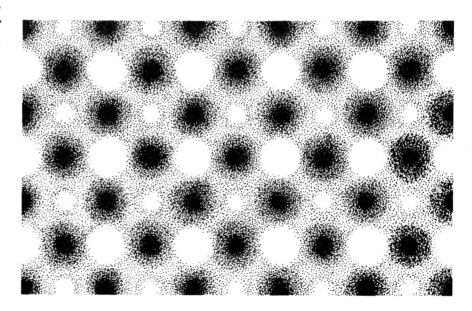

The atomic array (zirconium and oxygen in zirconia).

Plato and Perfection

The description of the cosmos as a sort of 'jumbled order' does seem to tally quite well with our ordinary perception of the world. In fact with hindsight it seems strange that it has taken the physical sciences so long to cotton on to this view. Is this because there is something basic in human nature that disdains the notion of an imperfect world? Without going too far into this, it is clear that we have to be careful not to treat any aspect of human nature as if it were more constant than any other aspect of the phenomenal world. We are on safer ground though in asserting that there is, in western culture at least, a distinct bias in this direction. This is a mode of thought that can be traced right back to our classical heritage, and to the formidable influence of Plato in particular.

The ascendency of Platonism, with its idealised and coherent attitudes towards the role of form and order, and the influence of these ideas on European culture over many centuries, can scarcely be exaggerated. In his book *The Sleepwalkers* Arthur Koestler, in referring to their massive contribution to European thought, describes Plato and Aristotle as 'twin stars' who alternated in visibility throughout the whole medieval period. Though the contribution of each of these philosophers was formidable, it is noteworthy that Aristotle himself was a self-avowed Platonist.

'The safest general characterisation of the European philosophical tradition is that it consists in a series of footnotes to Plato.'
Alfred North Whitehead

The sheer range of Plato's thought was prodigious: his authenticated dialogues alone are almost equivalent in length to the Bible, and there are certain themes that are consistent throughout his writings. Prominent among these are his theories concerning the nature of the sensible world. Plato was acutely conscious of the imperfections of the world, particularly those to be found in human society. One of the central and most tragic events of his life was the pointless judicial murder of his great mentor Socrates. It was a blow that intensified his doubts as to the possibility of ever improving his own, or any other, society by political means alone. This event, in fact, led to his final disillusionment, and it must also be said that his pessimism, so far as his own Athenian culture was concerned, was prophetic. By this time it had past its apogee and was fast approaching a crisis from which it never really recovered. In all of Plato's writings one detects a dissatisfaction with the world as he found it, and a yearning for sanctuary from its illusory values and transitory nature. It is easy to sympathise with this view even now when one sees the state that the world is in; surely things could have been arranged a little better?

The feeling of a general falling short of perfection in the visible or material world that seems to pervade all Plato's thought led him to formulate his somewhat mystical concept of 'universal forms'. This notion came essentially from his attempts to establish certainties in the field of knowledge. Plato felt that our ordinary use of language relied too heavily on general terms, such as dog, tree, rose etc., and that for these terms to have any real meaning we would have to understand what they really signified. To do this, he insisted, it was inadequate to point to any particular example of animal or plant since the example was subject to all manner of transformation; if we are to understand the world properly we must go to the source of these transitory manifestations, to the universal or archetypal models of things. These *universals* he saw as belonging to a world of forms, a transcendent domain that was at the same time a more real and unblemished version of our familiar, but illusory, world of sensory experience.

Plato did not believe that his ideal forms were directly available to the senses, but that they could be determined only by a turning away from the shadow world of sense-impressions, in order to locate the forms in the inner consciousness. This notion of a separate other place, uncontaminated by the imperfections and evils of the mundane world, can be seen as a version of the 'blissful region', common to many mythologies. Indeed Plato's concepts of ideal forms were later to exert a powerful influence on the course of Christianity, and on Christian notions of an afterlife. In actuality however these idealistic theories presented a problem: despite the fact that they were central to his metaphysical speculations Plato experienced considerable difficulties when it came to objectifying his ideas in this respect and he constantly changed his mind as to the exact nature of the forms. The ideal, it seemed, was not so easily defined.

Plato's failure to be objective over his ideal, perfect forms has an interesting parallel in contemporary science, where many of the more compelling discoveries have a Platonic ring to them. The consensus of current theories on the origin of the universe see it as a sort of descent from a state of perfect symmetry at the beginning of time, and space and matter, through a protracted and involved process of symmetry-breaking, to the great complexity that it now presents. Plato's central intuition has been vindicated: the phenomenal world is, in its very essence, imperfect.

Science, Monotheism and Theodicy

Although we live at a time when science is providing a most convincing and complete account of the workings of the universe, it is always worth reminding ourselves that its entire development has been marked by the overturning of established beliefs, both its own and those of society at large. It may even be the case that the majority of great discoveries have had this effect, of disturbing some convention or other, even though they themselves might have gone on to become part of the matrix of orthodoxy. This is a perfectly natural progression, and is as much a feature of the evolution of religious and philosophical ideas as of scientific ones. Indeed, particularly momentous discoveries can hold implications for all three departments; the affirmation of the heliocentricity of our planetary system being a case in point.

The evolution of scientific theories has been as uneven as that of any other body of ideas, but its own tenet of orthodoxy, objectivity, has tended to distort perception of its own progress. Science has exerted a massive and increasing influence on all our lives and this influence, as with any set of ideas, reflects a particular value system; because of this it is never really as objective as it believes itself to be. As L. L. Whyte has put it, 'The awkward fact is that Reason is never aware of its hidden assumptions.'

The roots of science run deeply into various ancient cultural strata, but its prevailing attitudes derive from a fairly specific cultural inheritance. Prominent among the articles of faith that it has almost unwittingly taken on board is the basic premise of the cultural monotheism of the European tradition. The notion of dualism has been as much of an anathema to science as it was to the early and medieval church, and the idea of a single, complete explanation of events is deeply ingrained in western consciousness. To judge from the tone of the definitions of it in most dictionaries, the cultural bias against any form of dualistic interpretation is still extant. The very term is something of a blunderbuss that fires off in so many directions that without further qualification its semantic intention is likely to remain unclear. Dualisms are 'inconsistent', 'unresolved' and 'unsatisfactory'; indeed the general impression that one receives is that the term has a whiff of taboo about it, if not of downright heresy. In science, until quite recently, a dualism has represented a conflict of evidence, an inconsistency that would have to be resolved. The underlying intention here is much the same as that which led Xenophanes, in the fifth century BC, to declare that 'if God is the best of all there can be only one'; and that which led Plotinus, in the third century AD, to state that 'if they are two we must find that which is before this duality'. These attitudes can be traced back to the period that saw a decline of belief in the gods of antiquity, and the 'resolution' of their unwieldy pantheon into a monotheism; that is to say, with the gradual forging of the Judaeo-Christian tradition.

There was an element of plain logic in this process of theological reductionism which undoubtedly contributed to its success in establishing a new and formidable cultural ethos. This monomial habit of thought continues to influence our attitudes to this day and tends to obscure the fact that there are many ordinary circumstances where a two-fold interpretation of phenomena seems perfectly natural and consistent: every right has a left, every up a down, and there are the familiar divisions of day and night, good and bad, male and female and so on. There are plenty of these complementary pairings abroad in the world, but our cultural inheritance makes it difficult for us to see how, in all their variety, they could amount to a consistent interpretation of phenomena.

In spite of an overall decline in religious belief that has seen the erosion of the concept of a sovereign and omnipotent creator, and the widespread acceptance of a more materialistic and atheistic view of the world we, in the west at least, are probably far more influenced than we realise by the assumptions of our cultural monotheism. Clearly, to have provided such a firm cultural foundation in the first place, this belief system must have satisfied human needs on many levels, intellectual as well as spiritual. Profound as this solution has been, and still is for many, it is beset by a central and intractable unconformity; the problem, which has probably occurred to everyone at some time or other, is that of reconciling the idea of a perfect creator with the obvious imperfection of the creation. 'Why do the wicked flourish and the just suffer in a world that is supposed to be divinely ordained?' All monotheistic creeds are confronted by some variation of this problem, and their diversity arises in great measure from their different solutions to it. Difficulties of this kind led Christianity into its own somewhat dualistic stance which envisages a continual and remorseless struggle between the powers of good and evil, a position that owes a great deal to neo-Platonic influences on the early Church.

Any theory that attempts to reconcile the perception of a perfect creator with the evils and imperfections of the mundane world is known as a Theodicy. There have been many responses to this basic problem which, naturally, was a focus of apologetics. The difficulties were addressed, long before the establishment of the Christian mission, by the Stoic Epicurus, whose blunt conclusion was that no theodicy is possible – 'Either God would wish to suppress evil and cannot, in which case He is good but not all-powerful, or He is able to, in which case He is powerful but not good.' This argument, on the face of it, has an irrefutable logic, but of course it is the main task of theologians to repair such rents in the fabric of faith, and in doing so they sustain and build the various systems of belief.

It is not only theologians who have to defend the faith; scientific theories and philosophical systems also require fairly constant patching. It does seem that whenever the law is laid down, about any aspect of the world, sooner or later it gets up and walks away. The cosmos is highly amenable to theories, and will support all manner of interpretations, but only for a while; the solutions to its mysteries are strictly rationed – 'Nature loves to hide.' All attempts to uncover the nature of the absolute are subject to the same influences that made it so complicated in the first place; which is to say that ideas about the universe are as perfectly differentiated as everything else in it. So it is that no religion is so sublime that it is proof against schism, and no philosophy so complete that it is beyond criticism. Even scientific laws, whether they are referring to 'things' or 'processes', are not the eternal truths that many scientists would have us believe, but are so many observations of regularities that give us an expectation, and really no more, that the future will resemble the past.

2
'The Two Forces of Nature'

Dualism and Determinism

These days the question of whether the cosmos might be the product of one, or of more than one, agency is likely to be regarded as a somewhat arcane matter, a subject of purely theological interest. Of course the issue was not always so remote. In medieval Europe, around the turn of the millennium, the Church became increasingly alarmed at the appearance of certain overtly dualistic creeds that had appeared from the east. These heresies were actually of Gnostic origin, and traced back to the very earliest centuries of the Christian era; although they saw themselves as true Christians the Gnostics were perceived by the established Church, of both eastern and western Christendom, as a serious threat to their divine authority. When persuasion had little deterrent effect on these sects, the ecclesiastical authorities, as was usual in these cases, resorted to more repressive measures, with the usual tragic consequences.

There are difficulties in identifying with the intensity of passion generated over this issue. Now it seems to have been a relatively mild deviation from accepted belief, but history tells us that these creeds were persecuted with a vigour and ferocity that was horrible even by the rather brutal standards of that middle Christian period. In 1118, by the personal order of the Byzantine Emperor, the Patarenes of the Balkans were condemned to be burned alive *en masse*, and a century later the Cathari of northern Italy and south western France were to suffer a similar fate. In 1220 the then Pope, Innocent III, launched a crusade against the peaceable but heretical Albigensi in their stronghold in Aquitaine. This campaign amounted to nothing less than a programme of genocide, and on its completion the persecution of heresy was formalised into the notorious institution of the Inquisition. Behind the sheer medieval nastiness and ecclesiastical despotism of these and similar events there must have been a genuine apprehension on the part of the established Church; the spread of these beliefs must have been felt as a challenge, not only to its authority, but to the entire moral and social fabric of the time. It is also clear that the dualistic nature of these heresies touched a particularly raw nerve: the Church had been grappling for centuries with its own dualities of good and evil, whereas to the Cathari and their followers the solution was clear. For them the entire cosmos was a battleground between two radically opposed forces of light and darkness. Matter was intrinsically evil and therefore could not possibly be the creation of a benevolent God. This Manichaean doctrine was, needless to say, utterly unacceptable to the established Church; in the event it became clear that the Cathari were as committed to their beliefs as were the adherents of the Catholic faith, and they were in the end prepared to die rather than renounce it. Sadly this was the fate they were called upon to endure in town after town of the provinces which they inhabited. The holocaust that finally extirpated religious dualism from Europe marks one of the most unhappy episodes of the whole medieval period (see Glossary).

Although the influence of Cathar dualism was finally eradicated it can be seen to have presaged the end of the hegemony of the Catholic church in western Europe. In the two centuries following the suppression of their ideas there were further, and more forceful, challenges to its authority that culminated in the great sea-change of the Reformation. The advent of the

Reformation and the Renaissance also saw a distinct softening in the perception of the role of the creator, a marked departure from the somewhat oppressive medieval concept of a deity who, despite his remoteness and omnipotence, was felt to take a detailed interest in the most minute affairs of his creation. There was also, from the time of the Renaissance, a gradual ascendancy of more materialistic and scientific explanations of the world, ideas which, when developed into astronomical and physical systems, led to a further disengagement between creator and creation. By the time of Newton's great synthesis of planetary gravitation there was a fashion among scientists and intellectuals for the new cosmography of Deism, a view that perfectly reflected the preoccupations of that period. Since this was an age that counted amongst its highest achievements the construction of elaborate mechanical instruments it was natural that the supreme being of Deism should have been imagined as one who would have set the world in motion, according to his own supra-rational principles, but who then played no further part in its affairs. This was God the watch-maker who, having built and wound up the divine clock simply allowed it to run its course, though in an entirely predictable way.

In its essence the Deist position was an attempt to reconcile the increasingly confident scientific view of the world with that of older, Christian values. This theory, of course, still had to contend with those problems already mentioned that face all monotheisms. One response was that which posited the notion of a pre-established, harmonious creation that had been set to run for all time by a benign creator, and which, necessarily, had to be the 'best of all possible worlds', despite all appearances to the contrary. This philosophical stance became known as Optimism, and is most closely associated with the figure of Liebnitz, the great mathematician and scientist. Liebnitz set out his philosophical ideas in his *Theodicée* (1710), but these views, highly developed as they were, were severely criticised by more rationally minded thinkers, notably Voltaire, who ridiculed their claims in his satire *Candide*.

The deterministic view which saw the world as a piece of giant clock-work was to have a pretty good run. The triumph of Newtonian physics ushered in the classical era of scientific discovery. Both for those who were inclined to accept Liebnitz' contention that ours is the best of all possible worlds, and for those who were rather more sceptical, the underlying presumption of scientific enquiry for the following two hundred and fifty years was that of the inherent predictability of the cosmos. The essential task of scientific investigation, it was felt, was to uncover the natural laws that constituted the mechanism of the 'great plan', and in this enterprise its achievements were prodigious. From an everyday point of view we still live in a world that is governed by the play of those forces that Newton first described in the *Principia Mathematica* (1687). At a deeper level however the picture is very different; the discoveries that have been made in the course of this century have entirely transformed the conceptual base of science. To paraphrase Yeats, it is 'all changed, changed utterly; a terrible beauty has been born'.

The changes that were wrought by two major revolutions of scientific thought, relativity and quantum physics, brought to an end the confident, predictable universe of classical determinism. These new theories were no mere extension of older ideas, but represented a radical departure which involved abandoning significant parts of the old interpretation of phenomena. The full implications of this perceptual revolution however have so far failed to make any serious inroads into what might be termed our cultural consciousness. This is partly attributable to the difficulties associated with making an objective visualisation of its propositions, but, as is often the case, the greatest obstacle to the acceptance of a new solution lies in a reluctance to abandon older explanations; our notion of God, for instance, is still a predominantly medieval one. However it is inevitable that just as our perception of the nature of physical reality will have to change so also will our perception of the nature of the primary causative principle (or principles) that brought it into being.

This is bound to be a demanding process; even Einstein experienced serious difficulties in accepting quantum notions of the absolute and inherent unpredictability of events at the elementary level, a view that he expressed in his declaration that 'God does not play dice'. He was wrong in this, but his difficulties in coming to terms with an indeterminate, but continuously creative, dynamic universe, is a hurdle that will be encountered on a more general cultural level. For if God is found not to be 'in charge' of the universe how *does* the thing work?

Attraction and Repulsion

We have seen that many of the earlier Greek philosophers were much concerned to develop a theory about the nature of reality that would account for all they knew of it, but there was one group of thinkers of that period who decided, metaphorically speaking, to throw in the towel on that particular issue. These were the Sophists, who were more inclined to devote their efforts to the development of social techniques whereby people (or at least their clients) could adapt most successfully to the society in which they found themselves living. The Sophists had a some-what sceptical outlook; they felt, for example, that it was impossible either to prove or to disprove the existence of God; for them man was the 'measure of all things' (Protagoras). Because of their ethical egoism (i.e. their belief that the individual might use any method to improve his circumstances) they became the focus for the disapproval of other, more profound thinkers, such as Socrates and Plato, and much of their teaching was repudiated by these higher moral philosophies. However they had one central premise that is as interesting and relevant now as it was in the Greek world of the fifth century BC, where they were travelling scholars. Their contention concerns the art of rhetoric, at which they were particu-larly adept; they observed that in any dispute there would be at least two viewpoints and that consequently at least two arguments had to be considered before any case could be decided. Now, although the Sophists were not particularly interested in theoretical philosophy this simple observation has quite deep metaphysical implications.

It is clear that within any social organisation, of whatever scale, there is always potential for dissent and factionalism. In fact a group only holds together so long as there is a consensus of intent or purpose, or at least a high degree of one. On the greater scale, at the level of an entire culture, the dominant social ethos is bound to involve complex and subtle patterns

'For even as they (Strife and Love) were aforetime, so too shall they ever be; nor ever will boundless Time be emptied of that pair.'
Empedocles

of behaviour, and it is this mode, this particular way of being, with which its members can identify. But the attractive force of group loyalty that binds members of a particular society or culture together is also responsible, more than any other factor, for the 'diffraction' of humanity as a whole. For every 'us' there will be a 'them', the others who are different from us, and there are therefore pressures towards conformity and social alignment within all societies.

These, in fact, are universal processes, and are fundamental to evolution in the widest possible sense of the term. It is just these tendencies, towards consolidation on the one hand and diversification on the other, that have led to all the differentiation and variety of nature.

Our ideas about ourselves, and the view that we hold of the world, are conditional on the particular place that we occupy in it. We cannot help but be deeply influenced by the complex assemblage of ideas, attitudes and beliefs that we inherit from our cultural 'location', wherever it may be, but every individual, even the most conformist, is far more than the sum of these influences. Each person is unique; we are originals because, like every other part of the cosmos, we are perfectly differentiated. No two people are entirely alike, even identical twins, no two trees, even of the same species, are ever quite the same, and this principle of individuation traces right down to the microscopic level, to the very basis of physical matter in fact.

The substantial appearance of materials derives ultimately from the orderly confinement, in discrete arrangements, of their component particles. We are frequently reminded by scientific writers that we must not think of these particles as occupying space in any familiar sense of the term, and that as purely electronic entities they have no individual identity, but as their very term of description implies, each quantum 'event', whether it is seen as particle or wave, as matter or energy, is unique and original.

It is difficult even to begin to conceptualize the realities of matter at the atomic level, where most of our familiar notions of cause and effect simply do not apply. In trying to comprehend this region we have to discard all familiar ideas of an objective reality and instead try to visualise a domain that is entirely comprised of energy patterns. The scene here is dominated by all manner of accidental collisions, shifting alliances and the constant transmutation of form and energy – all occurring at incomprehensible speeds! It is clear, despite its inaccessibility to direct sensory perception, that the apprehension of quantum realities has enormous philosophical, as well as scientific, significance. This interpretation of phenomena now underpins the greater part of our understanding of nature, and the great corpus of scientific knowledge is itself coming to exert an increasing influence on our general outlook.

The world of the infinitely small will always hold a particular fascination; it is all about us, but at the same time it is indescribably remote; its ruling principles may be of a different order, but since they underlie the familiar world of our sensory experience they inevitably have a direct bearing on it. It also follows that such principles, which operate both at this foundational level and at our own, must be of the most universal and significant kind. So what might these be? One of the most upsetting discoveries of the new physics involved the uncertainty principle which, in effect, pronounced the cosmos to be inherently unpredictable. This aspect of existence, which might seem familiar enough to many of us, was the most difficult proposition of the new physics for classical science to accommodate. It transpires, as a consequence of uncertainty, that the cosmos, at all levels, is both organised and disorganised; even in the lawless world of fundamental particles, which is chiefly characterised by its unceasing, ever-changing flow of energy, there are forms. If we look for further refinement of principles, to the ultimate reduction, we get surprisingly close to the 'love' and 'strife', or attraction and repulsion, of the fifth-century philosopher Empedocles. We now know how correct was his intuition and that it is precisely these forces that account for the shapes and movements of events, whether at the 'higher' levels of human interaction or within the community of infinitesimal particles.

The Two Essences

At this stage it seems appropriate to recapitulate some of the general lines of reasoning that have been covered so far. At a point almost exactly half way between the two world wars an international group of scientists made a series of discoveries that are likely still to be commemorated when the memory of those apparently far more cataclysmic events will have faded. The quantum findings that culminated in the so-called Copenhagen Interpretation of 1927 brought about a conceptual revolution in physics. These were momentous discoveries, which placed the whole scientific enterprise on a new footing, and which saw the introduction of powerful new mathematical tools that were greatly to enlarge our understanding of basic phenomena. These revelations have had the most profound effect on the world of science but their conceptual implications have not, as yet, made much impression on the wider consciousness. In the longer term however their absorption will be unavoidable, because taking up these new terms has involved letting go some of the most basic assumptions of the older physics, on which so much of our conventional view of the world is based. The quantum physicists revealed that the world is not constituted in the way we had always believed it to be, and eventually we will all have to catch up.

I have also mentioned that it was the pioneer physicists themselves who were the first to appreciate the broader, philosophical implications of their discoveries, and they too who first noted the correlation between their ideas and those of certain older belief systems. Niels Bohr, who was a philosopher as well as a physicist, was particularly struck by the parallels between his complementarity principle and the traditional complementarities of Chinese modes of thought. Those ancient Chinese philosophies, which emphasised the constant motion of the world and its perpetual action and reaction, fit surprisingly well with the outlook of the new physics and its focus on the simultaneity of organisation and disorganisation in the universe at large. But there is an important difference: in China these processes have always been seen as deriving from a dualistic mode of activity, known as the two essences, *ti* and *t'ien*. In their standard cosmogony it is the interplay between these two principles that give rise to both heaven and earth, and to man. This outlook was so deeply ingrained in Chinese life and thought that its polarities were institutionalised

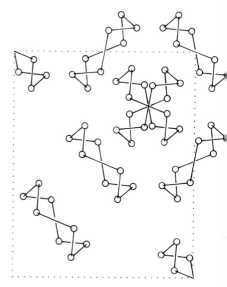

'We might characterise the only two components required for the understanding of the universe in terms of modern science as organisation on the one hand and energy on the other.'
Joseph Needham.

'There is no Li *without* Ch'i, *and no* Ch'i *without* Li, *both are eternal.'*
Chu Hsi

in a two-track system that was represented for centuries by the opposing, but complementary, philosophies that we have come to know as Confucianism and Taoism.

The roles of these complementary modes of thought were well delineated in traditional Chinese society. The Confucians (the *Ju Chia*) were principally concerned with the formal structuring of society and with the orderly administration of its affairs. They were humanists in so far as they saw people and society at the centre of things, as the Sophists did, but their conservative ideals, to provide and sustain the best of all possible societies, slipped all too easily into the maintenance of the *status quo*. The Taoists, by contrast, were unconventional and detached from society; they were scornful of the orthodox proprieties of Confucian doctrine and sceptical of the high value that this school placed on the role of humans in the world. For them any attempt to formulate fixed ideas, whether with regard to the structuring of society or in the interpretation of phenomena, were, in the last analysis, schematic, absurd and doomed to failure.

There are parallels to this division of attitudes in all advanced societies. There will always be adherents to those views that emphasise the values of order and formality, and others who will argue for change and vitality. In China however this dialectic was itself formalised: the philosophical polarities of Confucianism and Taoism each reflect something of the eternal qualities of the two essences to which, ultimately, they devolve. Although it was essentially paternalistic, Confucianism was always socially orientated; at bottom it was firmly committed to the advancement of society, and believed in the maintenance of peace and justice and the promotion of the general advantages of wealth and education. In the Confucian view the only way to secure these benefits was through the proper administration of society, which necessarily entailed a continuing involvement in all its affairs.

'How did the myriad things take their rise? The Yin *and* the Yang *reflected on each other, covered each other and reacted with each other ... likings, dislikings, avoidings and movements towards ... then arose in all their distinctions.'*
Chuang Tzu

Characteristically the Taoists had a completely different perspective; they were forever pointing out the failure of the best intentions of those in authority, and of their interference in a more general way. 'Those that would gain from what is under Heaven by tampering with it, I have seen that they do not succeed.' (Lao Tzu) They even went so far as to declare that 'love for the people is the root of all evil to the people' (Chuang Tzu). Now although there is a clear divergence of attitude here we have little difficulty in identifying the rationale, and indeed the virtues, of both sides of this polemic. The argument is essentially that between the posture of social involvement and that of non-interference. It also demonstrates a certain divergence between a rational or logical approach to a problem and a more intuitive response; one can find similar expressions of these standpoints rather closer to home. The former attitude, for instance, is epitomised in Burke's famous dictum that 'for evil to triumph it is sufficient for good men to do nothing', which, effectively, justifies every kind of political involvement. We also know that in practice even the highest ideals are subverted and that 'the road to hell is paved with good intentions'. These are the inevitable divisions of opinion that the Sophists warned us to expect on every conceivable issue; but the fact remains that in arguments like the one above it is usually difficult for any of us to accept that there can be merit in both sides of any set of opposing ideas; we usually opt for one or the other.

We can draw a parallel here with the situation that faced theoretical physicists in their first encounter with the unexpected peculiarities of quanta in the early years of this century. Apart from the enormous problems posed by the mathematical calculations that were involved, they were faced with certain conceptual difficulties which, it turned out, could only be surmounted by recognising an unwitting bias that had existed in science up to that time; this was the one-sided determinism that was, in fact, culturally reinforced. When, for instance, scientists tried to discover the position of an electron and, at the same time, to measure its velocity, they found that it simply could not be done. A natural law that had never previously been encountered intervened to prohibit this. The solution of this and similar problems, only came with the acceptance of the manifest *duality* of matter, with an awareness that these particles and waves were, in fact, abstractions whose properties could only be observed and defined through their interaction with other systems, and that knowledge of certain aspects of their properties was bound to exclude knowledge of others.

It is interesting, to say the least, that an important principle which has been found to be operating at the very foundation of physical reality, should accord so well with the precepts of an ancient Chinese cosmology. The pioneer physicist Niels Bohr became deeply interested in Chinese thought, and became convinced of the notion of a universal, harmonious mutuality. It is worth emphasising here that although there were, in the course of Chinese history, many interpretations of the nature of the 'two essences' they were never regarded as irreconcilable forces, but were always seen as an interdependent duality, with each principle needing the other to find expression.

Chinese dualisms were never radical, so their essences could not be objectively reduced, as was certainly possible with the opposing principles of Persian dualisms. Moreover there was always a high degree of relativity involved in the attribution of these distinctions; just as within China itself there existed the complementary systems of Confucianism and Taoism so for us in the west Chinese thought as a whole seems to be rather more 'dragonlike' (i.e. intuitive and receptive) than our own. But the west does have its own complementarities, the notions of form and energy being a case in point. As principles these two are entirely interdependent; in the phenomenal world at least there can never be an absolute separation between them, and they must be seen as different aspects of a primordial and unknowable source (see Glossary).

Crystal Form : The Ordering Principle

Scientific interest lies in the phenomenal. The reality behind phenomena cannot be known and is not of scientific concern. Although we might reasonably characterise the present understanding of the universe as consisting entirely of 'enformed energies' (or 'energised forms'), the abstract notions of *form* and *energy* have not, in themselves, any real scientific standing. When it comes down to it the meaning of these terms is obscure even in ordinary usage; we might feel that we have an intuitive understanding of what is meant by the term 'energy', but we are usually referring to one or other of its manifestations, and the conventional

'Morphic processes build up the hierarchies of structure, while entropy processes tend to disperse ordered units and to break down hierarchies. This is an intriguing vista of two great tendencies in the universe and their contrary effects on the hierarchies of structure. Exact science has only recently begun to study this in a systematic manner.'

L. L. Whyte

'Perhaps we will eventually be able to combine the western tradition, with its emphasis on experimentation and quantitative formulations, with a tradition such as the Chinese one, with its view of a spontaneous, self-organising world.'

Ilya Prigogine

'The perfection of mathematical beauty is such that whatsoever is most beautiful and regular is also found to be the most useful and excellent.'

D'Arcy Thompson

'The function of geometry is to draw us away from the world of the senses and of corruption to a world of the intellect and the eternal. For the contemplation of the eternal is the end of philosophy as the contemplation of the mysteries is the end of religion.'

Plutarch

'Geometry enlightens the intellect and sets one's mind right. It is hardly possible for errors to enter into geometric reasoning because it is well arranged and orderly. Thus the mind that constantly applies itself to geometry is not likely to fall into error.'

Ibn Khuldun

scientific definition of energy as 'the capacity to do work' also ducks the question. The essential nature of energy, the 'thing in itself', is ultimately mysterious and so also is the principle of form.

So what do we understand by the word 'form'? In most dictionaries it is associated with matters of 'shape', the 'arrangement of parts' and 'the visible aspect of things'. But clearly there are senses in which this term goes beyond considerations of purely spatial relationships since music can have form, and so can purely abstract operations such as mathematics; even ideas have a form. In addition there is the verb. To form is to impart the quality of form. The term is a very general one since all 'things', at every level, possess the quality of form to some extent, whether they are inanimate, organic, man-made or even complete abstractions.

It is questionable to ascribe spatial relationships to matter at the very deepest level, but atoms and their components certainly do have form. The characteristic form of an atom derives from the relationships between its constituent parts, which are comprised of a set of electrical entities (electrons) in conjunction with the complex system of the nucleus. Although electrons, even within this arrangement, tend to fly off in all directions, they do, for the most part, remain at a predictable distance from the nucleus, producing a sort of three-dimensional cloud, or 'shell'. Each of these shells has a particular quantum number and is differentiated into separate energy levels; the number of these shells and the numbers of electrons within them determine the form of the atom, and from this there follow all the physical and chemical properties of the various elements.

Matter is generated when atoms are brought together in such a way that an equilibrium is established between their forces of attraction and repulsion. The nature and extent of any perceptible form above that of the atomic level is entirely determined by the stability of this equilibrium. The fluid and solid states of matter that we recognise as 'high-level' properties are simply an expression of these lower, molecular phenomena. In the gaseous state the attractive molecular forces are unable to overcome the agitation induced by heat motion and therefore matter in this condition is found in its most formless and disordered state. Interestingly the words 'gas' and 'chaos' both derive from the same Greek root. In the liquid state matter is far more condensed, but its molecular order is transitory; here there is a continuous breaking down and reforming of molecular linkages, so that form in liquids is an ephemeral condition. At relatively lower temperatures molecules shape up into regular and stable assemblies to create the crystalline, or solid state. Here we get to the heart of the matter of form: the solid state has a greater degree of form than either the liquid or gaseous ones because it manifests an ordered array. Its constituent parts, in this case molecules, bear a well-defined relation to each other. Form is tenuous in liquids precisely because this relation is tenuous, and it is non-existent in the gaseous state for similar reasons.

Form of any kind then is an expression of a certain regularity of structure. Moreover we are able to recognise this because we ourselves have a structured point of view. At bottom the process of recognition consists of the engagement of one set of patterns with another. Hence the study of form is the study of relations, whether they are of a material or an abstract nature, whether they are to do with the ordering of matter in space or of individuals and their functions in society.

The relations operating within crystalline structures are few and relatively simple, which accounts for the austere geometric forms to be found in individual crystals. By contrast most organic forms are far more complex and subtle. This is precisely because they derive from relations of a higher, more complex order. But even these more complex natural forms demonstrate a structural coherence that is not usually found in the artificial. It is generally quite easy to distinguish natural objects from man-made ones because the former invariably have an underlying and integrated complexity. Any living organism has continually to adapt to its environment, to establish an equilibrium within its surroundings, and it is this balance of nature, sustained by the process of evolutionary adaptation, that is ultimately responsible for the beautiful integration of all living things. To generalise, the symmetries regulating the equilibrium between an organism and its environment become translated into the complex structures of animate existence, but the ordering principles underlying the dynamic system of an organism are rarely apparent; natural forms that manifest any obvious symmetry are the exception rather than the rule. Such a case, when it does appear, might be compared to a well-formed crystal in the sense that both make visible a great, but generally occluded, principle of order.

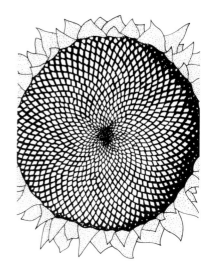

A plan of the Borabadur stupa, central Java, 'a fabulous summary of the arts and science of its period'.

The notion that there might be a regulating principle behind the apparent chaos and complexity of the world has always been a potent one: it is, in fact, the common assumption of both religious belief and scientific enquiry. However long before either of these impulses was differentiated human societies would have had an order of their own, and the ways in which they were ordered would naturally have been bound up with a perceived world order. This is to say that the ways in which we behave in a social setting, and the way that we see things, are both formalised to a degree that we do not normally recognise. The progressive development of human societies, as with all evolutionary change, has always been towards greater structural complexity, and this increase in social complexity

Natural forms that manifest symmetrical arrangements can be compared to crystals in that they make visible an ordering principle that generally remains occluded.

43

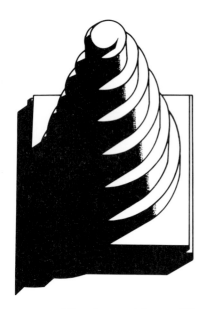

The ziggurat form of the minaret of the Great Mosque at Samarra.

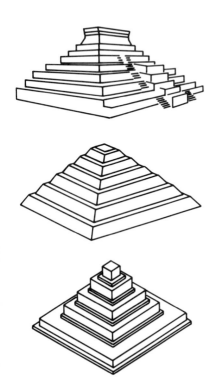

Step pyramids: Mayan, Egyptian and Mesopotamian

has naturally been reflected in the increasingly formal aspect of society. It is clear for instance that, despite their subtle nature, social relations in tribal societies are simple by comparison with those of the later, so called 'mature' civilisations. To begin to appreciate the world views held by the inhabitants of ancient Egypt or Babylon we have first to realise that these were intensely structured and extremely rigid societies in comparison with the more primitive modes of existence that they displaced. That these and other ancient mature civilisations in different parts of the world, had a far more self-conscious dedication to the abstract principle of order is quite evident, both in their art forms and in the massive 'crystalline' monuments that so many of them chose to erect. The awesome symmetries of pyramids, ziggurats and the like were not only the 'link between heaven and earth', but models of the formal hierarchical structures of the societies that produced them. In the more general sense, the element of any society that is concerned with the maintenance of its order and identity always inclines to adopt formal modes of expression, whether in art, architecture or simply in ritual. This is the reason why, throughout the ages, the upholders of temporal and spiritual authority have used the symbolism of symmetry as a communion with what they perceived to be a higher ordering principle. Among the more impressive achievements of the ancient mature cultures, made possible because of their advances in such new fields of knowledge as astronomy, mathematics and geometry, and in many ways the intellectual equivalent of their great monuments, were their successes in extracting important, previously unnoticed, regularities from nature. Many discoveries in these fields were made independently in the older civilisations and were naturally linked to the prevailing belief systems, but in their attempts to establish certainties in the field of knowledge many of their achievements must be regarded as having a strong element of the proto-scientific. There are many lines of cultural genealogy that connect the ancient civilisations of the Middle East to what has become the western scientific tradition, but perhaps the most important of these, from the point of view of the history of science, was that of the Pythagorean/Platonic stream of philosophical and scientific speculation.

There is a remarkable synchronicity between the lives of Pythagoras, Buddha and Confucius, all of whom were born and died within a very few years of each other (*c*.560 BC – *c*.475 BC). This is so remarkable, of course, because the ideas of each of these original thinkers had such a massive cultural influence. In each case this influence has lasted right up to the present. Pythagoras can be seen to have contributed as much to the foundation of European culture as Buddha and Confucius did to that of eastern Asia. It is not easy to summarise the aims of Pythagoras and his school, which had many of the traits of a religious order, but one could say that, like many religious sects before and since, they hoped to achieve a spiritual purification. Their version of catharsis was a highly original one since the divine essence to which they dedicated their contemplation was firmly identified with the order of pure mathematics. Pythagoras, in fact, is credited with saying 'All things are made of numbers.'

This elevation of the role of mathematics was itself of great moment to the evolution of western thought; it inclined the Pythagoreans to apply their numerical mysticism boldly to a whole range of subjects: to music, for instance, and astronomy. In doing this they laid the foundation of the western scientific tradition. The notion that numbers might have a separate life and existence of their own not only had a great aesthetic appeal but also proved to be very productive in the narrower, purely scientific, sense. Time and again nature seemed to confirm the Pythagorean intuition that they had indeed encountered a divine principle. It was through the later philosophies of Plato and Aristotle, both of whom greatly admired Pythagoras, that his concept of the sublimity of mathematical order became incorporated into the mainstream of later classical, and subsequently Christian, thought. Plato, in particular, was deeply influenced by the notion of the separate existence of a sublime order, and went on to develop his theory of universal forms, of which I have already spoken. This grand, and essentially mystical, vision had to be seen in part as Plato's personal reaction to the imperfections of his own society, and of the world at large. His deliberations on its many and various shortcomings led him to the belief that the world of appearances, which is to say the ordinary world of our sensory experience, is merely the temporary recipient of forms that properly belong to the transcendent world of ideas. In this view our ordinary world cannot support the forms for long because the order they bestow is being continually dissipated. Because of this the visible world is in a constant state of flux and its perceived forms are little more than illusions.

The mathematical ideas that were first advanced by Pythagoras, and which Plato found so inspiring, were primarily concerned with geometry. Both Pythagoras and Plato were fascinated by the pure relations that operated within geometric figures, particularly in the solids. Part of the appeal of these constructions was aesthetic, but even now it is easy to see how such figures, with their precise relations with each other, should have become identified with the sort of other-worldly perfection that was central to each of these philosophies. Both schools were haunted by the feeling that geometrical figures might, in some way, provide the key to the secrets of the universe; and in a sense their intuition has been vindicated. The enthusiasm that led to the uncovering of the mathematical regularities within geometric figures was the beginning of science proper. It was the first attempt at reductive analysis, and from this method there arose the genuinely scientific impulse towards the classification of natural forms in general. All this, of course, was an entirely novel concept: the great force and originality of thought of the Pythagorean/Platonic stream of philosophy lay in its conviction of the existence of order as an inherent natural principle, and not simply a construct of the human mind. Ultimately the entire scientific tradition rests on that belief.

Dragon Power : The Moving Spirit

There is perhaps no better indication of the thorough-going self-confidence of modern scientific thought than that shown by the recent speculations on the origins of the universe. Although there is some wrangling over details there is now a general consensus of scientific opinion as to its main features. Our universe started out with a Big Bang. The precise moment of the event of creation is beyond reach, as yet, but physicists have succeeded in reconstructing the sequence of events following the initial act of creation to within millionths of a second of its genesis. From these accounts it would appear that the cosmos materialised as an inconceivably

'The elucidation of the meaning of the sentence 'everything flows' is one of metaphysics' main tasks.'

Alfred North Whitehead

dense, rapidly expanding fireball which soon became a swirling confusion of quanta. At this early stage mass and energy were not at all differentiated but were freely converting one into the other. Only gradually did this primordial concentrate cool sufficiently for nuclei and atoms to form, and only at a later and greatly expanded stage were the galaxies, planets and stars able to condense out.

In this now generally accepted model the interactions of all fundamental quanta are seen as 'asymmetrical'. They are, in essence, the remnants of a primal symmetry which is presumed to have existed up to the moment of the original, explosive creation, although any state of being 'before' the creation of time is, of course, utterly unimaginable. Since everything is ultimately made up of quanta it would seem that all nature is a manifestation of this disturbed symmetry. As to the question of ultimate causation, the best indication that science has provided to date is that the universe came out of a vacuum. It has been calculated that, taken together, the various masses and energies that are abroad in the universe even now come close to cancelling each other out and that they amount to zero!

It is interesting to compare the most recent scientific cosmological views with those expressed in the *Tao te Ching*, one of the oldest and most important canons of Chinese Taoism.

> In the beginning there was something undifferentiated and yet complete Before Heaven and Earth were produced, Silent! Empty! Sufficient unto itself! Unchanging!

And after this prior condition. . .

> When One came into existence there was One, but it was formless . . . then came the movement which gave life, and things produced in accordance with the principles of life had what is called Form.

In their interpretation of phenomena the emphasis in these early Taoist texts, just like that of contemporary science, is on the processes of motion, change and transformation.

> All the various species of things transform into one another by the process of variation in form. Their beginning and ending is like an unbroken ring of which it is impossible to discover the principle.

To the extent that this religious philosophy recognises a causative principle at all it is identified with a term that might be translated as the 'vital spirit', *ch'i*. *Ch'i* is conceived as an omnipresent force that both vitalises and disturbs every part of the cosmos; it is 'the very breath of the universe'. As with our more familiar notion of energy it is seen as being essential to all natural processes. In every sphere, and at every stage of existence, down to the most infinitesimal detail, energies are being exchanged and matter transformed. In Taoist terms this is accomplished by the flow of *ch'i*. There is an extraordinary resonance between these more ancient views, which envisage a world that is permeated by mysterious patterns of energy, and those of modern physics with its notions of non-substantial 'fields' and 'events'. Both recognise the essentially dynamic nature of the world with its constant flow of movement and change and there are other remarkable points of contact, particularly with regard to the role of relativity.

The doctrine of the relativity of attributes has to be seen as one of the central tenets of Taoism. The Taoists were continually emphasising the absolutely relative nature of time and space, and were fully conscious that it is only our habituation to a particular scale in these things that causes us to regard our own standards as possessing a greater objective reality. For the Taoists such qualities as size, colour and beauty could only ever be relative. What was real, and therefore the focus of their attention, was the energy principle itself.

> How it floods in every direction! This way and that, there is no place where it does not go.

There was no inert or passive matter for the Taoists. Substance was neither solid nor material in any objective sense, but was rather a temporary expression of the unceasing operation of intangible forces.

The parallels that can be drawn between the outlook of modern science and that of Taoism and other older, more mystical traditions are all the more interesting for the fact that science, in the course of this convergence, has not itself become more mystical or poetical. On the contrary the

One of the greatest revelations of modern physics is that of the essentially dynamic nature of all matter. Particle tracks from a bubble-chamber photograph

Illustration: Brookhaven National Laboratory

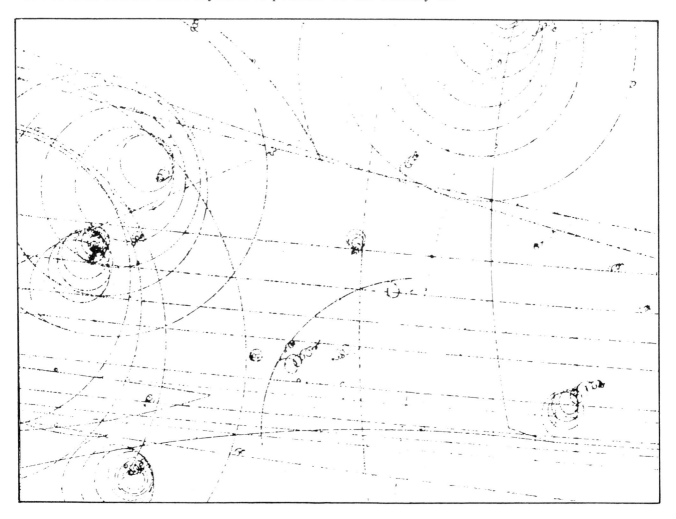

scientific view of nature has, if anything, become more rigorous as it has become more comprehensive, and its development has been entirely self-consistent. So there is something of a puzzle here; it seems extraordinary, on the face of it, that the scientific approach to phenomena, backed as it is by a great body of empirically acquired knowledge, should have come to anything approaching such similar conclusions with respect to the ultimate nature of physical reality as those of older and more intuitive systems of thought. But of course the subject of these, and of all such descriptions, is the same, whether it is the 'nature' of science or the Tao of the Taoists; the differences are primarily those of interpretation.

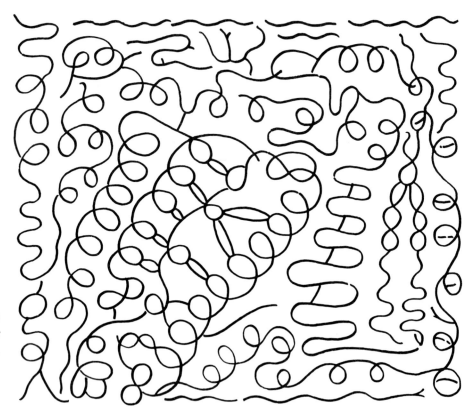

Occult diagram used in popular Taoism: 'The Space Song of the Blue Sky'.

It is extremely interesting that these contrasting lines of approach, which are epitomised by a logical and systematic method on the one hand and by an intuitive process on the other, should recently have been found to correspond to a functional separation of our higher cognitive faculties. Recent neurological research seems to indicate that these different perceptual modes might actually have a physiological basis, the so-called left/right brain asymmetry. These discoveries would appear to indicate that separate parts of our brain have quite different, though equally powerful, capabilities, with subtly different lines of approach. Although these distinct perceptual modes, which are located in the separate halves of our brain, combine together for the most part, there are indications of a certain division of labour, so that each of us, in a sense, operates a dual system of thought. It is even possible that these findings might have some bearing on our understanding of certain cultural divergencies, particularly those obtaining between the east and the west, which can now be seen as deriving, in part at least, from the different emphases of these distinctive modes of interpretation.

These absorbing discoveries are examined in greater detail in the next chapter. Suffice to say here that they offer a tentative explanation for the cautious progression in science from preoccupation with form to interest in function. It would follow that a line of thought that is essentially systematic, literal and 'crystalline' in its approach should only gradually come to an appreciation of the 'dragon' aspects of nature, a side of things that was intuited from the outset by the Taoists.

We have seen that science, in the west at least, began as an attempt to determine the eternal and unchanging aspects of the world. From this initial impulse evolved the characteristic methods of science: measurement, comparison and classification. It was perfectly natural that science should first have been focused on the static, simply because it is easier to measure things that are still. The great achievements of Greek scholars lay in such fields as geometry, astronomy, engineering etc., and were more concerned with the *structure* of things than with their *motion*. It was not until the great revitalisation of the Renaissance that scientists began to investigate the transmission of force properly. The gradual transition of the focus of scientific enquiry from geometric shape to dynamic motion, which began with Kepler and Galileo, soon ushered in the first great system to take dynamic forces into full account. The writ of Newton's theory of gravitation paved the way for the great classical era of scientific discovery.

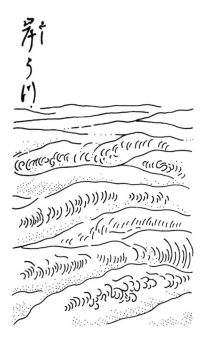

From this time on society itself became more dynamic and so began the detection of a whole series of other forces. The enormous potential of thermal, electrodynamic and ultimately nuclear forces completely transformed society. It was the introduction of new devices, such as the heat engine which made possible the direct tapping of the vast reservoirs of natural energy, that brought about the industrial revolution. This technological progression was part of an increasing tendency within the world body of science towards energy-based systems, a change of emphasis that can be seen to have culminated in the late nineteenth century with the declared intention of Lord Kelvin to establish a physics that was entirely based on energy principles, that is to say one without any allusion to an underlying model. Kelvin's hopes, of course, have been very largely realised and we now live in a world whose structures are seen to be entirely conditioned by dynamic principles, where the interpretation of all phenomena refers back ultimately to the play of mysterious energies, and where the very notion of material substantiality has given way to that of the 'invisible organisation of energy'.

With its present emphasis on energy as a primary causative principle western science has come strangely close to that ancient Chinese view of the world whereby the dragon was seen as the agent of all cosmic change. Dwelling as he did in the swirling vortices of mists and water the dragon was generally characterised as being sudden and unpredictable and in possession of enormous power. He represented a primal energy that could be both creative and destructive, the irresistible moving force of the universe.

'Mountains and seas are but copies of swellings and hollows of things nearby. Life and movement are the elementary principles of contour and texture lines.' Tao Ch'i (Taoist painter).

Nine dragons appearing through clouds and water. Detail from a famous Taoist-inspired scroll.

'Divine Order' and the 'Spirit of Nature'

One of the ways that we can begin to get a feel for the inherent values of an unfamiliar culture is by way of its creative output and, of all the modes of expression, it is perhaps those in the field of the visual arts that can make the most immediate impression. Two chapters of this book are entirely dedicated to an examination of particular art forms from non-European traditions, but although the cultural alignment of each of these is quite different from our own, and from each other, their art is, I believe, perfectly accessible to us. It is as easy for us to identify the artistic intentions of the particular aspects of Islamic art that are dealt with in the first of these two chapters as it is to respond to that Chinese art of Taoist inspiration that is referred to in the second. The reason for the inclusion of these particular artistic traditions in this context is that these seem to me to provide the most graphic expression of those abstract principles of form and energy for which the 'crystal' and 'dragon' of the title are metaphors.

It soon becomes apparent, when the works of these two artistic traditions are considered together, that they form a clear and deep-rooted contrast. The art of Islam is to a great extent the art of decoration. Its preferences are for intensely organised and highly symmetrical forms and its predilection for complex patterning is well known. It is fair to say that, at least during certain periods, Islam has demonstrated an almost obsessive fascination with pattern and symmetry, a genre that seems to refer directly to the pure geometry of crystalline order. By contrast those arts of China that show the influence of Taoist sentiments are aschematic and, if anything, show a preference for asymmetric composition. In this art there is no underlying structure and no adherence to form, but rather a constant evocation of the 'vital spirit' of the Tao, the source, it was felt, of all creative energy. In Taoist art every line is charged with symbolic intent, again contrasting with the more geometric art of Islam which is entirely devoid of symbolism as such, and refers only to a notion, Platonic in origin, of perfect form.

The contrast between the works of these distinctive and highly evolved artistic traditions naturally reflects many of the attitudes and much of the orientation of the cultural milieus that produced them. Taoism, as a coherent philosophy, emerged in the China of the third century BC, and has remained since that time a major influence on the arts of that country. Islam burst onto the world stage in the seventh century AD and rapidly established itself in territories from Spain to China. Its spiritual mission was soon translated into a new social prescription, and a new cultural identity that in turn gave rise to wholly original and confident art forms. It is fascinating to trace the points of origin of these respective cultural and artistic modes which present views that are as polarised as any to be found amongst the religions and philosophies of the world. Islam is a creed that

An inscription, in square Kufic, declaring 'Allah, there is no God but he', with the 'he' emphasised by a darker tone. This characteristic piece of Islamic calligraphy seems to epitomise the formal, managing and masculine aspects of the Islamic ethos.

emanated from and disseminated into regions of sparsity, the deserts and wastelands. Its temperament has always been affected by a rather severe dedication to the revealed truths of its faith, which it has always regarded as providing absolutely immutable rules of conduct to which successive generations must submit (the term Islam itself derives from a root that implies submission). The *Sharia*, the traditional system of Islamic law, was based on the *Qu'ran* (which Muslims regard as the revealed word of God), and was thus given a divine authority. It was concerned not only with basic moral principles, but with every aspect of existence, for which it laid out the most extensive and detailed rules of conduct. It was, in short, a prescription for an ideal human existence.

*The 'divine order', as expressed
by the favoured Islamic art-
form of pure Platonic
geometric patterning.*

In contrast to the central place of the revelations in Islamic culture Taoism has a more peripheral, though persistent, role in Chinese life. Far from advocating any specific code of conduct Taoism displays an instinctive scepticism towards the value of laws of any kind and it rather commends non-action and withdrawal from society.

Push far enough towards the Void,

Hold fast enough to Quietness,

And of the Ten Thousand Things none can be worked on by you.

*The 'ten thousand things',
meaning the whole cosmos,
represented as a meandering
river.*

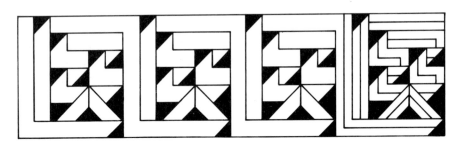

In Islam, however, such a withdrawal is decried. 'Islam is not the monkish way.' The faithful are obliged to marry if they possibly can, are urged to earn their own living, and are even advised to eat in company with others. The emphasis here is very much on the relation of man to others in society, whereas Taoism as a philosophy is not in intention a way of life for ordinary people at all, and its focus is on the greater world of nature.

There are revealing comparisons also in the respective views of the past held by Islam and Taoism. In Islam the period before the revelation has always been considered as a time of darkness, error and superstition. Taoism however has not only held a great reverence for the past but has consistently recommended 'the way of the sages of old'. In all the principle Taoist canons there is an underlying assumption that an ideal society, a sort of golden age, once existed, and that true reform can only be achieved by a return to the conditions of this remote past. It has been pointed out that this ideal must have been very remote indeed, for, as far as one can make out from a study of Chinese history, which is recorded back to the eighth century BC, no trace can be found of anything much more promising than the sort of political turmoil that prevailed at the time of the writing of the main Taoist texts.

'By beauty of shape I want you here to understand not what the multitude generally means by this expression, like the beauty of living things or of paintings resembling them, but something alternatively rectilinear and circular, and the surfaces and solids which one can produce from the rectilinear and circular, with compass, set-square and rule. Because these things are not, like the others, conditionally beautiful, but are beautiful in themselves.'

Plato from his dialogue *Philebus*

'Destroy arcs and lines, fling away squares and compasses. Those who cannot make perfect without arc, line, compass and square injure the natural constitution of things.'

Chuang Tzu

Tree motifs, from Islamic and Chinese sources, reflecting their respective cultural responses to the principles of form and energy.

There are many other aspects of these major cultural influences that could be cited to demonstrate the contrasts between them, but even in those that I have mentioned so far we can begin to see the origination of those quite opposite tendencies of thought that are represented by their respective artistic traditions. For one the law had a divine quality whereas the other regarded all laws as being practically worthless. Islam is an assertive and proselytising religion that is greatly concerned with the conduct of people and the structure of society. Taoism, as a philosophy, is yielding and unassertive, and is extremely sceptical of the outcome of any attempt to improve human society. From this it follows perfectly naturally that the former would employ the pristine clarities of geometrical form in its art, and that the latter should be attracted to the more vital aspects of nature and the metaphors of fluidity, such as water, smoke and flame, which are all favourite Taoist subjects.

The art of calligraphy plays an important part in both traditions, but here again the lines of approach are quite different. The method in Islamic calligraphy is almost invariably measured, contained and precise, whereas in all Chinese scripts that are of Taoist inspiration the emphasis is on spontaneity and the flow of natural energy, and the same is true in the allied art of painting in China. It is characteristic of Islamic art that it has no iconography of the sort that is found in the art of many other major religions such as Hinduism, Buddhism and Christianity, but in spite of this its art forms do manage to convey a distinct sense of the spiritual, and much Taoist art has a similar nobility of purpose. When it comes down to it neither are concerned with the mere world of appearances. In Islam the physical realm has always been secondary to, and derived from, the world of archetypes. Metaphysics comes first, being the point of departure and return (*mabda* and *ma'ad*). There are comparable sentiments in Taoism where, as it is expressed in the *Tao te Ching*, 'the only motion is a returning'. The origin, aims and content of the art that issues from these traditions are as different from each other as any in the world, but they are perfectly accessible to us by virtue of the intensity with which they express a communion with each of the fundamental principles of nature, of pure form and pure energy.

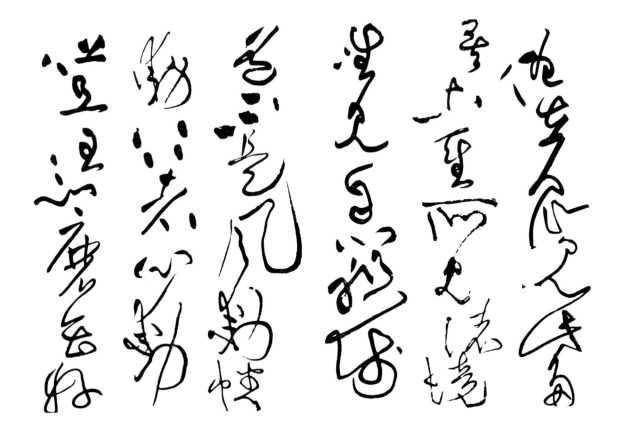

The wild, cursive script of the monk Huang Tingjian, described as evoking thoughts of 'surprised snakes and sudden storms'.

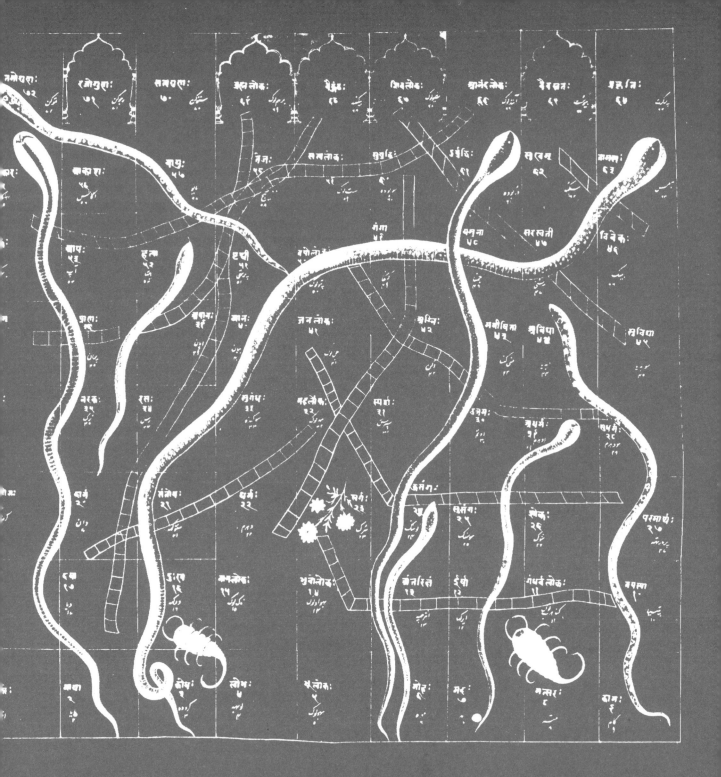

3
Snakes and ladders

Rule of Law, Law of Change

> I compare fortune to one of those violent rivers which, when they are enraged, flood the plains, tear down trees and buildings, wash soil from one place to deposit in another. Everyone flees before them, everybody yields to their impetus, there is no possibility of resistance. Yet although such is their nature, it does not follow that when they are flowing quietly one cannot take precautions, constructing dykes and embankments so that when the river is in flood it runs into a canal, or else its impetus is less wild and dangerous. So be it with fortune. She shows her power where there is no force to hold her in check; and her impetus is felt where she knows there are no embankments and dykes built to restrain her. *Machiavelli*

> The Empire is a divine trust and may not be ruled. He who rules, ruins. He who holds by force, loses. *Lao Tzu*

Aristotle observed that man is a social animal, but of course he is not unique in this respect. A high proportion of animal species live out their lives as members of an organised society, and they do so in an incredible variety of ways. The real distinction between the social behaviour of man and that of other social animals is that whereas their responses are entirely instinctive those of man are not. Our instincts incline us to follow a social existence, but not in any specific way; there is a great variety too in the ways that we express this social tendency and in the ways that human societies choose to organise themselves. The way in which human societies are organised, whether 'primitive' or 'advanced', will always be bound up with a system of belief, and reflect a particular cultural outlook. The problem of how society should best be organised only rose to the surface consciousness when the older magico-religious beliefs were found to be no longer adequate, when man left the state of existence that has been termed mythological. This was the transition that Lucretius referred to as the period when 'men first defiantly raised their eyes to the knowledge of what could and could not come into existence'.

It was just these circumstances that were met by the vigorous and changing societies of the Greek world of the sixth and fifth centuries BC At this period, when all manner of new social forms were appearing, the problem of social organisation was of far more than academic interest, and for this reason the literature of the period seems overly preoccupied with the nature of power and justice and with the relationship between them. The Greeks, with their characteristic thoroughness, brought the full weight of intellectual enquiry to bear on the matter: how, they wondered, should the law be constituted, and how could this law be reconciled with human nature (whatever that was)? In the event, these problems proved to be as intractable as any to which the power of Greek logic was applied. In a sense we are still looking for the answers, and it would begin to appear that an ideal, just and balanced society is, after all, unattainable.

Some Greek philosophers seem to have felt that the problem of finding the best way to organise society could be addressed in the rational methodical way that had proved so successful in revealing the inner laws of nature, but this was not to be: the shortcomings of both human law and human nature are still as familiar to us now as they were to the Greeks. It was a matter of deep concern to many early philosophers that whereas people were capable of the highest thoughts and actions they could also descend to unimaginable depths of savagery: the fifth-century Greeks were in fact extremely conscious of this from their own recent experience. The fact that in our own century we have seen that people are still capable of extremes of barbarism, and this after millennia of civilised existence, testifies at least to the difficulties involved in the complex problem of the relationship between people in society.

It was natural for many of the early philosophers to hold the view that people rose to their greatest potential at times when the constraints of law and conventions of morality were most fully exercised, and that savage and ungovernable behaviour inevitably followed when, for whatever reason, these sanctions were removed. This is a compelling argument and, of course, one that provides the justification for systems of law and morality everywhere. Indeed it is a fairly universal belief that human society is held together by constraints, moral, religious and legal, on individual freedom.

The Greeks themselves were quite familiar with the dire consequences of the breakdown of social values, and the 'ravages of individualism', and they had good cause to come to grips with the problem of maintaining social equilibrium. This is the theme that runs through the work of the greatest of the early historians, Thucydides. In his descriptions of the revolution at Corcyra and of the plague at Athens there are the most graphic accounts of all manner of brutal and 'inhuman' behaviour, which, with some justification, he attributes to the breakdown of social order, a microcosm, as he saw it, of the more general decline of Greek society at that time. It is a melancholy thought that such events are, unfortunately, still liable to occur in almost any part of the world, in spite of centuries of moral induction and the rule of law. There is always the temptation to attribute social ills to the degeneration of conventional mores, but to follow this line of thought blindly is to ignore the fact that an excess of order in a social structure brings its own dangers, not least the injustices and repression of tyranny.

There is a long history behind the supposition that draws an analogy between the order that prevails in nature and the ordering of human society. That there is a powerful ordering influence in nature is quite evident, but many influential thinkers have gone further and felt that there was a direct relationship between the laws of nature and those of human society, and that the latter were in some way dependent on the former. The Danish scholar Bartholinus exemplifies this cast of mind: 'If a law of Nature were to be changed by a kind of disorder, the Glory of human law would also perish.'[1] (Interestingly he made this observation in the context of a dissertation on the arrangements found in crystalline structures.) There are, however, obvious limits to the extent that a theory, or set of principles, that apply in one domain can be extended to another of a quite different order. Laws and conventions can be seen as providing a sort of structure for society comparable to those prevailing in the solid, or crystalline, state; the solid and fluid states are frequently referred to as 'conformist' and 'individualistic' states of matter, although such 'social' analogies only hold if one disregards important distinctions in the relative complexity of these different 'orders'. It is certainly the case that there is a high level of structure in human society, and that there is a general premise that underpins all social groupings – that is, that its members sacrifice some of their individuality for the collective benefit. At its most basic this means that society, like a coherent mass of any kind, is held together by the symmetrical forces of reciprocation.

People being what they are, the enduring patterns of human societies are necessarily complex, in primitive as in our own more 'advanced' systems. In fact there are no genuinely primitive rules of conduct in any society, any more than there are any primitive languages. The norms of tribal societies are maintained by customs and practices that are as complex in their own way as the legal institutions of the modern state. The underlying intention of laws and conventions of all kinds is to instil in the individual a sense of obligation, and in all societies this rests ultimately on deep religious or moral attitudes. It is somehow not surprising then to discover that the root meaning of religion is 'to bind' (*religio*). In the most general sense the force that binds humans together into a social order is the same as that which binds atoms together into a molecular order; but it is only in these most general terms that there is any real comparability between the natural laws of the physical world and the laws of societies.

The notion of symmetry attaches itself to all basic scientific laws; the law of the conservation of energy, for instance, implies a translational symmetry of space and time. Physical laws such as these are regarded in science as absolute, as verifiable in every part of the universe, but social laws and moral decrees can never be absolute in this sense, much as those in authority throughout the ages have tried to insist that they were. The patterns of society, however, do run very deep, and like patterns of all kinds they have an inherent tendency to persist. Social order is sustained by the regulating influence of laws, conventions and moral attitudes into a complex of interacting symmetries but, in common with ordered structures of all kinds, human society is subject to the disturbing influence of change so that its symmetries are being tested constantly. Much of the underlying pattern of European culture can be traced back to the social framework of the classical world, ultimately to the city-states of Athens and Rome, with of course the major modifying influence of the Judaeo-Christian religious tradition. It is worth noting, by way of an aside, that the potent appeal of the Christian ethic itself owes much to the primal symmetry of its central message: 'Do unto others. . .', 'Love thy neighbour as thyself'. But the essential grid of western civilisation was provided by that system which has been described as the 'richest legacy of the ancient world', namely the complex system of Roman civil law, which became the most highly organised legal system that the world had ever known. The watchword of Roman civilisation was order; indeed it was this sense of orderliness, rather than that of art or science *per se*, that became the most enduring characteristic of the Roman spirit. This was a civilisation that was firmly and self-consciously based on the values of *imperium* and *potestas,* i.e. of order and discipline in the state and family respectively. The origin of our reliance on the institution of properly constituted authority derives directly from this tradition.

Romans saw their system of law as the very foundation of the empire and the *Pax Romana*, and it had all the virtues and shortcomings of a rigid and disciplined system. Roman law was highly organised and intended to cover all possible contingencies, and it was notoriously inflexible. When the Christian emperor Justinian recodified this law he genuinely believed that he had created a system that was so perfect that the possibility of further improvement was not admitted; nothing was to be allowed to be taken from, or added to, this body of law, and even commentaries on it were forbidden![2] It was this system, revived at the end of the medieval period, that formed the basis of modern civil and common law in all European countries, and of course in all those parts of the world that in turn came under their influence. Since this came to mean that a substantial proportion of the world as a whole had adopted, or had at least been deeply influenced by, the Roman pattern of society, it must surely be counted as an extremely successful model.

One of the greatest events to influence the development of this social pattern was the Roman conquest of Greece in the second century BC Even before this Rome had admired Greek culture, but the increased contact resulting from the conquest led to an even greater enthusiasm for almost every aspect of its civilisation. In fact in the whole of history there are few instances of the veneration of one culture by another to compare with that of Greece by Rome. Rome, at the time of the conquest, had nothing to compare with the great artistic and scientific heritage of Greece, and was keen to preserve what she could of its superior culture. Perhaps the most important and enduring aspect of this legacy, however, lay in the realm of ideas. All the major Greek philosophical traditions made an impact on Rome: Epicurianism and Stoicism came, at different times, to exert a powerful influence on the early empire, and later there was a great revival of Platonism. The adoption of this latter philosophy in particular was of great significance for the future since, together with that of Aristotle, it was to provide the intellectual continuity between the ancient and the medieval worlds. Neo-Platonism was, in fact, to play a direct part in the development of Christian theology, and was therefore an important component in itself in the formation of European moral attitudes.

The sort of ethical notions that underlie much of western thought, for instance regarding criminal acts such as theft or murder as wrong in an absolute and objective sense, owe a great deal to this Platonic inheritance. It is also true that there is a somewhat authoritarian, even totalitarian, strain in Plato's thought that seems to have carried into the western tradition. We get the best indication of Plato's prescription for society in his dialogue, *The Republic,* where he sets out his ideas in great detail. The sort of ideal society that he envisages here is an extremely orderly, highly regulated state, predicated on the basis that 'reason and principle demand restraint'. According to Plato this rather rigid ideal can only be achieved by the establishment of a precisely delineated hierarchy, indeed by a total fixity of social role.

> In our state we shall find the shoemaker sticking to shoemaking, and not turning pilot as well; the farmer sticking to his farming, and not taking on court work as well.

All other social virtues are subservient to stability; in fact Plato seems always to argue from the point of view of the state *vis-à-vis* the individual, rather than the other way round. In short he adopts a thoroughly 'crystalline' viewpoint.

It is a testimony to the power and originality of Plato's thought that his ideas for the best of all possible human societies are still capable of provoking intense debate. There is no doubting the sincerity of his belief in the value of order in society, and his ideas probably reflect much of his own temperament, but the sense of urgency that comes across in the presentation of his social theories can be more completely understood in an historical context, for while Plato was formulating his prescription for an ideal society the one in which he was actually living was in imminent danger of disintegration. The intense social and political disturbances in the Athens of the fourth century BC, where 'individualism threatened to carry all before it', made a sad contrast with the ideals of order and harmony that had characterised the golden age of the fifth. This terrible decline made the deepest impression on Plato and coloured all his theories. A return to a more disciplined and regulated social order must have seemed an obvious remedy.

Plato is known to have greatly admired the arts and music of Egypt and, in his comments on these, he notes with obvious approval that they were bound by rigid laws and rules. He was fully aware of the great antiquity of Egyptian civilisation and the contrast that it made with the seeming fragility of his own. Egypt was highly regarded in the Greece of this time for its mathematical and geometric skills, and it is significant that the stages of preparation Plato envisaged for his ruler, the philosopher-king, involved an extensive tuition in precisely these disciplines, together with reason and astronomy. It is entirely characteristic that he was far less concerned that his charge should learn to deal with the less predictable aspects of a social existence, such as human nature, a fact that points to the greatest deficiency in his ideas, since moral knowledge is not in any way analogous with scientific knowledge and the great flaw in Plato's reasoning was that he believed it could be.

If there is one moral that we can draw from history with a fair degree of certainty it is that no society, even one as enduring as that of ancient Egypt, is immune from the vagaries of change. Change is inevitable, and it can arise from causes both internal and external to the body politic. There are always likely to be tensions in a given social structure between those whose advantage lies in maintaining its fabric and those who are likely to benefit from change. These greater and lesser beneficiaries are bound to take quite different views of the status quo. It is as natural that the rulers, and those identified with them, should disapprove of any tendency towards disruption or non-compliance with the 'established procedure', as it is for lesser breeds to see advantage in such activities. All advanced societies have their conservatives and their radicals; here is a quotation from a Confucian commentary that epitomises the perennially jaundiced view of the administrator.

> The inferior man is not ashamed of unkindness, and does not shrink from injustice. If no advantage beckons he makes no effort, if he is not intimidated he does not improve himself, but if he is made to behave correctly in small matters he is careful in large ones. This is fortunate for the inferior man.[3]

The views of the 'inferior' man are, of course, not generally recorded to history, and more often than not he was getting too much of the dirty end of the stick even to consider 'improving' himself.

Despite these inevitable conflicts it is clear that the overriding instinct of people in society is towards conformity, with those who dare to flout convention meeting with general disapproval: furthermore all advanced societies have a range of agencies to support their conventions. The family and school are as instrumental in this process as the law and the framework of religious or moral beliefs. There have, however, in the course of history, been many notable occasions when governments have felt that these instincts towards social conformity were inadequate, and there have been various attempts on the part of rulers, usually in the wake of a period of turbulence, to control the actions and the thoughts of their subjects by means of a rigidly enforced and thoroughly comprehensive system of law. Such drastic experiments, which have been tried in both ancient and modern times, are generally characterised by two distinct features – they are usually of relatively limited duration, and they invariably bring in their train a great deal of human suffering.

One of the most notorious such attempts occured in China in the third century BC, with the rise to power of the *Fa Chia* with their ideology of legalism. The objectives of this frankly totalitarian movement was to entirely replace morality with a strictly enforced law.

> Severe laws and heavy punishments are what the people hate,
> but they are the only means by which order can prevail.[4]

To further their ends the *Fa Chia* claimed an identity of the 'good' with the requirements of the ruler. Their ideology had a brutal simplicity: 'right', to them, was 'what the rulers want', and 'wrong' was 'what the rulers do not want', and they instituted draconian measures to endorse their views. As well as insisting on an absolute obedience to the law they introduced a system of forced labour, and advocated the elimination of whole classes of people of whose mode of existence they did not approve, including scholars and academics. This, also, was the time of the notorious episode of the burning of the books; all literature that did not support the legalist credo, i.e. practically everything, was disallowed, including agricultural manuals! The reign of the Legalists (or Realists), as it turned out, was fairly short, but far from sweet. This brutal regime bore many of the familiar hallmarks of the totalitarian excesses of more recent times, and only came to an end with the death of the emperor that it had vaulted to power. Ironically some of the measures that it introduced, such as the standardisation of writing, weights and measures etc., gave China a cultural homogeneity that it has retained to this day.

It is not only in ancient times that governments have attempted to control the lives and minds of their citizens by the imposition of detailed laws of behaviour. In the German society of the sixteenth century, for instance, there were laws covering such fine details of existence as the number of guests that might attend a wedding, the sort of clothes that they should wear and the number of dishes permitted at the wedding feast! The problem always, in imposing such rigid standards of orthodoxy, is not simply that they tend to stifle creative thought, but that they tend to produce uneven and divisive attitudes of mind. This can lead to double standards, cynicism, and even a contempt on the side of the rulers for their subjects.

It is interesting, in this context, that the political theories of the Chinese legalists, like those of Machiavelli, were presented in the form of an 'advice to the ruler', and they demonstrated the same unhealthy combination of high-minded rhetoric and cynical practice: the law was absolute for the citizen, but not for the ruler. In a similar way Plato saw the need for the ruling elite of his ideal society to resort to the stratagem of the 'noble lie', by which the citizens were to be duped into eugenically sound marriages. All dictatorships are flawed in this way, and most of their propaganda is intended to conceal the fact. The justification of repressive measures by those in authority is usually that these are preferable in the longer term to the dilapidation of society. The sort of political reforms that Plato advocated in *The Republic* were motivated by his concern for the increasingly desperate conditions in the Greek world of his time. The Legalists too were driven to action, as they saw it, by the fearful turmoil of the period of the Warring States. Reactionary movements are generally characterised by an intention to establish a disciplined social order, whether on an old or new pattern, and a subsequent resistance to change.

The impulse to institute and maintain order in society is bound to be conservative, and this conservatism is very likely to express itself in 'crystalline' modes of behaviour and dress, in ritual and uniform for example. We can see the emergence of such features in any enduring system, particularly in the regulatory and protective wings of the state, in the legal, religious and military spheres. Within these institutions there is likely to be a strong emphasis on ritual, and their members will almost always be marked out by a distinctive formal dress. All long-established social institutions show these traits, and those that aspire to their position affect the same standards. It is not too far-fetched to draw an analogy between the order of the well-regulated state and the molecular order of the physical world; in fact the ceremonial display of massed military ranks at state occasions are probably the nearest human equivalent to the disciplined ranks of atoms in the solid state. The almost universal inclination towards ritual and uniformity on the part of vested authority can then be seen as a perfectly natural expression, an alignment with a more general ordering principle.

For the clearest exposition of the significance of ritual to authority, and the perception of its necessity for the well being of the state and of society at large, we can turn to Confucius: the Analects are constantly emphasising the virtues of ritual in all things as the 'right way of outward action'.

> Respectfulness without ritual becomes laborious bustle; Carefulness without ritual becomes timidity; boldness without ritual becomes insubordination; straightforwardness without ritual becomes rudeness.

Confucian edicts always manage to convey the impression that they are in accordance with some greater ordering principle, a common assumption of those in authority; 'After all,' they seem to say, 'if the correct proprieties were not insisted on things would simply fall apart.' Certainly Confucius himself believed that heaven knew and approved of his activities, and it was just this sort of pomposity that provoked such an opposite and subversive response from the proponents of that great rival to his social philosophy, Taoism. The Taoists had an entirely different view of the value of ritual .

> Ritual is the mere husk of loyalty and promise-keeping. Indeed it is the first step towards brawling.[5]

To the Taoists the Confucian schemes of government, far from being sublime, presented a ludicrously narrow view of the world; they regarded any such attempt at social organisation as doomed to failure, simply because it did not allow for the relentless forces of change and was therefore bound, sooner or later, to become inappropriate. The structuring and ordering of society from above can never be much more than interference.

> The people are difficult to keep in order, because those above them interfere. That is the only reason why they are so difficult to keep in order.[6]

And even if the government were, by chance, well intentioned:

> There is nothing more fatal than intentional virtue.[7]

To try to govern men by laws and regulations is about as effective as trying to tunnel through a river.

> That the scheme of Empire is in confusion, that the conditions of life are violated,
>
> That the will of God does not triumph, that the beasts of the fields are disorganised,
>
> That the birds of the air cry at night, that blight reaches the trees and herbs,
>
> That destruction spreads among creeping things, this, alas is the fault of government.[8]

It is all the fault of the government! A familiar enough complaint even today, but the humour of this intentionally overstated diatribe has a serious point – however well intentioned, and however effective their administration, schemes of social management can go seriously awry. At worst they produce the very opposite effect to that intended. Prisons, as the 'universities of crime', can promote law-breaking instead of deterring it; the military establishment may be far better at provoking war than at keeping the peace, and so on. In our own century we have seen the way in which high socialist ideals have been subverted into a repressive tyranny, and how 'realistic' measures intended to crush the spirit of a defeated nation created instead a war machine so aggressive that it threatened the entire civilised world!

Nothing is easier, it would seem, than to take sides in a dispute concerning the 'proper organisation of society', not simply in the narrower political sense of 'left' vs 'right', or 'wet' vs 'dry', but also in those more general but equally familiar polarities of 'social responsibility' vs 'personal freedom', ' conventionalism' vs 'free expression' etc. and, having adopted a stance, nothing is more difficult to accept than that each of these sets of opposing principles can be traced back to a more primal division: that neither aspect will ever have a monopoly of the truth, and that there can be no last word in any of these matters.

NOTES

1. In *De Figura Nivis Dissertatia* (1660).
2. The *Corpus Juris Civilia,* the body of civil Roman law, recodified in the 6th century AD.
3. From a Confucian commentary on the *I Ching*, the Chinese Book of Changes.
4. Han Fei Tzu, quoted by Waley (see Bibliography).
5. Lao Tzu, the *Tao te Ching* (see Bibliography).
6. Ibid.
7. Chuang Tzu (see Bibliography).
8. Ibid.

Style and Structure

> If there were no others, there would be no 'me', if there were no 'me' they would not be perceived. *Chuang Tzu*

> We dissect nature along lines laid down by our native language. Language is not simply a reporting device for experience, but a defining framework for it. *Benjamin Lee Whorf*

For a biologist the behaviour of a particular animal species is as distinctive and predictable as its appearance. There are thought to be in excess of a million separate species on earth and each of these is distinguished both by a specific physical make-up and a unique set of behavioural patterns. The factors determining both, of course, concern adaptation to environment. The most successful animals are those that are best adapted to their surroundings; the criteria for adaptation are comprehensive, and involve both the physiological relationship of the species with its environment and its social relationship with other members of its own group. In fact all species conform to innate behavioural patterns to within fairly narrow limits. The only animal to have transcended this species type-casting is *homo sapiens*, but if we think of people in terms of their very different cultural identities, rather than as a single animal species, then the differences are less marked.

It is useful here to speak of style. Human cultural styles, like the styles of animal species, are complex and cohesive; they demonstrate a sense of their own separate identity, and have reached this sense of separate identity by an evolutionary process. The cultural behavioural patterns of humans, like those of animal species, are the direct result of their evolutionary experience; a cultural style, like a species style is, in its very essence, a complex set of responses to the outside world. In other words it is an impressionable structure. Style, of any kind, is a structured response.

'Being, in itself, out of relation, is itself unthinkable.'

Herbert Spencer

As individuals we absorb, from birth, a whole range of cultural and sub-cultural influences. Our sense of identity, the way we see ourselves in relation to society and the greater world, is largely formed by the complex of interconnected beliefs and attitudes that constitute a particular social framework. Whether or not we recognise or like the fact, our sense of ourselves is underlaid by this group identity, the ethos of which is likely to be a subtle blend of religious, national, regional and even familial influences. Even though we might subsequently react against this conditioning we are likely to retain more of it in our own outlook than we realise, since social orientation is fixed at an early age. By the time we are nine, it seems, most of us will have adopted the general outlook that will stay with us for the rest of our lives.

All of us, then, are deeply affected by the social and cultural influences that we are exposed to, particularly in our formative years; it is this that marks us as a special sort of social animal. Indeed it has been discovered in fairly recent times that an early involvement with a social milieu of some kind is actually critical for our individual intellectual development. Most of us will have wondered, at some time or other, just how different our personalities would have been if we had been brought up in a quite different social setting, or none at all; what would our true selves be like without such influences? There is a famous Arabic story, *Hayy ibn Yaqzan* by *Ibn Tufayl*[1], that conjectures the fate of such an uninfluenced mind. This book tells how a shipwrecked infant boy is washed up on a remote, uninhabited island, and manages to survive, initially by being nursed by a gazelle. The child grows up in complete isolation, unsullied by the corrupting influences of civilisation: as the story develops the youth learns to reason methodically and manages by degrees to construct an ordered cosmology for himself, coming ultimately to a philosophical contemplation of God. The book is actually a vehicle for the author's neo-Platonic ideas, but in one essential respect, that of the effects of social deprivation on a developing mind, it has to be judged as quite wide of the mark.

It would, unfortunately, be far more likely that an individual who had been subjected to such an ordeal would be seriously mentally impaired. It is known that this would be the outcome because various rather cruel experiments, in which monkeys were reared in isolation, resulted in their developing severe psychotic conditions; moreover it was subsequently found that important sensory areas in their brains had actually failed to develop. We can be sure that the effect on human subjects, similarly deprived, would be even more disastrous. It would appear that the higher primates, and to an even greater extent humans, are phylogenetically constructed so as to have a positive need for the complementary conditioning of a social pattern; without it we simply do not develop as mature individuals. On the other hand each of us, even the most conforming individual, is much more than the mere sum of these social influences. We all have a sense of ourselves as separate, unique entities by virtue of our possession of that most extraordinary phenomenon, consciousness. This duality has always presented something of a dilemma to those concerned with matters of moral and ethical behaviour; to what extent can anyone be said to operate as a free agent, and therefore be culpable for their actions, when so much of our behaviour is affected by prior conditioning? As individuals we have the profound sense that most of our actions contain an element of choice, but then so does a man who has been hypnotised into believing that he is a dog, or that he is freezing to death, or whatever. The problem of the incongruities of free will and determinism is one of the oldest and most intractable questions in philosophy. It is, in fact, insoluble: none of us is a completely free agent, since so many of our responses are pre-determined by our conditioning to the values of a particular cultural frame, but nor are we entirely 'programmed'. In human behaviour, as in every other aspect of the universe, there is no absolute separation and no absolute symmetry.

'Look that thou make them after their pattern, which was showed thee on the mount.'

Exodus 25:40

To return to the matter of style in the sense of which I spoke earlier, i.e. as an expression of both human and animal identity, it is clear that language is one of its most important components. The essential function of language is *communication*, an obvious requirement for all social animals; it is inconceivable that any human society could operate without language, but in fact there are few, if any, animal species that live out their lives without contact of some kind with members of their own group. This is the point of language; it enables one member of a species, or social group, to influence the behaviour of another within that group. Animal species manage to communicate in a great variety of ways, using visual, auditory and even chemical means. For them language is a relatively simple and unvarying procedure, part of their inherited behavioural patterns, and it has a dual aspect. For it to be effective at all, that is to say for a message to be accepted as such, the sender must be 'placed'; he must first be identified as a member of the same species, and in addition may need to declare his social and sexual status, and must act in a recognisable way, i.e. by conforming to a familiar set of responses.

Just as is the case in animal species, where language is a unique and integral part of their social identity, or style, so it is with us humans. Nothing 'places' us so readily as the style that we project in our speech, manner and mode of dress, etc. From the point of view of the individual this is part of the process of identification with a particular group, or his or her role within society to which others, in turn, can make the appropriate response. A great deal of what passes for polite conversation is, in fact, to do with this business of 'social alignment', but the patterns of human society are even more complex and fluid than those of animal societies, and the 'fixity' of style in such matters as language and dress are only relative. It is true of style, in the most general sense, that to remain effective it must evolve to reflect changing circumstances, and this, of course, is the underlying dynamic of all fashion. Changes of style, in whatever sphere, are always made in relation to a 'previous model'; the lineage must be recognisable, but there must also be presented a more 'advanced' and original view. Seen in this light, fashion is far from being the trivial business that it sometimes appears, in that there is a sense in which it is the very nub of existence. We exist because we are in fashion – for the moment at least!

Human language, as we know, is also subject to the vagaries of fashion. In order to persist in its dual function of communication and identification it has to evolve continuously; all languages, then, are highly evolved structures that support and are part of a particular cultural standpoint. There was a time, in the early 1920s, when a certain group of philosophers[2]

'Human social behaviour is permeated by cultural ritualisation to a degree which we do not fully realise for the very reason of its omnipresence. Everything that is called manners is, of course, strictly determined by cultural ritualisation. 'Good' manners are, by definition, those characteristics of one's own group; and we conform to their requirements constantly.'

Konrad Lorenz

posited the notion of a 'perfect' language: that is, a means of description and communication that had none of the ambiguities and inherent prejudices of all existing languages. In this way they hoped to side-step all the time-consuming arguments about the meaning of words that bedevilled their debates. Their aim was to create a terminology that would reflect the world in an ideal way, rather as a map serves as a reliable guide to a given terrain. However this attempt to construct an entirely formal and 'pure' language met with insuperable difficulties, and was eventually abandoned, but it was an interesting failure. If nothing else this exercise affirmed the infinite subtlety and the essentially organic nature of language. A language is not to be synthesised, it has a life of its own and is the creative expression of an entire culture.

The characterisation of language as a 'tribal machinery' is particularly appropriate, since it emphasises the point that patterns of speech are completely bound up with patterns of thought, and that there is implicit in all languages the sense of a unique cultural style. Such phyletic designations as Celtic or Semitic are essentially language-based; language is the principal medium of group cohesion in all human societies; indeed it is impossible to separate those instincts that go to create a cultural identity from the complex evolution of ideas and attitudes that they embody. We can think of this as an evolutionary process. Ideas and attitudes have a momentum of their own; like any organism they tend to persist and to propagate themselves, they are receptive to similar structures and resist others, they can fuse and recombine, which enables them to evolve, and moreover to evolve selectively. It follows too that there will be evolutionary advantage in those sets of ideas that constitute a cultural style; a sense of style imparts a cultural unity, it provides a norm to which and with which members of a group can respond and identify; it creates a sense of confidence. Most people do belong to social groups that influence their opinions and judgements, and it is clear that there are obvious advantages in adopting a group attitude. It is far easier, for instance, for members of a group to make a generalised, rather than an individual, response to situations that present themselves, to be able to classify events according to a particular outlook. In this way even a prejudiced point of view could be held to confer evolutionary advantage, i.e. survival value. Group attitudes will, naturally, be self-perpetuating; expectations of behaviour are themselves a powerful influence on behaviour. It is also the case that the extent and manner in which new ideas are accepted within a group, of whatever scale, depend on how they fit with the pre-existent constitution or psyche of that group, or entire culture. Although it is intangible a shared cultural frame is as real as anything that we are likely to experience; when it is undermined, as has sadly happened to many tribal communities in the past with the impact of more 'advanced' civilisations, the results can be utterly disastrous.[3]

In general, however, cultural patterns are resilient; like graphic patterns they might be transformed by all manner of changes and additions and yet survive in their essential form. History is full of examples of deeper and more ancient patterns of belief resurfacing in different guises. An example of this in recent history was the way in which Marxism unwittingly incorporated into its revolutionary creed many far older, mythological beliefs; in the notion of 'dictatorship of the proletariat', for example, we can detect the ancient notion of the 'just', or 'chosen' people; the imminent arrival of the 'classless society' was, in essence, a version of the millennialist expectation of a golden age; the 'inevitable decline of capitalism' a replay of the 'final battle between good and evil', with of course the expectation of the triumph of the former.[4]

Humans have a strong genetic disposition towards a social existence, but it is unspecific. Although most animal behavioural patterns are far more intensely prescribed by genetic conditioning than those of humans there are useful parallels. Many bird species, for instance, inherit a disposition towards a certain mode of song, which provides the basis for individuals to learn the particular, current language of their own group or locality. In the same way people have to learn to adopt a particular social style, though if ethnology has demonstrated anything it is the sheer variety of ways in which this social tendency can be expressed. There are differences too in the kinds and degree of conformity required by various societies: some, it could be said, are more 'crystalline' than others, i.e. requiring a greater degree of conformity to the norm, and, of course, there are bound to be variations in individual response to the norm. There are, however, certain universal forms of social behaviour that could reasonably be described as amounting to an innate group psychology.

There is a willingness on the part of most members of social groups to recognise their own rules of behaviour as the norm, and to invest the authority of leadership in particular individuals. There are interesting connections between this predisposition towards social conformity and individual susceptibility to hypnotic suggestion that give this trait an unsuspected social value. Within the group, however, leaders themselves are fully expected to conform to established and familiar patterns of behaviour; typically authority figures will adopt a pose that is considered appropriate to their position and a distinguishing mode of dress, but whilst in office they are expected to act within certain prescribed limits. The urge towards social conformity is concerned, ultimately, with the reassurance of continuity; to belong to a group and to have an assured position in a particular social grid seems to fulfil a basic human need. This is the reason that the loss of one's position in society, through unemployment say, or retirement, or marriage break-up, is frequently accompanied by a loss of self-esteem, social disorientation and introspective depression.

Another indication of the importance of the value of social identity can be seen in those circumstances where, for whatever reason, an individual chooses to reject some or all of their familiar social values. In these cases there is likely to have been a 'conversion' of some sort, where many of the old allegiances are replaced by a whole different set of attitudes. It is well known that a convert is usually far more fervent in his new found beliefs than more established members of the group to which he aspires. This is easily understood as part of an attempt to emphasise the new identity, to establish a personal position within the new set of principles or social framework. George Orwell, in the 1930s, was constantly berating those 'rebels' who, whilst rejecting the bourgeois values of capitalist imperialism, were rather less critical of the shortcomings of Bolshevik imperialism.

This business of social alignment is closely related to style. It is the most interesting aspect of fashion that as new sets of ideas spring up from within a social group and attract a following, they are accompanied by new and distinctive modes of dress, manner of speech, etc. (This is almost obligatory when the young begin to assert their independence.) By contrast those elements of society that see their business as the maintenance of the social pattern, the Church, police, legal profession etc., almost invariably affect styles that demonstrate their resistance to change. This is certainly true in Britain at least; here the police uniform is a modified version of a nineteenth-century original, the law persists in a seventeenth-century fashion of wigs and gowns, and ecclesiastical attire is positively ancient. All societies, even primitive ones, have the equivalents of this sort of ritualistic conservatism which may appear solemn or ridiculous according to one's standpoint. Styles themselves, then, can be 'crystalline' or 'dragonlike'. The function of the uniformity and conservatism of official dress, and the repetitious nature of ceremony, is to demonstrate the continuity of a particular social pattern. On the other hand most advances in fashion are clearly intended for a quite different purpose, usually to mark a distinction between a new style and that of an existing order. Fashion is identified with change, but if it is successful it too will be incorporated into the norm, and there is a sense in which this is a universal principle.

Style is an expression of the originality, of the uniqueness, of ourselves as individuals, of the group within society, of the larger society itself, even of species. By definition no species, societies or individuals are quite alike. Yet we can never think of ourselves as entirely separate from the social framework that was our formative influence; it is part of our very essence. These then are the terms of existence: there is a distinction between the particulars of all phenomena down to the most minute detail, but there is no absolute separation. How better to explain this basic paradox of the discrete continuity of phenomena than as the result of the play of two eternally co-existent forces of order and energy, of the 'crystal' and the 'dragon'?

NOTES

1. Interestingly this work was first published in English just a few years before Defoe wrote *Robinson Crusoe*, and it is thought likely to have influenced his writing of it.

2. The 'Vienna Circle' of Logical Positivists.

3. 'To kill a culture it is often sufficient to bring it into contact with another. The people of the subdued side then tend to look down upon everything they previously held sacred, and to ape the customs which they regard as superior.' *On Aggression* by Konrad Lorenz.

4. I owe this observation to Mircea Eliade (*Sacred and Profane*).

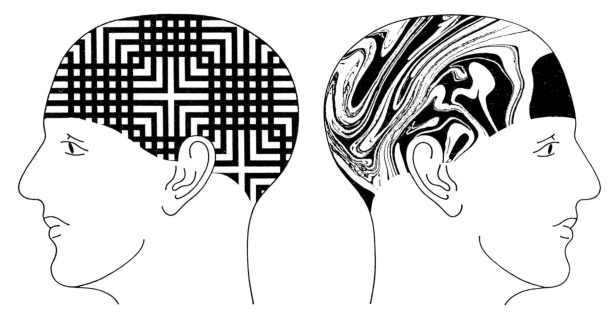

Crystal Mind, Dragon Mind

One of the most obvious facts about the human cerebrum is that it is double. One hemisphere is structurally the gross image of the other. That is, the other side is not only structurally the same, but is working just as hard. I submit that the informational capacity of one is just as great as the other, or put differently, the other side is not only working just as hard, but also just as intricately. *Joseph Bogen*

Most of the gods of Roman mythology have their equivalents in the Greek pantheon – Venus is Aphrodite, Cupid Eros, Mercury Hermes and so on – but there is one notable and interesting exception in the enigmatic figure of Janus, the two-faced god, who is an exclusively Roman deity. Janus is undoubtedly a god of ancient origin and before he was superseded by Jupiter was in fact the most important of all Roman gods. We learn from Ovid that, at the time when air, fire, water and earth were a formless mass, Janus was called Chaos, and that it was only when these elements separated out that he assumed his familiar name and appearance. Quite often he was portrayed as bearing an alarmed or surprised expression, as if to reflect the confusion of his original state. It is possible that Janus, as he is depicted in Roman mythology, is actually a survival from a far older set of beliefs and that he represented an animistic dualistic principle of a kind that is found in the beliefs of tribal societies in many parts of the world.

Wherever he is found this bifrous or double-countenanced figure, who is forever staring in opposite directions, presents a particularly striking and evocative piece of imagery. Like so many mythical figures he embodies a range of symbolic intentions that support a whole variety of interpretations. Janus would probably have taken on a rather different significance when he was adopted as chief god by the Romans, and may easily have undergone earlier metamorphoses – this is the essential quality of myth, that it has the

The higher levels of human brain function take place in the cerebrum, the largest and most recently evolved part of the brain; the cerebrum consists of two distinct halves (the cerebral hemispheres) and it has been discovered that these separate regions process information in different ways and have their own areas of specialisation. The left side is more logical in its approach, the right more intuitive and syncretic.

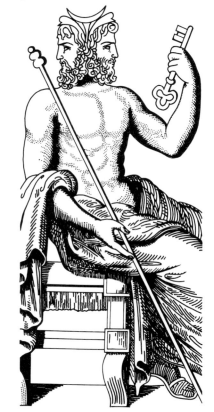

Janus, the two-faced deity, was at one time the Roman 'god of gods'; among other attributes he was felt to be responsible for the civilising of the human race.

capacity for regeneration and therefore of reinterpretation. For us in the late twentieth century the Janus myth has acquired a new and unexpected significance, and it is one that may only have been dimly intuited in the past, for recent research into the way the human brain functions have revealed that the unity of our conscious experience derives from an underlying duality. Humans themselves, so we are informed by neurologists, are quite literally two-minded beings.

An appreciation of the implications of some of the remarkable discoveries in recent neurological research is bound to involve a digression into the physiology of the brain, and this subject, I realise, is not everybody's cup of tea. I apologise for this in advance and being of a squeamish disposition myself will treat the matter as briefly and as delicately as possible.

Anatomists had long realised that the cerebrum, which accounts for some 90 per cent of brain mass in humans, is comprised of two distinct halves, the cerebral hemispheres. Later it was discovered that the higher levels of brain function take place here, and also that these are the most recently evolved parts of the brain. As long ago as 1911 the psychologist William McDougall put forward the somewhat macabre hypothesis that a surgical splitting of these parts of the brain might lead to the existence of two 'selves', each with independent streams of consciousness and self-awareness. Somewhat surprisingly this alarming proposition has since been verified: it is indeed the case that when the connection between the hemispheres is severed two independent psychic entities, a veritable dual consciousness, are brought into being. This is true not only for humans, but for all the higher animals.

Dramatic confirmation of the functional dualism of the brain came in the early 1960s during studies on the effects of drastic brain surgery on severe epileptic patients. The results of these early findings had enormous implications, both for neurology itself and for the study of the human psyche in general. From these investigations it became increasingly clear that normal consciousness, that most precious of gifts, derived from the subtle integration of the mental processes of two psychic compartments, each with an independent capacity for learning, remembering and perceiving. As may be imagined this discovery received a great deal of attention and raised a host of further questions, not least of which was the basic problem of just why the human brain should have been arranged in this way in the first place. Why should nature have indulged in this apparently unnecessary duplication of such a huge range of our neural activities? Why, in short, should we need two brains instead of just one?

The key to the form and function of any aspect of any living organism is, of course, evolutionary advantage. To begin to understand the reasons why the human brain is constructed in the way it is we have first to look at the evolution of sensory systems in a more general way. The main reason that our brain has a double structure, in common with the brains of all other higher animals, is because it is an integral part of a nervous system which itself follows a gross morphology that is laid out on bilateral lines.[1] This is an arrangement that goes back to the very earliest developments of neural circuitry. In fact the origins of this preferred form go so deep as to be bound up with the emergence of perception itself. At the most elementary level

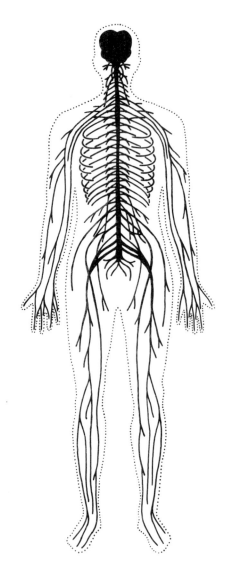

The gross morphology of the human nervous system (of which the brain is an integral part) follows the general plan of bilateralism found in the body.

an organism only exists by maintaining its separate identity in the face of an indifferent, or even hostile, environment, with which it is continually reacting and interacting. Paradoxically, this entails the construction of an isomorphic representation, or map, of the outside world, with respective features occupying the same position with regard to each other as in the actual world.

Very simple creatures, of course, create very simple maps, and the more complex the perceptual system the more complete its reconstruction of its map of the world. There is however a basic problem with maps, one that most of us will have experienced at one time or other, and that is in determining one's own position in relation to it. In simple terms, to know which way is up. A sense of gravity is, in itself, a useful device for orientation, but it transpires that a bicameral approach is a virtual necessity in the process of perceptual map-interpretation, particularly for visual systems owing to the technical necessity for lens-reinversion. Complex brains, such as our own, derive from earlier models that might be described as having a twin-analogue system, and although ours is a far more complicated piece of apparatus it preserves many of the original, essentially bilateral features.

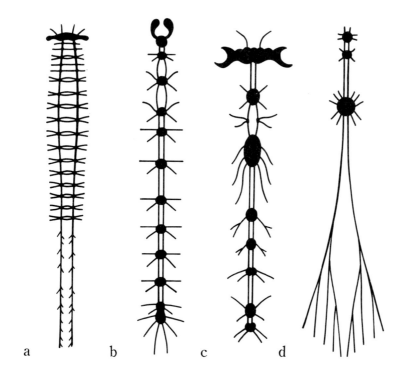

The emergence of a 'duplicated' structure, somewhat resembling a rope-ladder, can be seen in these primitive developments of nervous systems, the ganglia forming accumulations of nerve cells at the points where the 'rungs' and 'struts' cross. (a) Primitive crustacean (b) Caterpillar (c) Honeybee (d) Water-bug. (after Buchsbaum)

Bilateralism, it has to be said, has been a tremendous success in evolutionary terms; it is a very good format for getting around, whether on land, in the sea or in the air, and this, after all, is what animals, unlike vegetables, want to do. Animals have an appropriate symmetry for their needs, but their locomotive habits have also required them to develop complex nervous systems. Virtually all nervous systems then are constructed along bilateral lines. Our own, like that of most animals, has a dual structure to deal with the paired arrangements of our arms, legs, eyes, kidneys etc. This neural bilateralism also applies to the structure of the brain itself, particularly to its uniquely developed 'higher' structures, the cerebral hemispheres. Each hemisphere is the mirror image of the other and each side works as hard as the other. In purely physiological terms they are virtually symmetrical, but there are important differences in the way that they operate and they are now generally regarded as being functionally *asymmetrical,* that is to say that each brain half has its own *modus operandi* and its own areas of specialisation.

The cerebral hemispheres are bridged by great bundles of nerve fibres known as commisures (shaded black), the most important of which is the corpus callosum. (a) The corpus callosum allows for reciprocal connections between corresponding centres in the cerebral hemispheres. (b) The thalamus acts as a relay between the cerebral cortex and lower level structures of the nervous system.

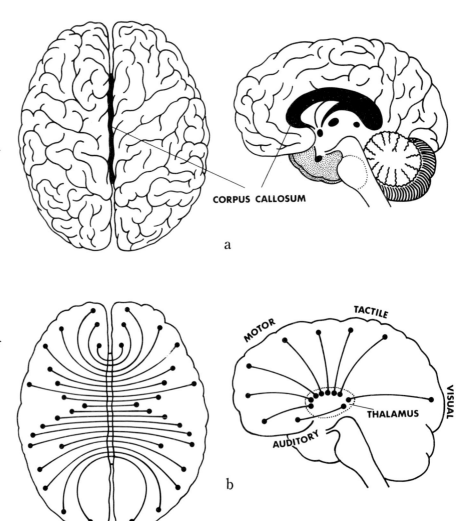

One of the most conspicuous indications of this functional asymmetry, or lateralism, is the phenomenon of 'handedness' (right or left). Far more dramatic evidence though has come through the observation of the effects of damage to the respective hemispheres. If a part of the left hemisphere is affected by accident or disease it can seriously impair certain higher intellectual faculties, such as speech, in a way that seems not to happen if the damage is sustained in the corresponding part of the right side. Accumulated evidence of this sort led nineteenth-century neurologists to ascribe a 'dominant' role to the left hemisphere, a view, which although it has some foundation, has been greatly modified by more recent discoveries. The current idea is that both hemispheres are involved in higher cognitive functioning, but that there is a division of labour, and fundamental modal differences between the two sides.[2]

These differences, as I have already mentioned, first came to be appreciated through observation of the contrasting effects of left- and right-brain damage: typically a patient with damage on the left side may be unable to comprehend a given statement, but may be able to recognise its emotional tone, whereas a patient with a right hemisphere disorder can usually understand the meaning of what is said, but often fails to recognise its emotional content, whether it is spoken in an angry or humorous way for instance.[3] Effects such as these are an indication of the functional duality of the brain; in general terms there seems to be a divide between logical and intuitive lines of approach. The right brain is better at recognising things that are not easily put into words, whereas the left strives towards order and logical consistency. It has been shown that each hemisphere has the ability to perceive, remember and learn quite independently of the other, and that they perform these functions idiosyncratically; that is to say that the two hemispheres process information differently, and are organised differently. It is not surprising, in view of the fact that they are separate entities, that they should have differing views of the world.

In spite of their marked differences there is a modal complementarity in the functions of the separate hemispheres: one could generalise and say that the left tends to think in words, and the right in images, but the division and specialisation of their respective talents go much further than this. For comparison we can list their characteristic modes of thought.

Left	Right
logical, rational	intuitive, emotional
verbal	non-verbal
analytical and convergent	syncretic and divergent
sequential	simultaneous
linear	spatial

Perhaps the most appropriate generalisation that could be made in respect of the differences between left and right brain function would be to say that the former is 'crystalline' in its approach and the latter 'dragonlike'.

There are fairly obvious risks attached to a brain that operates on a double-plan system, the most outstanding being the danger that the two separate mental domains might vie with each other for control over the organism. In all developed brains where this is a potential hazard the problem is averted by the establishment of neural pathways that form a connective 'bridge' which allows information to be exchanged freely between the two parts of the brain, and which facilitates the co-ordination of their mental activities. In the human brain these consist of massive bundles of nerve–fibres that establish reciprocal connections between corresponding centres in each hemisphere, and are known as commisures. The most important of these is the corpus callosum which is, in effect, a massive communication cable that carries something in the order of 200 million lines! If, for whatever reason, these connections are seriously impaired the two parts of the brain do indeed operate as if they were two individuals inhabiting the same body.

According to Sperry[2] the corpus callosum performs the important function of allowing the hemispheres to share learning and memory, and this happens in two ways: by transmitting the information at the time the learning takes place and by supplying it when required on later occasions. Interestingly though the information that is transferred seems always to be of a 'ready-processed' and 'high-level' nature. In other words each half of the brain thoroughly analyses and processes its own perceptions before passing on any information. Although the hemispheres are thoroughly connected by the informational linkage system of the commisures there are 'Chinese walls' between them, enabling each side to retain an independent mode of thought. This bilateralism, where the experiences of one side are not always useful to the other, might, on the face of it, appear to be a rather inefficient system, but it now seems likely that the net result of this dual-perceptual approach is to maximise the productive capacity of the brain as a whole.

The normal mental processes of the brain then involve a subtle and complex integration of distinct and specialised talents, a function which is largely mediated through the corpus callosum. Although we are not consciously aware of it, our perceptual focus constantly 'switches' from one mode to the other, with the most appropriate taking over for the particular task at hand. In certain unusual circumstances, such as in hypnotic or drug-induced states (and possibly schizophrenia), a double consciousness may come to the surface. Presumably here the normal dominance-determining mechanism has broken down to some extent. At its most efficient though the brain engages in the sort of activity that Einstein referred to as a 'combinatory play', combining the intuitive leaps of the non-verbal right with the rational, analytical method of the verbal left. The right brain is essentially more 'fluid' in its approach, and can achieve rapid and complex syntheses that are far beyond the capacity of the left. It is more skilled at tasks involving mental association and ideation, but it does not have the intellectual equipment to express these verbally: it has little aptitude either for arithmetical problems, being unable for instance, to calculate 'even to the extent of doubling the numbers 1 – 4' (Sperry). Serial tasks of this sort are really the province of the left brain, which is more logical, literal and systematic, one might say 'dry', in its approach. If we draw on the well-used, though rather limited, analogy of brain function with computer operation then the left is essentially *digital* in its method, and the right *analog*.

In answer to the question why the brain should divide its functions precisely along these lines we have to assume that it is for reasons similar to those that influenced its evolution as a bilateral structure in the first place, i.e. that it is a more efficient system and therefore confers evolutionary advantage. To begin to understand what is involved here we have to adopt the Platonic premise that the real world can never be known. Whatever sort of organism we might be, our knowledge of our environment is based on the best reconstruction of it that our sensory apparatus can reproduce. In the case of human beings this perception is a product of the combination of the separate experiences of the two cerebral hemispheres. It is useful to draw an analogy with the phenomenon of binocular vision, itself a perceptual device that gives us a richer and more 'realistic' concept of three-dimensional space. We can manage reasonably well, of course, with just one eye, and by the same token we can get by without the minor hemisphere or the connective commisures, but there is no doubt that, just as stereoscopic vision is far more useful, the combination of the two perceptual systems is far more effective than one on its own. In other words we are *stereocognitive*, and this perceptual arrangement is particularly effective because its dual aspects respond to a world that itself manifests a similar combined duality.

The brain of every individual, of course, is organised in subtly different ways, its psychic configurations creating unique patterns of ability and personality. Each individual psyche makes its own response to the inherent dualism of the mind/brain just as it responds to the cultural dualisms that are a feature of all social structures. In general these preferences are made as unconsciously as those of the left/right dominance determining reflex itself: we are quite 'naturally' of an artistic or scientific cast of mind, or, for that matter, political orientation. There is evidence, derived from experiments involving a sample of students, that seems strongly to support the premise that those individuals who habitually rely more on their left brain tend towards scientific subjects and adopt an intellectual approach to problems whereas those who depend more on their right side incline more towards the arts, and have a generally higher emotional response. These results are interesting, but not entirely surprising. It has been suggested though that similar criteria might apply on a cultural level. The psychologist Robert Ornstein has put forward the idea that the divide between eastern and western modes of consciousness traces back to cultural emphases on the different hemispheric modes of perception. This goes much further into the realms of speculation, but it is certainly the case that such an influential eastern philosophy as Taoism, which always advocated non-verbal, non-logical and 'fluid' methods, has no real equivalent in the history of western thought. The doctrines and art of Taoism, and its spiritual successor Zen Buddhism, always emphasise the importance of immediacy and non-angularity, and are distinctly right-brained in spirit.

This cultural bias against left-brained modes of thinking, if it is indeed the case, would go some way to explaining the reasons why Chinese civilisation, for all its prodigious achievements, never developed an enthusiasm for science comparable to that of the west.[4] Science, indeed, can be seen as an institutionalisation of left-brain activity. Sperry takes the view that our culture is too one-sided in this respect, and feels that it tends to undervalue non-verbal forms of intellect and that the educational systems of the west actually discriminate against the right hemisphere.[5] One is reminded here of the Taoist reservations concerning the 'scholastic illusion' – that information that is classified is felt, often mistakenly, to be thoroughly understood. Psychologists involved in the study of brain asymmetry have noticed that the left brain has a distinct tendency to 'take over' and feel itself responsible for all the actions of an individual, even to the extent of rationalising those decisions made by its right partner that it has played little or no part in making. There is surely an analogy here between this response and the rationalisation of governments and rulers of all kinds, that they know best; and of course it is the overbearing attitude of authority that leads to the sometimes 'subversive' quality of right-brain activity. As well as the social polarisation of authoritarianism vs libertarianism there is a whole range of other traditional dualisms – intellect vs intuition, science vs art, the logical vs the mysterious – that are traceable, not simply to the cerebral activities occurring in different parts of our brains, but to a deeper, fundamental phenomenal duality.

One of the philosophical problems thrown up by the confirmation of the dual mechanism of the brain concerns the nature of consciousness. It began to appear that most of the criteria ordinarily adopted to describe the start of conscious awareness could equally well be applied to the independent cerebral activities of the separate hemispheres – where then was the 'self'? This is a characteristically twentieth-century problem; relativity and quantum theory had earlier performed the same sort of vanishing trick on energy, matter, space and time. The answer, in a sense, to both problems is the same, that these and all phenomena exist only on the cusp of interaction between the respective *theos* of the crystal and the dragon.

NOTES

1. Bilateral is used here in its more usual sense, meaning a three-dimensional reflection about a plane; strictly speaking the form of symmetry described in this way is dorsiventral. If we were genuinely bi-lateral we would have faces on the backs of our heads as well as the front.

2. Dr. Roger Sperry of the California Institute of Technology won the Nobel Prize for Physiology and Medicine in 1981 for his pioneering studies of 'split-brain' patients.

3. 'Specialisation of the Human Brain'. Geschwind, N. *Scientific American*, September, 1975.

4. Science likes to divide, quantify and measure activities in which the Taoists were reluctant to engage: it is entirely characteristic of Chinese metaphysical speculation, for instance, that it should lack any 'atomist' theories.

5. *Lateral Specialisation of Cerebral Function in the Surgically Separated Hemispheres*. 1973.

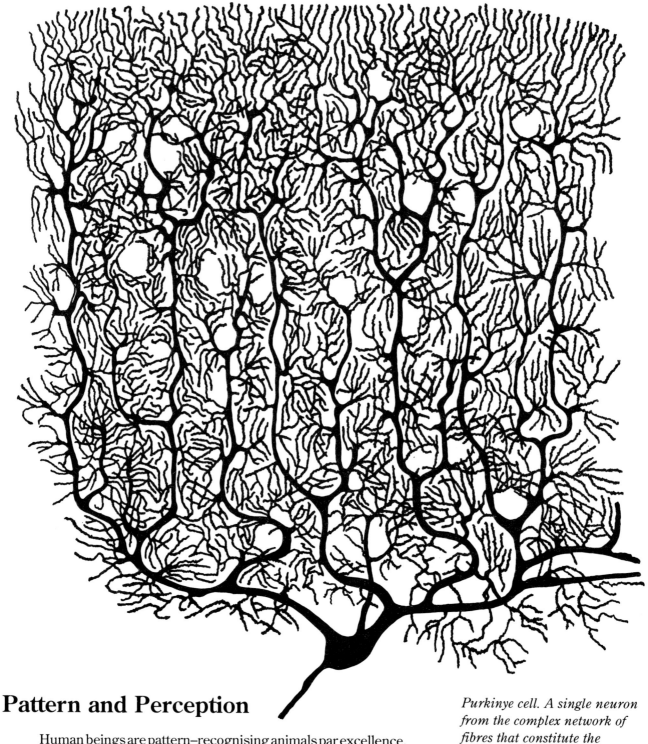

Pattern and Perception

Purkinye cell. A single neuron from the complex network of fibres that constitute the human nervous system.

> Human beings are pattern–recognising animals par excellence.
> *Heinz Pagels*

There is a Chinese tradition that attributes the superiority of man, and his separation from other animals, to his ability to weave. This piece of folklore, as is often the case, shows a canny piece of intuition; first because it links the notion of intelligence with the faculty for pattern recognition, and secondly because it acknowledges that human beings are particularly good at this. In fact it is precisely our capacity for abstract and systematic thought that enables us to identify and reapply the many patterns that we

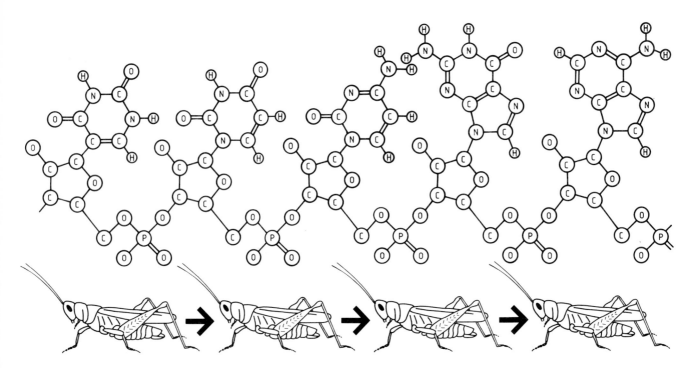

Life-forms first emerged through their capacity to recognise pattern; the metabolisms of even the most simple forms are controlled by regulatory patterns of great complexity, and all species are able to persist only by virtue of the invariant arrangements within their genetic code.

observe: it is these skills, exactly those required for weaving, which give us the edge over all other animals. Of course all organisms, right down to the most humble unicellular creatures, are consummate pattern recognisers; all living things persist by recognising their particular needs amongst the uncertainties of their environment, and will, in addition, have acquired the skill of perpetuating their pattern of existence by means of replication. There is a sense in which the beginning of life is identical to this aptitude for pattern manipulation, and consciousness is simply its ultimate development. One way of looking at the human nervous system, with its arrangement of some ten billion nerve cells, is that it is the finest instrument that we know of for detecting and utilising patterns in a cosmos that is itself thoroughly imbued with pattern.

The tremendous impact that evolutionary theory made on biology in the middle of the last century tended to overshadow other developments in that field which were to have equally far-reaching implications for human thought in general. It was at around this time that scientists were beginning to grasp the essential distinction between living and non-living matter. Many, for instance, were beginning to dispute the long-held notion of a vitalising *élan vital*; it was also becoming clear for the first time that there were no chemical elements that were peculiar to the constitution of living creatures, but rather that they were made up of nothing more or less than the materials that were available to them in their own environments. It was becoming apparent that the physical basis of life lay not so much in any mystical vitalising force, or in some peculiarly magical constituent, but in the ways in which ordinary, elemental, materials were reconstituted into higher and more complex forms.

At the same time that biologists were making these radical assertions, chemists, for their part, were beginning to recognise and classify the essential and irreducible constituents of all matter, both living and non-living. The classical notion that all the matter in the world was somehow made up of the elements of earth, air, fire and water had long been

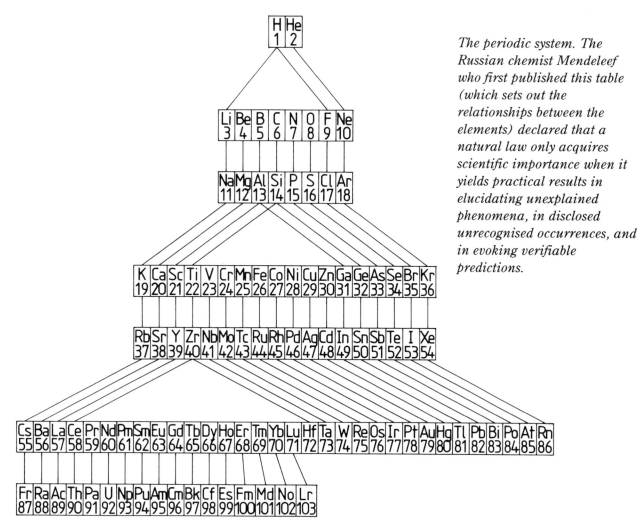

discounted as a credible proposition, and had been gradually replaced by a more methodical system that classified elements according to their chemical and physical properties. This process culminated, in 1869, in Mendeleef's proposals for a periodic system of elements. This new system of classification was so successful that it not only corresponded very well with all observed data at that time, but also predicted the existence of previously undiscovered elements. But its principal achievement was to establish the correlations between the properties of the various elements and their atomic weights. Through Mendeleef's table an elegant pattern of relationships emerged which placed all chemical elements in a clear and immutable system, a system moreover that is valid for every part of the cosmos. As another pioneering chemist put it (in terms that would have delighted the Pythagoreans): 'The properties of the elements were found

Water is formed when two hydrogen atoms share their electrons with a single oxygen atom in an extremely cohesive molecular arrangement.

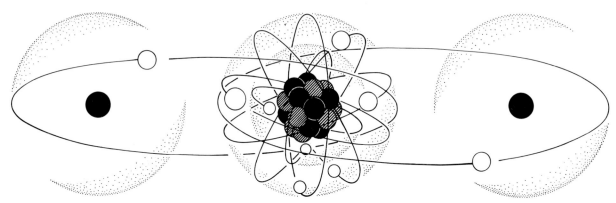

81

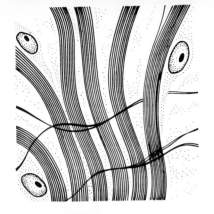

a

b

c

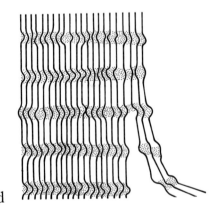

d

Biology as 'the study of fibre': the fibrous hierarchy of collagen at different magnifications: (a) a molecular chain (b) a fibril consisting of parallel chains (c) a single fibre composed of many fibrils (d) collagen fibres in connective tissues.

to be the properties of numbers.' In time the table of elements came to be better understood as the expression of the arrangements of forces within the atoms that constituted the elements. The chemical properties of every sort of material were, it turned out, entirely conditioned by the numbers of its electrons or protons.

Among the great problems for the early chemists were those difficulties that they encountered in trying to analyse the chemical nature of such everyday materials as wood, bone, animal and vegetable fibres etc., but gradually it became apparent that the basic elements of which these materials were constituted could also be found in inorganic form. Then there arose the problem of how this organic material, in all its diversity, could be made up of the carbon, hydrogen and oxygen of which it seemed mainly to consist. Eventually it became clear that all the differences of texture and strength in natural materials derived from their internal, molecular structure in arrangements that drew their cohesive power from that of the molecular bond. So the macroscopic structures of all living creatures are, in essence, based on microscopic interactions of the same order as those of crystalline morphologies. Living organisms are, for the most part, made up of giant molecules, the production of which from less complex materials is one of the main functions of organic metabolism.

Some of these organic molecular components are very large indeed; a typical arrangement within proteins for instance might consist of tens or even hundreds of thousands of atoms. The characteristic form of these structures consists of a regular 'chain', the staple of which is based on repetitious sequences of particular groups of atoms. These strands, the 'chains of life', are the foundational units in the ascending series of fibrous structures of which all living things are constructed. (Indeed biology has been well characterised as the 'study of fibres'.) In all organic materials the basic macromolecular units go to make up colloidal particles, which, in turn, form the essential material of all cell structures. Although a great deal of this macromolecular material is actually in solution within living cells its arrangement is intensely proscribed; molecular orientations within cell structures are infinitely more complex than those of any inorganic crystal form, but they are so structured that there is little about these arrangements that is truly fluid. There is, of course, a prodigious variety of cell types, all of which have evolved to meet specific functional requirements; there is no such thing as a typical cell. To get some idea of this diversity we have only to consider the range of types of cell structure in our own bodies, such as bone, nerve and muscle, not to mention such highly specialised materials as those used in our eye lenses or nervous systems. It is truly astonishing to think that the constitutions of all the plants that grow, and of all the creatures that walk, fly and swim about the surface of the earth are like this, that is to say that they are comprised of level upon level of interactive, and interdependent patterns of organisation.

(Opposite page) Organic molecules (proteins and nucleic acids) are the basic components of all living organisms, both plant and animal. These complex molecular arrangements are seemingly endless in their variety; no two species of any organism, for instance, share the same form of protein. (a) A typical fat. (b) Carbohydrates. (c) Protein. (d) Nucleic acid.

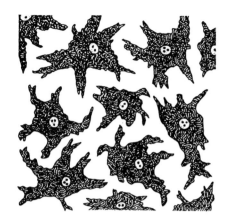 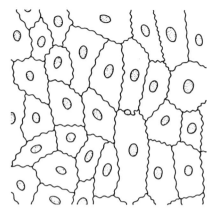 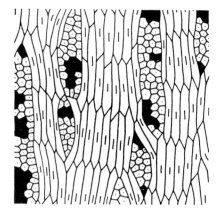

So one picture that we might form of nature is that of a structural hierarchy; just as the various and distinct properties of the elements rest on the arrangements within their component atoms, so these arrangements in turn give rise to all the possibilities of molecular compounds, right up to the incredible complexities of the electrochemical exchanges involved in organic metabolisms, and from this, of course, on to the infinitely complex patterns of animal behaviour. From this sort of morphological standpoint it is all too easy to see the temptations of a purely deterministic interpretation of the world, i.e. a perception of an order of nature as an elegantly interconnected complex of causes and effects. This view however has been gradually superseded by a science that has become increasingly more enthusiastic to develop an understanding of nature in terms of the energy transfers involved between its various levels of organisation. In fact the deterministic presumption was finally and fatally undermined by the advent of the quantum revelations with their new description of matter at the sub-atomic level. It was found that the principal actors of that world, the infinitesimal particles, behaved in the most erratic and uncontrolled ways. Far beneath the stately order of the ranks of the elements in their periodic array there existed a particulate madhouse of chaos and randomness. Further, it was found to be impossible to describe simultaneously the whereabouts and the actions of these entities: a purely deterministic interpretation was unable to account for these disturbing events in what should have been the very foundation of their cosmic constructions. Heisenberg's uncertainty principle, which gave quantum theory its mathematical foundation, had devastating implications both for the notion of scientific objectivity and for its deterministic causality. The primacy of an ordered perception of nature gave way to an energy-based view: order there certainly was, but it could no longer occupy the pre-eminent role that old-fashioned determinism had tried to create for it.

Cell structure. Virtually every part of all plant and animal life is made up of cells, most of which have highly specialised functions. There is no typical cell structure, but many have common structural features.

'It seems to be one of the fundamental features of nature that fundamental physical laws are described in terms of a mathematical theory of great beauty and power, needing quite a high standard of mathematics to understand it. You may wonder, Why is nature constructed along these lines? One can only answer that our present knowledge seems to show that nature is so constructed. We simply have to accept it.'

Paul Dirac

The quantum revelations obviously brought with them some fairly profound philosophical implications, not only for science, which they put on a whole new footing, but also in a more general way, for our certainties (those basic assumptions that affect the way in which we see the world) are as likely these days to be founded on a scientific as on a religious base. In fact the matter of the relationship between the world as we see it and as it might 'really' be is a question that philosophers have long been concerned with. The problem, put simply, is this: to what extent can we be sure that our perceptual continuum tallies with the continuum of externally existent things? Does the order and coherence that we perceive as a feature of the external world have a genuine existence apart from the order that our perceptual habits might impose on it? Is that order an inherent part of nature, or do we select a convenient structure from what is actually a seamless web of events?

We know that there are, in effect, no clear lines of demarcation between the energy patterns of atomic structures and those of the molecular patterns of increasing complexity that can ultimately give rise to human thought processes, and to those convoluted arrangements that we choose to call civilisation. Clearly there is a consistency throughout the entire range of existence, but at the same time it is obvious that there is no possibility that the patterns of human existence could ever be predicted from the patterns of particle energies of which they are ultimately constituted. The 'cosmic consistency' though complete is not constant in any absolute sense. It is a disturbed consistency. The most notable disruption of the cosmic symmetry is the effect of time; the universe is cooling down, balls stop bouncing and we get older and not younger. Although individual atoms are not subject to this directionality the universe, for us at least, is a one-way street.

The cosmological view that seems to be emerging out of the radical discoveries of the physics of this century is that of a hierarchical succession of broken symmetries, a view that encompasses both structures and processes at all levels. This is a model that unfolds, with the advancement of time and entropy, from an original and perfect symmetry at the very beginning of things to the appearance of an increasingly complex pattern of events. The whole process of evolution, which inclines to ever greater refinement and complexity, has to be seen as a consequence of symmetry-dislocation, the play of lesser disturbances in a theatre of greater ones. Evolutionary progression however is never a uniform series of events, but is governed by all manner of accidents, errors and indeterminate 'pressures'; sometimes its progression is relatively fast, at others remarkably slow. (Some species have persisted with little change for tens of millions of years!) There is an intriguing paradox here then, in that the order of living things, indeed the whole order of nature, should have been brought about by the disordering of a presumed primal symmetry.

Symmetry relations are also involved in those philosophical problems already mentioned concerning the gap between the 'real' world and our perceptual construct of it. The awareness that we have of the 'outer' world involves our thought processes in a more or less continuous activity; our minds are not simply passive recipients of sensations from 'outside', but are engaged in a constant process of exploration and interpretation. Above all we tend to account for things according to past experience. What we see will be strongly influenced by our expectations; common sense tells us that there is a direct relationship between our experience of the world and its actuality, but philosophers have always been keen to point out that our senses can give us misleading, and even false, information. Our sensory apparatus was not, of course, designed to be forever presenting us with the ultimate truths of reality. It is far more concerned with the mundane task of getting us about in the world, and for this it is remarkably efficient.

The overriding impression that we form of the external world is one of stability and continuity; we do not expect the scenery to change radically every time we look at it (although it is constantly changing), and the world does not bob up and down as we walk along (unless the particular piece of brain-circuitry that deals with this is not working properly). This perceptual continuum, the maintenance of which seems to require little conscious effort on our part, in fact represents a task of prodigious computation. The pattern of impressions that impinge on the brain convey a perpetually shifting complex of shapes, tones and colours. We are able to assimilate and make sense of this mass of information by applying a grid of preconceived structures and theories (in much the same way that artists use 'squaring-off' techniques for accurate scaling down). In other words perception involves the application of knowledge: the world order that we create in our heads is the cumulative product of received impressions which our perceptual processes have tended to allocate to particular and familiar categories. Our ideas, memories and imagination tend, therefore, to run in set patterns. Different modes of perceptual classification are likely to lead to different interpretations; one might easily imagine that individuals from different cultural backgrounds could, quite literally, see the same events in quite different ways. This, of course, is one of the perennial causes of misunderstandings and conflict between people of different backgrounds.

'The forms of a person's thoughts are controlled by inexorable laws of pattern of which he is unconscious. These patterns are the unperceived intricate systemisations of his own language. Every language is a vast pattern-system, in which are culturally ordained the forms and categories by which the personality not only communicates, but also analyses nature, channels his reasoning, and builds the house of his consciousness.'

Benjamin Lee Whorf

No matter how hard we try to prevent them the parallel diagonals in this optical illusion appear to merge. Since our eyes can deceive us in such a simple example the question arises, to what extent can we rely on our visual or other sensory perceptions to give us a clear impression of the 'real' world?

The ways by which we acquire and interpret sensations has become far better understood with the gradual uncovering of the physiological processes involved in the reception of impressions and their transmission through the nervous system. The most useful aspects of all higher perceptual functions are those that enable us, and other creatures, to make predictions. To do this efficiently there must always be a firm correspondence, or congruity, between our perceptual model and the world outside. We now know, for instance, that in the process of visual perception the particular point that is being stimulated in the brain will correspond, at any given moment, to a point that is being excited in the retina, which, in turn, will be related to the point in space that is occupied by the perceived object. Whatever transformation this or any other object is subjected to there will be a 'linkage' of congruities between the original and our perceived impression of it. This linkage carries all the way through from the reduction of the three-dimensional reality of external objects, by way of a two-dimensional receptor system, into an electro-chemical neural message, and the re-formation of this information into a three-dimensional model in our mind/brain. The telephone provides a good metaphor for this sort of linkage; when we get a call from someone we know we usually have little difficulty in recognising their voice, even though it has been transformed into a series of electrical impulses and back again. (In fact the sensitive cells in our ears perform much the same task.) So what is involved in cognition at the most basic level is the reception of complex patterns of impressions, their transmission through the nervous system to the brain and the reconstitution and differentiation of this information. Since it involves *invariance,* this is a symmetrical process; we create the outside world in our own heads just as a mirror recreates the world in its reflection.

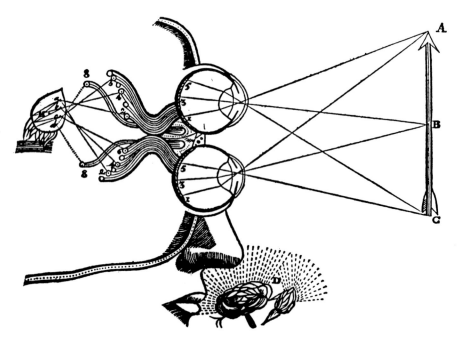

The nineteenth century saw the beginnings of scientific enquiry into the nature of perception and the differentiation of the purely physical problems involved from the associated philosophical difficulties.

Illustration from Descartes' *L'Homme*

Just as perception might be characterised as a 'quest for certainty' so the term might equally well be applied to the whole enterprise of science. There are obvious parallels: our thought processes involve a continual setting up, or modelling, of the outside world, and rely on a continuous feed-back to confirm and qualify this model. In fact normal thought processes can only be maintained in a constantly changing environment.

Where there are no stimuli to feed back we are likely to enter a disorientated state of sensory deprivation. Similarly the scientific method involves the setting up of hypotheses which may then be tested against a body of established knowledge; if it were not involved in this continuous process of postulation it too would probably go completely haywire. It seems very likely then that science, like the ordinary thought processes of which it is an extension, will always need to be a dynamic and continuing process. This, of course, runs counter to those notions that see science as 'closing in' on reality with a grand Theory of Everything. As I've said, there is a sense in which science already has a complete Theory, but from any objective viewpoint it seems in no serious danger of finding out Everything. The universe would appear to be so constructed that, given sufficient enthusiasm for the task, there will always be further mysteries to probe.

The comprehensive picture of the world built up by science over the past 300 years or so has been gradually pieced together from the observation of regularities within the 'mundane world of appearances', rather than through any search for absolute knowledge in the Platonic sense. But through empirical methods of scientific enquiry a body of knowledge has been established that can be defended with as great a sense of certainty as any in the entire previous history of thought. We can be as certain of the existence of the atom, and of the absolute standards that are built into its constitution, as of our own existence. And from this standard, of course, there arise all the regularities of the periodic series of elements which constitute the material basis of the world. Science is equally convincing when it speaks of the fundamental invariance of DNA, which provides a standard for the entire world of living organisms. As concepts these and other patterns that provide the basic framework of science would seem set to be around for a very long time to come.

Although on the one hand we are assured by contemporary science that the phenomenal world is no more than a plenum through which energies are ceaselessly flowing, on the other hand science itself is only concerned with the measurable, that is to say, invariant aspects of that world. Because of this science is advanced by the observation of consistencies. Our individual cognitive processes also work like this. Our perceptual habits of expectation and prediction are inclined to impose an order and coherence on the multiplicity of impressions that our senses receive. Our minds are very good at selecting those things that most interest us from this mass of information and in creating from these selections a consistent view of the world. It seems self-evident then that just as there are 'external' consistencies to be observed, they can only be observed in a consistent way. In fact in its very essence the process of perception involves the engagement of one set of patterns with another: we perceive, therefore we are patterned.

4

The Crystalline imperative

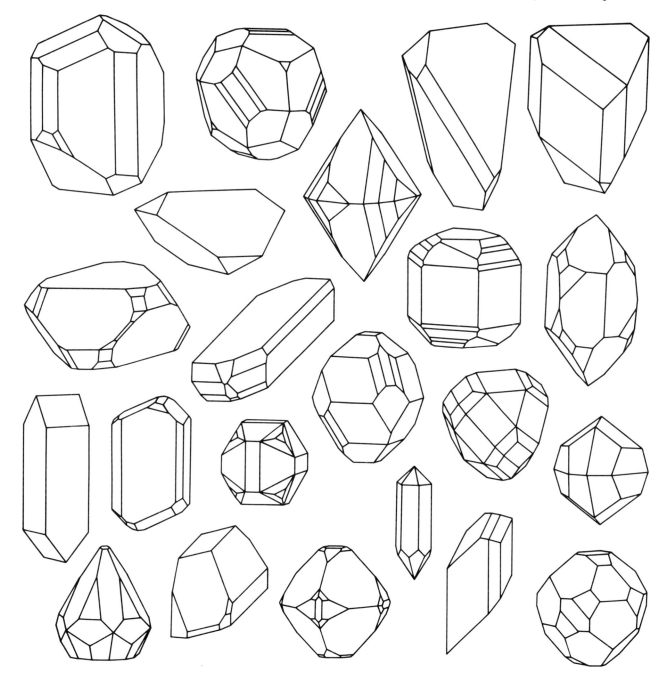

Iron Vapour – Solid Air

> There is something breathtaking about the basic laws of
> crystals. They are in no sense a discovery of the human mind,
> they just 'are' – they exist quite independently of us. The most
> that man can do is to become aware, in a moment of clarity, that
> they are there, and take cognisance of them. *M.C. Escher*

Crystals have always exerted a particular fascination. The sort of regularities that they display are extremely rare in nature, and it is easy to see how,
in more primitive societies, they would have acquired a magical significance. Well-formed crystals are special objects by virtue of their purity of
form, which stands in such direct contrast to the jumbled chaos of so much
of the natural world. Although the causative principles behind the elegance of crystalline formations are now well understood by science,
something of their magical aura tends to persist. In fact far from being

downgraded by this scientific demystification the crystal has assumed a new and exalted position in the world, and there is a real sense in which its magical potential is greater than ever before, as we shall see. Science has shown that these forms are our most tangible connection with the primal order that belongs to that mysterious domain lying beneath our ordinary impression of reality, the atomic underworld, and in doing so it can be seen to have vindicated those more ancient intuitions of the potency of crystal-line formations.

The confirmation that the geometrical form of a crystal derives from a deeper, molecular order, and indeed that this is the primary characteristic of most matter in the solid state, is a comparatively recent discovery and is bound up with that great revolution of scientific thought that has led us into the modern era. The extent, rapidity and confidence of the advances that have been made in this field can be gauged from the fact that in the opening years of this century the very existence of the atom as a distinct entity was itself a matter of intense dispute. Part of the problem then, of course, was the size of atoms; no-one at that time had devised a way to detect the existence of such infinitesimally small particles.

The idea itself was not new. In fact the notion of a fundamental and indivisible unit of matter had been around for well over two thousand years. The real difficulty for the atomic model that was being proposed around the turn of the century lay in the associated claims made by its proponents, because they were not far short of a demand for an entirely new perception of the nature of physical reality. It is perfectly understandable that such ideas should have encountered resistance, for acceptance of these revolutionary theories clearly involved abandoning many of the basic premises of the older, deterministic physics that had held sway for the previous two centuries – the very distinction between 'energy' and 'mass' was being challenged! The adoption of the new quantum propositions, and those of relativity, could not be a simple addition to the existing stock of scientific knowledge, as were many of the great discoveries of the nineteenth century. In the event the proofs of the new physics soon came, and their astonishing claims were substantiated. For better or for worse the dawn of the 'age of the atom' had broken.

As is often the case with great new discoveries their value, when fully realised, was proportionate to the difficulties of acceptance that they had initially encountered; with these new insights light was thrown into many of the darker areas of nineteenth-century physics, and several of the more bothersome problems of this period were resolved. Quantum theory, which was first presented by Max Planck in 1900, provided the first great step away from the 'deterministic continuum' of classical physics and led into the more modern perception of a universe of probability patterns of discrete but erratic particles. Material substantiality, the very stuff of reality, was now seen simply in terms of the disposition of fundamental particles, as 'the invisible organisation of energy'.

The great innovation of Planck's quantum hypotheses was the replacement of a continuous view of the world by a discrete one. A useful analogy to this theory can be found in the tones of a newspaper photograph. When examined through a magnifying glass these tones can be seen to consist of an array of apparently unrelated dots of various sizes; viewed

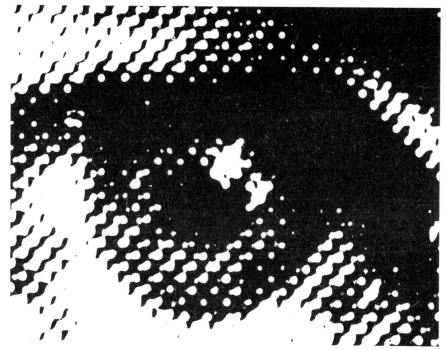

Max Planck, who in 1900 proposed that all radiant energy might be composed of quanta. At the left, a magnification of part of this photograph which reveals the fine 'screen' of dots that go to make it up.

photo: Paul Popper Ltd

normally of course this assemblage blurs into recognisable pictures. In a similar way, because the discreteness of physical quantities is so small, we are unable to perceive their separateness, and they too blur into a continuity. Apart from quite useful analogies of this sort it is difficult to arrive at a reliable visualisation of the micro-world of particles. There will always be problems here, and in fact the pioneer quantum physicist Werner Heisenberg was quite insistent that we should not think of atoms as 'things' at all, but rather as 'events'. This is a necessary attitude of mind if we are to distinguish between the individual and the collective properties of elementary particles. We cannot, for instance, think of individual atoms as experiencing heat or cold, or of being solid or fluid, or even of ageing; these are only the properties of particles *en masse*.

This is not to say that there is anything 'illusory' about our own perception of temperature, solidity, time etc.; it is simply that we experience these things as 'high-level' manifestations of 'low–level' phenomena. In contrast to this, the sense of order that we experience as a familiar aspect of reality has a direct counterpart in the order that is present in even the deepest reaches of nature. Occasionally the fabric of this universal order is so coincident as to allow a continuity from the world of the infinitesimally small to carry through to our more familiar perceptual level. This is what happens in the case of well-formed crystals. The pristine qualities of these forms derive entirely from their internal, molecular structure, and this rigorous arrangement derives in turn from the regular relations between their molecular components, which itself traces back to the highly structured relations within atoms themselves.

All the modes of existence of physical matter, whether in the form of gas or vapour, liquid or solid, are determined by just two conditioning factors, namely pressure and temperature. If either of these factors is changed the form of the matter which has been subjected to them is also likely to change. Water provides the most familiar example: here we have a liquid

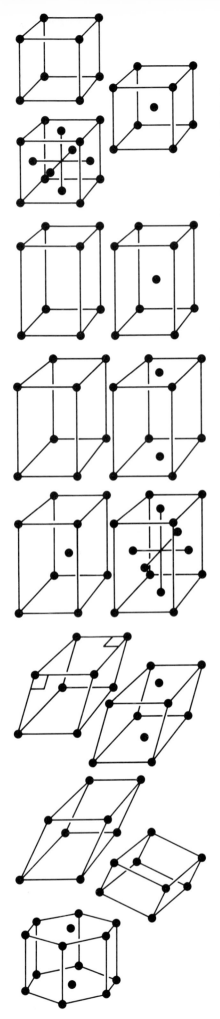

which freezes to a solid, ice, and boils to a vapour, steam. But water is by no means unique in this respect; in fact it is a general principle that the same basic matter can appear in quite different metamorphoses in different circumstances of temperature and pressure. It is quite as 'natural' for iron to exist as a vapour, and for oxygen to appear as a solid in the appropriate conditions, it is just that these conditions would be very different from those that we are accustomed to. The essential, modal condition of matter, that is to say whether it appears as a solid, liquid, gas or vapour, depends not on its elemental composition but on its molecular disposition, on the circumstantial arrangement of its constituent particles.

At all levels of phenomena the appearance of order is equivalent to the achievement of stability and equilibrium. It follows from this that the most stable arrangements on the micro-scale are those which show the highest level of molecular equilibrium which, in physics, is characterised as the *solid* state, a condition that is generally described as possessing long-range order. The *liquid* state is far less ordered, with only small regions having any degree of coherence at any one time, and even this transitory order is being continuously broken and deformed. A liquid of any kind therefore is seen as having only a short-range order. The resistance felt on running one's hand through water is a direct encounter with the tenuous molecular affiliations that characterise all liquids. In the *gaseous* state the molecular equilibrium is utterly disturbed, and its constituent particles behave in a quite individualistic and chaotic manner. This is the least ordered, and therefore the least regular, state; gases are insubstantial precisely because they have no inter-molecular bonding; a gas represents a particulate confusion.

In physics the term 'solid' has more or less the same meaning as in common usage, but 'fluid' is more general and includes the gases and vapours as well as liquids; fluids flow, solids do not. These categories by no means describe all the possible states of being, since there are some materials that occupy a sort of no man's land between the two and then there are the more complex orders of organic matter, which may incorporate all of these conditions. This latter state however is actually a rare and special case, for the greater part of matter can be conveniently located on a scale of solidity/fluidity. The point of this, so far as we are concerned here, is that this spectrum is nothing more or less than a high-level version of the molecular scale of order/disorder.

Though it is a common occurrence, the transition of matter from one of these conditions to another, say by crystallisation, is one of the most dramatic and astonishing phenomena in the whole of nature. When a substance enters the crystalline state its constituent molecules are instantly conscripted into the disciplined ranks of the crystal lattice, in battalions of the most mind-boggling uniformity. As molecules take up their position in

The unit-cell arrangements of the fourteen possible crystal lattices: (top to bottom) simple cube, body-centred cube, face-centred cube, simple tetragonal, body-centred tetragonal, simple orthorhombic, base-centred orthorhombic, body-centred orthorhombic, face-centred orthorhombic, simple monoclinic, base-centred monoclinic, triclinic, rhombohedral and hexagonal.

this formidable array they rapidly extend in every possible direction to form seemingly endless rows of identical components. Occasionally this disciplined scheme is disturbed by odd defects such as dislocations, misplaced atoms and wandering electrons, but such aberrations scarcely detract at all from the impressive display of conformity. In any crystalline arrangement irregularities are rare by comparison to the norm, which is tens or even hundreds of millions of identical, obedient molecules. It is worth re-emphasising that this scenario of almost unimaginable regularity applies to most crystal states, and that virtually all solid matter in the universe is crystalline!

At this point perhaps it is as well to make the distinction between a crystal pure and simple and a crystalline mass. In both cases the internal, molecular arrangement is dominated by the sort of regularity described above, but a well-formed crystal occurs only when this internal order determines outward appearance. Crystals of different substances adopt different and characteristic forms – every substance has its own unique form – but as they grow, various planes within the crystal generally grow at different rates so that a single substance can, in itself, appear in a great variety of crystal types. A crystalline mass on the other hand consists of a conglomerate of individual crystals that elbow into each other so that none reaches its true crystal shape. This latter arrangement is by far the most common, and metals and ice are typical examples.

It should be clear from all this that we can only refer to the properties of any substance by taking into account the particular circumstances of its inter-particulate relationships. Even if we could isolate an individual molecule it would not be appropriate to describe it in the sort of terms that we use for matter at the more familiar level. A molecule cannot, in itself, possess the condition of hardness or softness, nor, as I have said, can it be hot or cold; these terms are simply not relevant to molecules as individuals, but are collective descriptions. Liquidity and solidity are not immutable properties of matter, but are merely subjective conditions. When matter does opt for the crystalline state however it is under terms that are intensely circumscribed. In the first place practically all crystalline solids conform to one of fourteen possible lattices. Then within this basic constraint its molecular units must fall into just one of 230 space groups. Furthermore they will be confined to one of thirty-two crystal classes, in which they may express themselves in one of six systems.[1]

Almost all substances have their own unique and characteristic crystalline form, but there are rare and revealing exceptions to this rule in the phenomenon known as *polymorphism*, which allows for more than one form to occur. Carbon, for instance, crystallises both in the rather mundane form of graphite and also, in special circumstances, in the form of a diamond. The great contrast between these crystalline forms is entirely due to their respective molecular arrangements, one form being cubic, the other hexagonal, and the differences between the physical properties of these two are, of course, quite marked. Diamond is extremely hard – in fact it is the hardest known substance – whereas graphite is soft enough to be used as a lubricant. The underlying reason for this is that the atomic bonding in the tetrahedral arrangement is extremely powerful, whereas in the hexagonal structure of graphite the bonding is weak and layered, so

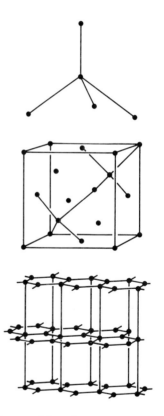

Polymorphism in carbon: the internal arrangement of carbon atoms in diamond as a tetrahedron (top), and its relationship to the cubic symmetry (middle). By contrast, the layered hexagonal arrangement of carbon atoms in graphite (bottom).

The molecular unit-cell, in this case of fluorite (CaF$_2$), that forms the basis of the crystalline lattice structure. Crystals can be regarded as being built up of millions upon millions of these basic units: as a face-centred unit-cell (above); as perspective packing drawing with the respective atoms in their proper relative ionic sizes (below).

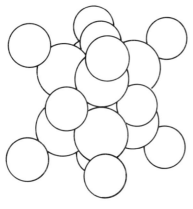

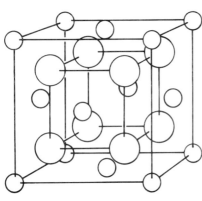

The basis of a wallpaper design, or any other pattern in two dimensions, is essentially the same as that of a crystal lattice in three-dimensions; both rely on the regular arrangement of a similar repeat unit.

that it appears as a soft substance that easily forms into plates that slide over each other. There are other significant differences between the two, in colour, in density and in their respective optical, electrical and thermal properties. To all intents and purposes diamond and graphite show themselves as if they were two entirely different substances, but they are both carbon – the differences are those of its 'invisible organisation'. It is impossible to separate the chemical and physical properties of any substance from its molecular disposition which, in the case of solids, rests on an electronic equilibrium that creates a distinctive series of points in space. Therefore the crystalline solid consists of an indefinite repetition of units (or cells) that go to form a coherent and stable mass.

An analogy can be drawn between this arrangement and the sort of regular design shown below. A pattern, whether of a wallpaper design or of the internal structure of a crystalline material, is essentially the same – it derives from an ordered array, the systematic repetition of a particular element. In graphic design this element is known as the *repeat*, in crystallography it is the *unit-cell*. It is clear that the element of order is essential here; a jumbled collection of repeats no more constitutes a wallpaper pattern than an incoherent grouping of molecular units would constitute a solid. This analogy can be taken further – the repeat element of this design has an inherent capacity to form a pattern, and only relies on its being laid out in a particular way to realise its potential, and the same criterion applies in crystal formation. Atoms, by means of their constituent electrons, can link up with their immediate neighbours; since all atoms of the same kind are identical this linkage is highly conformable. The result, in the appropriate conditions of pressure and temperature, is an atomic alignment of prodigious uniformity: the process of the transformation of any substance from the fluid to the solid state is that of an accession to order[2].

The process of crystallisation is easily observed even through a low-powered microscope, and the extraordinary rapidity and apparent determination of the process is intriguing as a purely visual spectacle, but it is all the more impressive with the knowledge that this performance involves the precision assembly of millions upon millions of obedient atoms, forming up into the prescribed ranks of their particular lattice. The accuracy and speed of this structure surpasses anything that could be imagined to occur in the gross macro-world; a typical rate of crystallisation might involve the accretion of some sixty to seventy million atomic layers per second! It is as if, as in some Arabian Nights tale, whole cities were to be built in the twinkling of an eye. In one sense there is little now that is mysterious about this process; science has uncovered all. Yet at the same time when we observe this single-minded compulsion to order it is easy to feel a sense of awe, to feel that we are witnessing the workings of a formative principle, an essential aspect of what will probably always be one of the central mysteries of creation.

NOTES

1. A *space lattice* is the dimensional, geometric pattern in which atoms arrange themselves and upon which a crystal is built. *Space groups* are groups of points, infinitely extended, and possessing the same elements of symmetry and the same translations as each of the 230 different arrangements that are theoretically possible for atoms in crystals. A *crystal system* is any one of the seven groups into which crystals are classified according to symmetry patterns. These seven groups comprise thirty-two different types of crystals and 230 different structural possibilities.

2. There are exceptions to this rule, notably in glass and glass-like substances which are perhaps best thought of as being very 'stiff' liquids.

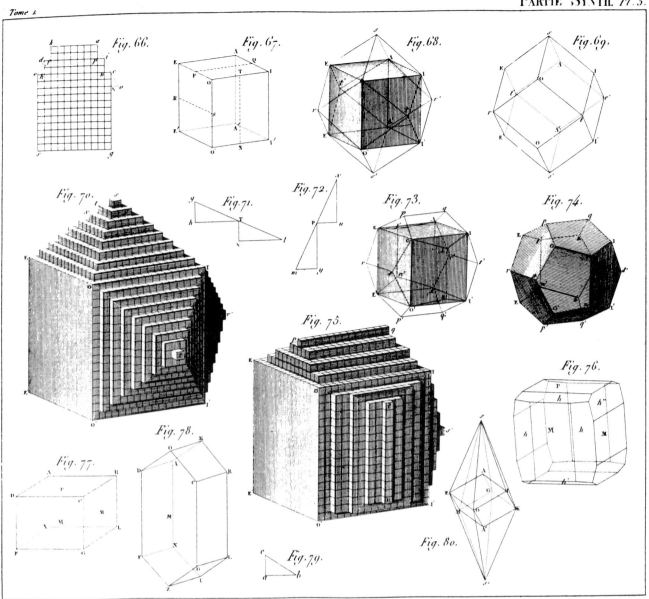

Haüy's arrangements of molécules soustractives *demonstrating his Law of Decrement. Taken from his* Traité de Cristallographie, 1822

Journey to the Interior

(In the atom) we have something which has existed either from eternity, or at least from times anterior to the existing order of nature. *Clerk Maxwell*

Sometime in the year 1779 the Abbé Haüy, a professor of geometry at the Museum of Natural History in Paris, was visiting a friend who, like himself, was an avid collector of minerals. It so happened that, whilst handling a particularly handsome example of calcite from his friend's collection, the crystal somehow detached itself from his grasp and smashed to pieces on the floor. In the course of his stumbling, apologetic attempts to clear the numerous fragments he was struck by their astonishing consistency of appearance: the crystal had shattered into many pieces of various sizes, but they were *all* rhombohedral! This incident so impressed the Abbé that, on his return home, he repeated the experiment on two calcite crystals from his own collection – and produced exactly the same result. It soon became apparent that calcite, whatever its origin, and no matter how it was fragmented, persisted in its rhombohedral form, and this even when it was powdered to a dust.

This phenomenon so intrigued Haüy that he began to investigate a whole range of mineral crystals, and in time was led to the conclusion that every substance had its own unique crystal form. Eventually he was confident enough to put his discovery forward as a law, and it was the acceptance of this, and of his later proposals, that marks the real beginnings of the study of crystals as a new and distinctive branch of science. The Abbé was not the first to apply scientific methods to the investigation of crystals, but his was the first systematic attempt to classify a great variety of crystal types. His law of *rational indices* still holds, apart from a few minor qualifications, and he is rightly regarded as the founder of crystallography.

Earlier speculations, on crystal formations in particular and on the constitution of matter generally, were marked by occasional flashes of insight rather than by the sort of sustained investigation that Haüy brought to bear on the matter, but the subject had attracted very great minds indeed. On New Year's Day, 1611, one Johannes Kepler presented a friend with a short but delightful essay entitled 'The Six-cornered Snowflake', a work that is essentially an examination of the tendency to geometry in nature. In this dissertation he reflects on such formations as the hexagonal structure of the bee's cell, the rhombohedral packing of pomegranate

Kepler's drawings accompanying his investigations into the partitioning of the plane. From his 'Harmony of the World' *(De Congruentia Figurarum)*

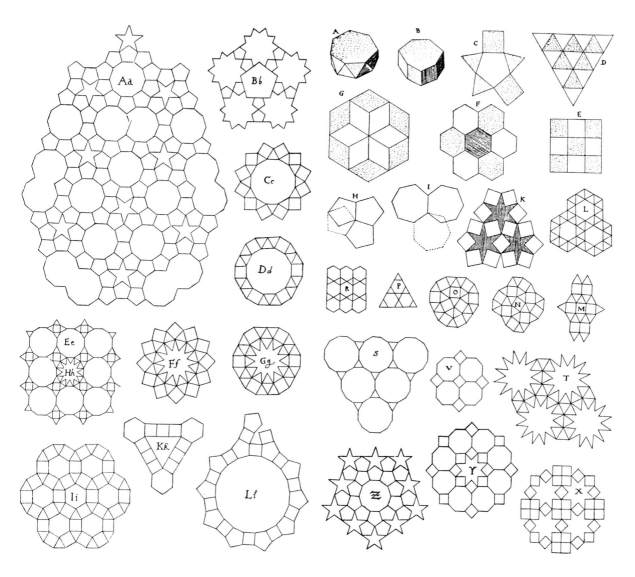

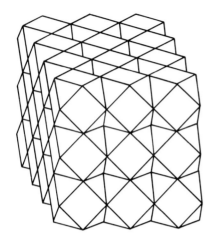

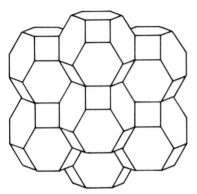

Two forms of the close-packing of polyhedra.

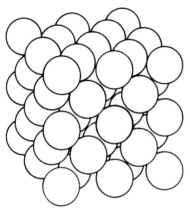

A cubic close-packed arrangement of spheres, indicating their internal regularity.

seeds, the geometry in crystal forms and the delicate symmetries of snowflakes themselves. He also deals with the purely mathematical aspects of the regular division of space, with the problems involved with the close-packing of spheres in space and of circles in the plane. Kepler was fully aware of the ideas of the Pythagoreans and was sympathetic to their notion that the ultimate truths of reality and the highest aesthetic qualities were in some way contained in number and geometry. His own great achievements in what was, in his day, called natural philosophy (i.e. science) can be seen almost as the by-product of his attempts to uncover just such a set of all-embracing, divine principles – 'Why waste words? Geometry existed before the creation, is co-eternal with the mind of God, is God himself. . .' In the event however Kepler abandoned the particular direction of enquiry that he started in his brief treatise on the snowflake, and the intuition that led him to associate the close-packing of geometrical figures with crystalline structures was not followed up. His instincts, as so often before, had put him on the right track, but his genius was destined to reveal the mysteries of the macro-world rather than the micro. For Kepler, the snowflake essay was an interesting diversion but he was soon embroiled again in his life's work of uncovering the laws of planetary motion.

There were other forays into this field. William Davidson was a near contemporary of Kepler and like him was convinced of a connection between form in the Platonic sense and crystalline structure. His books on chemistry (of which he was the first British professor) contain intuitive 'internal' drawings of crystals as well as more conventional representations.

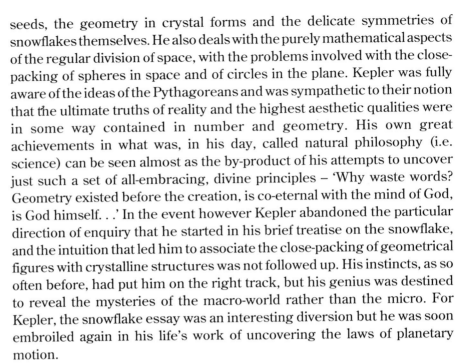

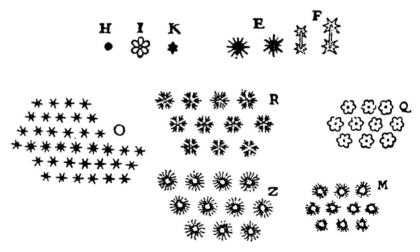

Descartes' drawings of snowflakes.

Another great mind to have been captivated by the diminutive symmetries of the snowflake was the philosopher Descartes, who noted that the hexagonal formations of snow crystals had 'six sides that were so straight, and six angles that were so equal, that it would be impossible for man to make anything so exact', and he went on to postulate a theory of 'symmetrical obligation'. These observations did little to advance the scientific understanding of crystalline structures, but are noteworthy just for the fact that this, of all natural phenomena, should have so engaged the curiosity of such an influential thinker at this particular time (1635). Descartes quite probably felt that there was a tantalising indication here of the sort of indubitable and fundamental certainty that he sought to establish as the basis of his rational philosophy. A little after his time, in the second half of the seventeenth century, the notion that crystals might be a subject worthy of investigation seems suddenly to have taken hold. It seems appropriate somehow that the attention of some of the best minds of this Age of Reason should have been so attracted to such 'logical' structures as crystals. It is certainly the case that many of the great experimental scientists of this period (Bartholinus, Hooke, Huygens, Steno etc.) made worthy and

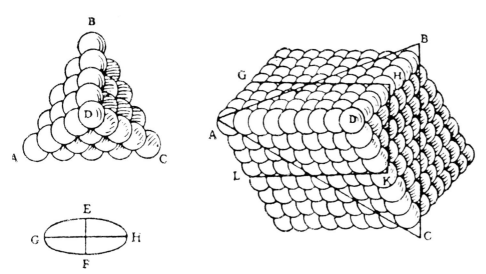

Huygens' inspired notion as to the internal, molecular structure of calcite, which gave an account both of its rhombic morphology and of the phenomenon of bi-refringence.

interesting observations on the subject. The general drift of these discoveries tended to support the notion that the external form derived in some way from the internal structure. There was also, around this time, a revival of atomic theories, but there were great difficulties in connecting these two matters. The problem was that atomic theories, however inspired, had to remain as just that, abstract theories without the means of experimental verification. It was not until the twentieth century, with the penetration of the crystal domain by X-rays, that the relationship between atomic and crystalline structure was fully exposed. Early atomist theories remained inadequate in the scientific sense, and foundered as a result.

The Abbe Haüy was himself indifferent to the notion of elementary particles, and proposed instead a system of *molécules soustractives*. Haüy did not see his 'molecules' as constituting the fundamental stuff of matter, but envisaged them as polyhedral building blocks that assembled in stacks to form crystalline structures. His theories, though later superseded, brought a good, rational solution to the different and varied crystalline configurations. He postulated that the *molécules soustractives* attached themselves to a central nucleus, in layer after layer, but reduced by single rows to form the cubes, rhombohedra and other typical crystal shapes. There is an intriguing question here as to whether he may have derived any inspiration for these ideas from any drawings or other descriptions of the Egyptian pyramids. It is one of those curious historical coincidences that soon after Haüy had published his pyramid-like theory of molecular structures (in his *Traité de Cristallographie*) Napoleon completed his conquest of Egypt at the Battle of the Pyramids. Haüy's theories had the profound distinction of being substantially correct. Molecules *do* act as the

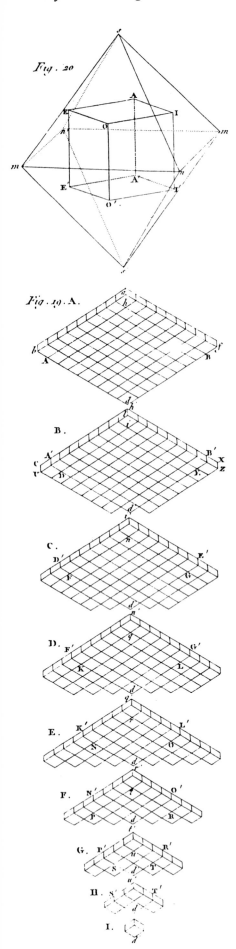

building-blocks of crystalline matter; they are not, as he supposed, constituted as minuscule polyhedra, and they add themselves to the crystal surface in great spiralling sweeps rather than in storied layers, but the essential point of the crystal state is well conveyed by his theories, namely that the internal arrangement of its constituents is intensely organised. Haüy, however, had no real conception of the scale of molecules proper, of the billions of atoms involved in even the smallest of crystalline formations.

The lack of a proper atomic theory hindered the development of crystallography as a science, so that in the nineteenth century its principal concern was with the systematic ordering of crystals into classes. These classifications were made solely in terms of the symmetrical relations involved, that is to say from purely geometrical considerations. The many varieties of crystal symmetry were determined entirely by the rational constraints inherent in the partitioning of space, and the necessities of repeatability in these three dimensions. Thus Bravais, by 1850, had described the fourteen space lattices that are known by his name, and Hessel and Axel had in the meantime classified crystals into their thirty-two classes. By 1890 all 230 possible space groups had been listed by the Russian Federov, a scheme that was able to account for every type of crystal that had then been discovered. Thorough as these systems were they remained essentially a description of the crystalline state and took no account of any possible internal, atomic disposition; this state of affairs was soon to be dramatically changed however with the introduction of a technique that spilled over from an entirely different scientific discipline – that of electromagnetism.

The German physicist Röntgen had, in 1895, discovered a previously unsuspected form of electromagnetic ray that would not be deflected by either prisms or magnets: their properties were at first so mysterious that he gave them the provisional term of X-rays. Some fifteen years later when their wave-length was published they were revealed to be extremely short, electromagnetic waves. It so happened that the new models of the atom that were also abroad at this time had diameters that were roughly of the same order as these X-ray waves. This coincidence was noted by Von Laue, another German physicist, who realised that this might allow for the possibility of an internal reflection effect, that a diffraction might be effected by directing a beam of these new rays through a crystal. An experiment was duly performed, and proved to be an immediate success – a sort of scientific 'hole in one'! A crystal of copper sulphate was chosen for this experiment, and a narrow beam of X-rays was directed towards it. Where these rays emerged on to a photographic plate they produced a number of symmetrically arranged dots, the results of the predicted diffraction effect, which was induced by the atomic layering within the crystal; effectively the crystal diffracted the X-rays as if they were passing through a single, giant molecule. By careful measurement of the relative positions of these diffraction patterns it became possible to calculate the positions of the actual molecules and their distances from one another.

Haüy saw his molécules soustractives *as polyhedral 'building-blocks' that reduced in rows to form the regularities of crystalline structures.*

This technique, which was revealed to the scientific world in 1912, marks a watershed in the history of crystallography, a point in time from which the whole focus of interest was directed away from the externals of the crystalline state and towards its internal constitution. X-ray crystallography was rapidly developed, and was soon helping physicists to determine the precise configurations of atoms, ions and molecules within crystals. Its pioneers were at first astonished to discover that one after another, practically all solids were in fact crystalline. (It turned out that virtually every element and molecular compound had the capacity to form crystals.) Man had, for the first time, peered into the crystalline domain, and had found there a world of the most rigorous conformity, of countless billions of identical entities arrayed in ranks of the utmost precision. Earlier theories that had suspected this sort of arrangement received their confirmation. The advent of X-ray diffraction analysis provided the final confirmation of the arrangements of atoms in crystalline matter and this discovery was as important to the new atomic theorists as it was to crystallography itself. The atom, whose existence was first postulated in the fifth century BC in Greece, was now casting its image on to a photographic plate.

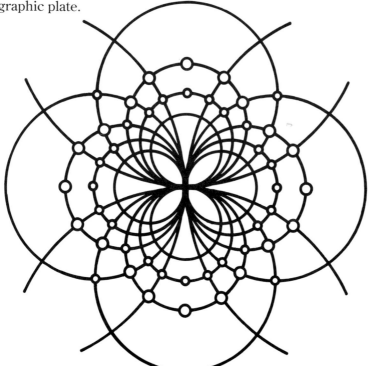

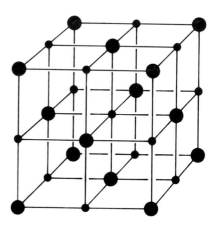

The molecular structure of common salt: as a face-centred lattice (above), and the diffraction pattern produced by directing X-rays through this lattice (left). Salt was in fact one of the first substances to be analysed in this way.

The early history of atomism is itself rather interesting. From an historical perspective it might seem no less remarkable that atomic theories should have developed at such an early date than that they were arrived at by pure deductive reasoning. The 'invention' of atoms is generally credited to Leucippus of Miletus. Leucippus' notion of the atom came from his attempts to resolve the rival and apparently incompatible cosmologies of two of the most important philosophers of his day, Heraclitus and Parmenides. The former claimed the principle of change as being the sole reality, but the latter asserted permanence as an essential condition of being. Leucippus elegantly reconciled these views by introducing the notion that matter might consist of various aggregates of indivisible particles. In this way all gross matter, which was constituted of such aggregates, was subject to all the transformations of the Heraclitian flux, but the particles themselves were indestructible and eternal and could therefore belong to Parmenides' 'world of being'.

This hypothesis, which of course was substantially correct, was taken up and elaborated on by Leucippus' successor, Democritus, to form a system of 'legitimate' knowledge, as distinct from that acquired from sense perceptions. The atoms of this system were of various sizes, were in a state of constant vibration, and could be arranged in an infinite variety of ways. All the observable characteristics of matter derived from different arrangements of these particles. These early atomic theories, which were far more elaborate than I have indicated, represented a quite extraordinary intellectual achievement, but they also show a visionary quality amounting to a sort of clairvoyance. However, these ideas were destined to remain *in vacuo* for the next two thousand years, as abstract notions that were never entirely forgotten but that were regarded as being beyond verification and therefore sterile.

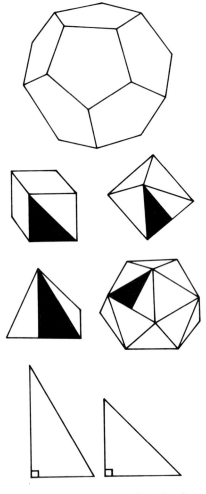

The atomists arrived at their conclusions as much from the need to resolve the problems of the mutability and pluralism of nature as from the need to establish a scientific explanation of natural phenomena. In the Greece of this period however, there was another line of enquiry that addressed the same problem but which, from the point of view of the development of science, was rather more productive. This was the Pythagorean/Platonic tradition. The ideas of the atomists were familiar to Plato and indeed influenced his own thought, but characteristically he developed his own theories as to the ultimate constitution of matter, ideas that were more in line with his general cosmological views. These theories are laid out in his dialogue *Timaeus*, a work that has a distinctly Pythagorean tone; here he puts forward the notion that the cosmos is derived from various combinations of the elements, air, earth, fire and water, an idea that itself traces back to Empedocles (though it is thought that he, in turn, may have borrowed it from Pythagoras). Plato advances this cosmology however by identifying these four elements with the first four of the so-called 'perfect' solids, each element being assigned to a specific polyhedron. In this scheme air is represented by the tetrahedron, the cube is the element of earth, the octohedron is fire and the icosahedron water. The fifth and, for the Pythagoreans, culminating solid, the dodecahedron, is taken to represent the cosmos as a whole. Plato goes on to assert that these solids may be further reduced to two constituent 'basic triangles' (with angles of 45°, 45°, 90° and 30°, 60°, 90° respectively), shapes that are now familiar to us as geometrical set-squares. So Plato puts forward the rather surprising idea that these simple figures form, in some way, the foundation of all physical reality! Clearly this is a very different view from that of the atomists, whose particles, though microscopic, were at least substantial, in that they were made up of some elementary material. Plato's triangles obviously had no substance at all, and were nothing more than formal, geometrical arrangements. Although the details of how these figures were connected to the gross material world are rather vague in this account, the general theory, like those of the atomists, is strikingly prescient; indeed many modern atomic theories have a distinctly Platonic ring.

Plato identified the four elements of air, earth, fire and water with his 'basic solids', themselves derived from two 'basic triangles'. The fifth and culminating solid in this scheme, the dodecahedron (top), represented the cosmos.

We tend now to count Plato's views on the constitution of matter among the more mystical of his speculations, and he probably felt about these, as he certainly did about the form of the good, that this was a form of knowledge that was incommunicable in any ordinary sense. Plato derived this quasi-religious attitude from the Pythagoreans, for whom number and ratio were expressions of the divine. In the more limited terms of science proper Plato's elements, perfect solids and basic triangles, would, in any case, have encountered the same difficulties of verification as did the ideas of the atomists, and as a result did little to advance the cause of science in this direction. However they could be said to represent the first perception of the importance of those principles of symmetry operating at the fundamental level of matter. There is a sense in which the two sets of ideas, those of Plato and those of the atomists, are complementary, since the theories of each touch on important aspects of present perceptions of the basic 'stuff' the universe is made of. Like that of the Sun-centred planetary system that was proposed in the fourth century BC by the Pythagorean, Aristarchus, these ideas were destined to go into cold storage, leaving a 2000-year hiatus in the story of the atom.

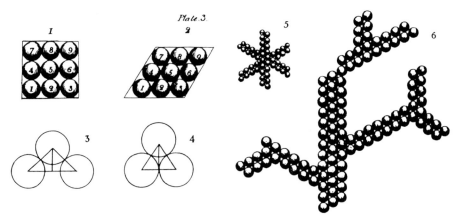

Interest in the atom, and in the ways that it might be arranged to form various materials, was only seriously revived in the eighteenth century, by the likes of Lavoisier and Dalton, when, with the development of chemistry as a science, it became an increasingly useful abstraction. The influence of classical ideas of atomic structure is quite evident in Dalton's famous work *A New System of Chemical Philosophy*, published in 1808, (see illustration). This work introduced the idea that all the varieties of chemical compounds, with their distinctive properties, might consist of elements that were in some way bound together in specific and consistent proportions. Dalton developed a working hypothesis that ascribed 'atomic weights' to various elements, and this system graduated from being a method of convenience to becoming the foundation of the modern system of classifying all the elements and their molecular compounds.

The turning point for the atom, its emergence from the realm of abstraction, came in 1905, when an obscure customs official published a paper on an equally obscure physical phenomenon, and in the process altered the course of science. In Volume 17 of the *Annalen der Physik* the young customs clerk and spare-time physicist, Albert Einstein, asserted that Brownian movement, a previously inexplicable quivering motion manifested by all very fine granular particles, was due to the effect of

Dalton's 'particles of water' in ice. From A New System of Chemical Philosophy, 1808

random atomic bombardment. In this somewhat off-beat way the atom made its entrance on to the world stage, for Einstein's predictions for Brownian movement were soon verified by experiment, and the scientific dispute as to the existence of atoms was finally settled. A great deal remained to be discovered about the properties of these entities, but their existence was never again to be seriously doubted. The journey to the interior however was far from over. The new atomic theories confirmed and made coherent much of the physics and chemistry of the nineteenth century, but also changed the whole outlook of science in the process. The establishment of the existence of the atom neatly marks the beginning of this transformation, which was like an awakening to a new reality. The encounter with the world of the infinitely small presented its explorers with many disturbing visions – atoms themselves were found to consist largely of empty space, mass and energy were found to be interchangeable, and here space and time had a quite different value to that of our more familiar world. Perhaps the most surprising aspect of this particulate world came with the realisation of its inherent unpredictability; the energy and organisation which appeared to be the ultimate constituents of matter were in themselves quite adequate, it seemed, to create the same blend of ordered and disordered complexity that is the most prevailing characteristic of the macro-world. With the atom and its even more fundamental constituents, science had encountered a profound and unforeseen dualism.

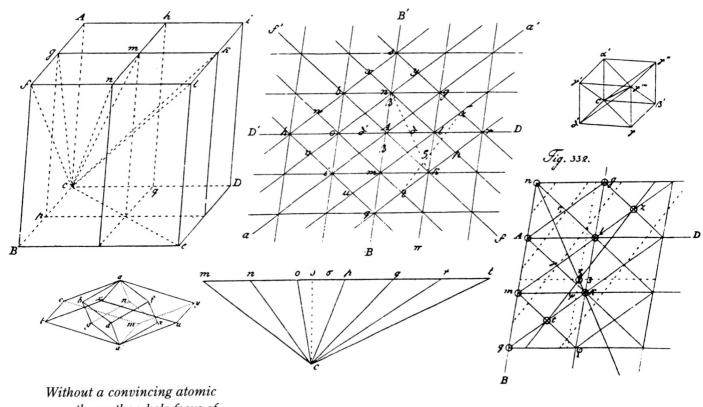

Without a convincing atomic theory the whole focus of crystallography in the nineteenth century was on the ordering of crystal types in terms of their symmetrical relations.

Snowflakes and the Solid State

'Why six-cornered?' Kepler in 'Strena seu de Niva Sexangula'
('A New Year's Gift: On Hexagonal Snow') 1611

Not all snow crystals are quite as perfect as those illustrated above; indeed not all are flat or even hexagonal in their general form. Snowflakes themselves often consist of a jumbled, inseparable mass of various individual crystals. Nevertheless when snow is in season and falling heavily from the sky it really is a simple matter to catch enough samples on the cuff of one's coat to see for oneself the formations that so stimulated Kepler's imagination. (A magnifying glass and warm clothing are recommended for this exercise.) Having caught some decent specimens and peered at them under the glass, two features of these small, evanescent forms soon become apparent. First there is a surprising similarity in the overall shape of most examples, and secondly there is an infinite variety in their individual detail. Now one might have thought that this phenomenon would have been observed and commented on long before it attracted Kepler's attention, but curiously there are hardly any references at all to these symmetries in the works either of antiquity or at any other time up to the New Year's Gift essay. Until they were singled out for that special attention, snowflakes, these intriguing forms, simply remained as one small part of the greater mystery of nature.

Kepler himself was a fascinating figure, a visionary and founder of modern science and yet very much a man of his time. He managed to combine an outlook in which we can recognise a thoroughly modern

Snow crystals: infinite variations on a theme. Each crystal displays the unique circumstances of its development twelve times over, in the manner of a kaleidoscope.

107

determination to uncover the plain facts of the workings of creation with a scholastic and medieval sense of awe at its mysteries. Both attitudes come across quite clearly in his treatise on the snowflake. He was a neo-Pythagorean and saw in these natural geometries evidence of the direct influence of the hand of the creator. There is little doubt that he felt, as did the members of the original brotherhood, that such regularities could provide a key to the divine mysteries. It is worth restating that from a purely scientific point of view this cast of mind, which is intellectually rigorous and at the same time deeply mystical, has over the centuries proved to be exceptionally productive. In fact it underlies the whole scientific enterprise.

In the New Year essay Kepler returns again and again, almost obsessively, to the essential hexagonal composition of the snow crystal. It is clear that he divined in these formations the play of an important, but elusive, principle. We know that he felt his essay to be important enough to warrant publication, and it was eventually published, though it attracted little attention. The snow crystal was, for the time being, to keep its secrets. It is not even certain that Kepler made the association between the process of crystallisation in ice and that occurring in minerals, although Robert Hooke certainly did a short time later in his *Micrographie* (1665).

Even now there are some aspects of the formation of snow crystals that remain somewhat obscure, but the underlying principles that account for their general form are well understood. Water freezes in a hexagonal form, a phenomenon that was familiar to the Chinese even in ancient times. Snow crystals are six sided as an expression of this tendency which derives from an internal, molecular disposition. When they are flat, as is frequently the case, it is due to their mode of accretion; ice molecules are deposited on the surface of the flake and tend to migrate across it to the growing tips. The 'branches' of any given snow crystal are similar because their growth occurs within a minuscule vapour field; as a result the conditions of growth

Ice forms in hexagonal plates, a fact noticed and recorded by the Chinese in very early times. A pattern from a decorative screen.

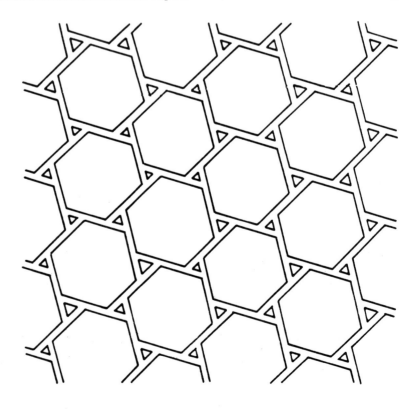

tend to be the same for each axis of symmetry. These are the principal factors determining the general appearance of snow crystals, but of course each individual example presents its own unique variation on this theme. The originality, or singularity, of every separate snow crystal is really no more than a record of the particular circumstances affecting its growth, its history in other words. The production of snow depends very much on air temperature, microscopic variations of which greatly affect the growth and appearance of the crystals. In addition the vapour field in which crystals develop is never perfectly uniform and this leads to the overall symmetry of individual crystals being slightly disturbed. In general, however, they exhibit a fairly high degree of conformity. Rather surprisingly it has been found that the instabilities involved in the formation of snow crystals – of freeze/thaw and refreezing, heat diffusion, surface tension etc., – tend to reinforce rather than detract from their overriding imperative towards six-sidedness.

There can be little doubt that Kepler would have been delighted by these explanations, and that he would have seen in them a vindication of his own intuition of the importance of these minuscule forms. Their significance is indeed far reaching, because the science that is able to provide such a complete explanation of these and other crystalline phenomena has, in the process, transformed our view of physical reality. This new understanding of the basic constitution of matter has, in turn, opened up whole new fields of technology. Inventions such as the microchip and the laser are really just the first fruits of modern solid-state physics. The discovery of the use of X-rays for the diffraction analysis of crystalline substances marks the beginning of this process, and from that time, in the early part of this century, there has been an increasing tendency to investigate the properties of materials in terms of their molecular microstructure. This revolution has meant that scientists are now inclined to regard solid material primarily in terms of the arrangement of its atoms, ions and molecules. The kinds of order, and of disorder, that are found at that level have led to a new and more complete understanding of the nature and potentiality of solid materials. One important result of this has been the development of a whole range of entirely new materials and, of course, it has given rise to all the possibilities of electronic microtechnology.

In today's physics the expressions 'solid' and 'crystalline' are virtually synonymous. In universal terms by far the greater part of solid material is crystalline in the sense that its constituent molecules are arranged in a regular pattern in three dimensions but, insofar as this conveys a picture of a perfectly orderly, frozen micro-world, it is misleading. For a start atoms that are bound together in this way are far from being stationary; the notional, idealised arrangement of molecules within the crystal lattice is just that, an ideal: their fixity is only relative. In fact molecules in the solid condition are in a state of constant motion around the points of their lattices, about which they are perpetually rotating and vibrating. This movement is referred to as their heat motion, and accounts for the property changes associated with temperature. At lower temperatures this motion is constrained into a relatively sedate molecular dance, the individual vibrations merging into a general wave motion, but when the temperature rises to a critical level the heat motion of individual molecules overcomes the force that binds them to their fellows and the lattice arrangement disintegrates. This transition, of course, represents the melting point of a given substance, and marks the upper limit of its existence in the solid state.

The dissolution of the lattice structure also occurs when a solid is dissolved in a liquid, such as happens with ordinary salt or sugar in water. If the water, or other solvent, is subsequently evaporated the solid, with its orderly molecular arrangement, will reappear. If conditions are particularly favourable this restructuring may be so complete that it is apparent on the outward form of the solid; that is to say, if a solution is cooled very slowly large, well-formed crystals will appear. There is sometimes a reluctance on the part of a substance to enter this solid state: it is, for instance, notoriously difficult to crystallise a very pure solution. In these cases it may be necessary to 'seed' the solution with minute crystals of the dissolved substance to induce it to crystallise, by way of example as it were. Interestingly in this form of induction it is not absolutely necessary to use seeds of the same substance – those of an entirely different material may do the trick, but they do need to be of the same general crystal class.

Another interesting and characteristic crystalline phenomenon is that of epitaxy, where crystals of one material grow on the face of another and adopt the orientation of the parent, forming in parallel array. Epitaxial growth is extremely useful in the manufacture of semiconductors, where it is used to deposit oriented layers of selected materials. Other traits of crystalline behaviour are rather less useful. In some cases crystallisation may occur instantaneously throughout a solution in a 'flash' reaction; this occasionally happens with cement or plaster, usually with disastrous consequences! The precise reasons for the 'flash set' are rather obscure, and there are in fact many aspects of crystallisation that are unpredictable and even mysterious.

The most complete and idealised manifestation of the solid state would be a perfect, single crystal. Such a paragon, however, does not exist in reality. At best this ideal is produced only within small regions of actual crystals, and well-developed crystals are themselves a comparatively rare phenomenon. Perhaps it is as well, at this point, to make the distinction between crystals *per se* and crystalline substances – salt and sand are both common crystalline materials, but whereas ordinary salt consists entirely of small, complete crystals, sand is simply made up of a conglomerate of crystalline particles; the external appearance of salt crystals is determined by their internal, molecular structure, but this is not the case with sand. These days the characteristic properties of materials tend to be explained in terms of their molecular constitution, and there is perhaps no better illustration of the ways in which the differences of micro-structure relate to familiar macroscopic properties than in the contrast between steel and glass. Steel is a particularly useful material because it is both strong and ductile; if it is stamped into the shape of a car body it stays that way. In common with all other metals it has the incidental advantage of being a good conductor of electricity. Glass, by contrast, breaks when it is bent, and is so poor an electrical conductor that it is actually used as an insulator. Glass is transparent, whereas a sheet of steel that is more than a millionth of an inch thick is quite opaque. The quite dramatic contrasts between these materials are traceable to the basic fact that whilst steel, like all

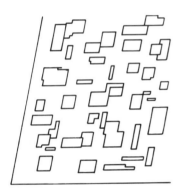

Epitaxy: crystals of one material growing on the crystal face of another, and adopting the orientation of its 'parent'.

metals, is an intensely crystalline material, glass is among the least crystalline of all solids. The micro-structure of metals lacks the complete uniformity of a crystal proper, but it has a relatively simple molecular structure, and a high degree of regularity.[1] In glasses and other amorphous solids there is far less of a sense of order between the constituent particles, and these tend to be much larger. These latter materials are now thought of as being quasi-crystalline.

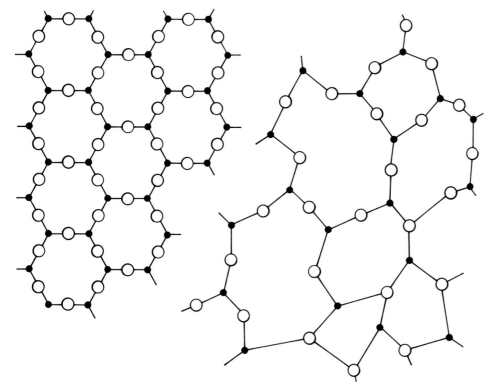

In glassses the molecular arrangement is somewhat irregular and they are therefore poor conductors of heat and electricity. (left) The regular, crystalline arrangement of silicon and oxygen atoms in cristobolite, and (right) in that of a typical glass. Each shows the silicon atoms surrounded by the same number of oxygen atoms, but the more amorphous glass lacks the long-range order that is characteristic of most solids.

When the molecular interior of matter was first laid open in the early days of X-ray crystallography a very high degree of order was assumed for the internal arrangements of all crystalline matter. This notion was fairly soon dispelled however with the realisation that disorder, in the form of defects of various kinds, infiltrated even this pure domain. In addition to this it was later found that there existed a whole range of substances whose molecular organisation lay somewhere between the crystalline and amorphous solids. Research into this latter area led to the surprising discovery of the existence of molecular structures, in the form of long chains, that lay quite outside the constraints of the 230 space groups. These findings, which had between them already seriously eroded 'classical' notions of crystallography, had profound implications for the future of the science. Very soon it was to be taken into entirely new areas of discovery, in fields as disparate as electronics and biology, and its role elevated to an importance that would have been inconceivable to nineteenth-century crystallographers.

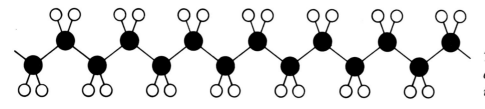

The characteristic 'zig-zag' arrangement of molecules within a polymer chain.

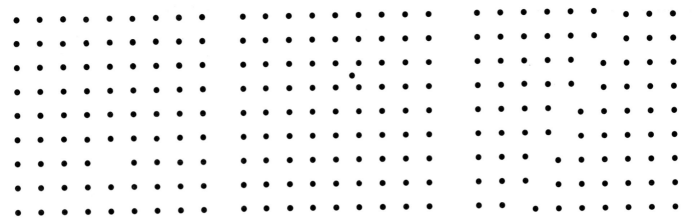

The principal types of defect in the crystal lattice are 'holes', 'crowdions' and 'dislocations'.

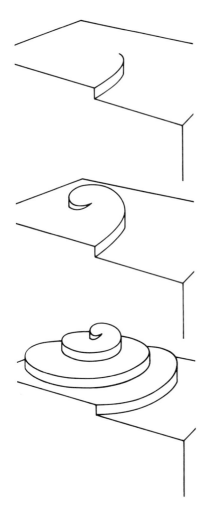

A 'screw dislocation' is a particularly dramatic form of defect, occurring as a spiral that pulls the turns upwards and sideways until they meet the boundaries of the crystal face.

It was not until the late twenties and thirties of this century that the presence of defects gradually became accepted as a normal feature of crystalline materials. For a while the view of the internal arrangements of crystals had been idealised, with the assumption of a perfect molecular order, but it gradually became apparent that there were disturbances in the atomic layering of every type of crystal. On the atomic scale these dislocations, holes and fissures are a comparatively sparse feature of the close-packed crystalline array, but such are the differences of scale that these defects can be found by the million in a square centimetre of any normal crystal surface. Since their initial discovery these imperfections have been the subject of considerable research, not least because of their relevance to the strengths of materials. Material failure, such as metal fatigue, almost always traces back to these micro-defects. It has been shown, in experimental situations, that any material that is relatively free from these flaws has greatly increased strength as a result. 'Whisker' growths of tin, which have comparatively few defects, have been found to be as much as a thousand times stronger than the same metal in its ordinary state! The implications for material development are obvious.

There are other irregularities of crystalline structure which have had an even greater bearing on the course of modern technology. These are to do with the very forces that bind atoms together and hold them in their position within the lattice, the electrons. The development of new semi-conductive materials allows for precise manipulation of these mercurial entities, and this has made possible all the technical wizardry of electronic microtechnology. In essence semiconductor devices operate by means of the skilful control of defects in the crystal lattices of specially selected, or formulated, materials. These materials have been developed so as to

Semiconductors depend for their functioning on known irregularities in their crystal lattices: (left) P-type with 'wandering holes'; (right) N-type with free negative charges.

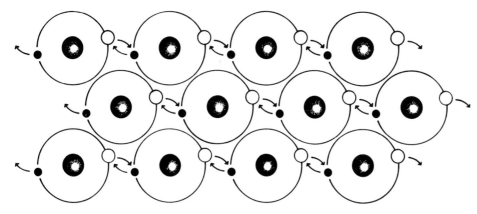

create 'holes' in some lattices, and 'spare' electrons with which to fill them in others. This expedient provides an accurate means of controlling the flow of electrons, which is to say the electric current, through the required circuitry. It is hardly necessary to comment on the extraordinary success of this technology. The range and capabilities of semiconductive devices that are available even now are quite astounding and they clearly have an even greater future. It is, of course, entirely fitting that this exploitation of the orders and energies of the micro-world should have become one of the characteristic technologies of the atomic age.

Impressive though they are these developments have been paralleled by other insights into forms of molecular structure that have, if anything, an even greater significance for the future of science and technology. As I indicated earlier, the great break with classical crystallography came with the realisation of the existence of molecular arrangements of an entirely different order from that of the massed uniformity of the crystal lattice. It was found, in fact, that molecules could combine to form long, extended 'chains', in arrangements that might involve hundreds or even thousands of particles. It was fairly soon realised that fibrous protein, which accounts for a great deal of organic material as a whole, was constituted in this way. Many of the new materials that have become a common feature of modern life are made up of similar, though rather less

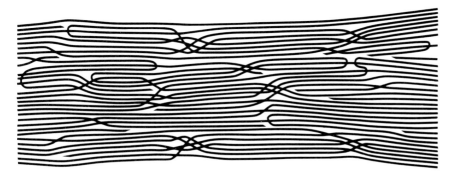

Many organic materials are fibrous, being made up of long 'chains' of molecules. These are partly ordered, in the crystalline sense, and partly not. The ordered regions confer strength in such substances, and the disordered regions give them their flexibility.

complex, long chain molecules. Plastics, synthetic fibres and rubbers combine strength with flexibility in a whole variety of ways and nature uses the same approach for the same reasons. Hair, wool, cotton and leather owe their durability to the fact that they are 'sort of' crystalline. Like the synthetic polymers mentioned above they have a molecular constitution that combines areas of crystalline regularity with others that are less ordered. Roughly speaking it is the crystalline regions that confer strength and the less orderly areas that give these materials their flexibility. The

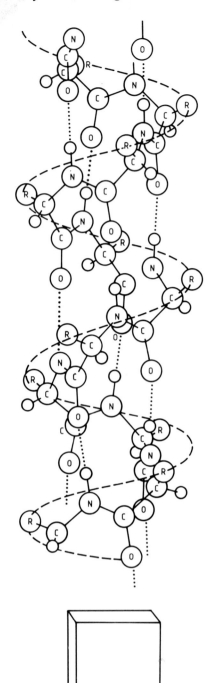

most important feature of these forms of molecular organisation is their sheer variety; the ways in which strength and flexibility can be combined has led to the creation of a virtually infinite variety of materials from a very limited range of component atoms. This is the means by which organisms have achieved their great functional complexity, and the reason why the possibilities of material development are now so enormous.

Research into the nature of large organic molecules, the 'crystals of the chains of life' was greatly intensified in the immediate post-war period, leading by 1950 to the discovery of the alpha-helix structure of protein chains. It was soon realised that all of these giant molecules lay in one or other of two great classes of organic substances, each with its own importance but quite separate function. These were the proteins themselves and the salts of nucleic acids; the former were deeply involved in the physical structure of all organisms, both vegetable and animal, whereas the latter appeared to be entirely concerned with the perpetuation of these complex and highly evolved forms through the transmission of genetic material. The culminating achievement of this new science of molecular biology was the discovery of the famous double helical structure of DNA, perhaps the greatest single scientific discovery of the century.

Although the importance of this breakthrough was immediately apparent to the scientific community, the assimilation of its wider implications into the general consciousness has been a far more gradual process. When these findings, which are as far-reaching as those of Darwin's evolutionary theory, are finally absorbed we can expect that they will have had a comparable influence on the general consciousness. Because of their direct bearing on the origin and continuity of life, which, after all, is of great interest to most of us, these revelations are bound to affect the way we view the world. What this new 'central dogma' has clarified above all else is the primary role of the 'crystalline imperative', the ordering principle, in life itself.

NOTES

1. Metals are perhaps best thought of as arrays of nuclei; a proportion of the electrons involved in this scheme are forever wandering around, creating a powerful electronic bond, the so-called Fermi Sea. It is this effect that makes metals malleable since groups of ions can be pushed about in a containing electrostatic 'aura'.

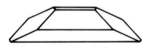

Surprisingly, in view of their molecular complexity, proteins form crystals with a high degree of perfection, often in two or more different forms: the helical form of part of a protein 'chain' (above); two types of haemoglobin (below).

5

Symmetry and beyond

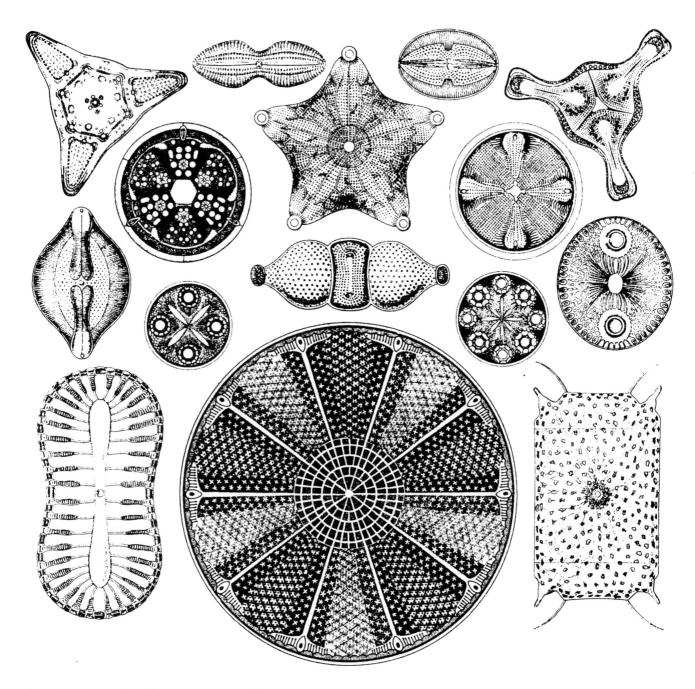

So What *is* Symmetry?

Marine symmetries. From Haeckels' *Kunstformen der Natur*

It is characteristic of this science of numbers and proportions that its aims are identical with the principles of being. *Al-Farabi*

God used beautiful mathematics in creating the world. *Paul Dirac*

If a stone is hurled into a still pond it will, for a short while, create a regular series of perfectly concentric ripples on the surface of the water. What has happened is that a random event has been transformed, at least in part, into an intensely symmetrical one. In contrast, if a vase is accidently shattered, its symmetry will be displaced. Events of this sort are familiar even to children, but they illustrate two of the most important and interesting

117

aspects of symmetry, those of its all-pervasive and yet uncovenanted nature. In fact every single event in the phenomenal world is bound to involve both the formation and the breaking of symmetries of some kind or another.

The symmetry principle, as we shall see, is inseparable from any notion of order, but the complexity and multiformity of nature is such that its regularities overlap and intrude upon each other in such profusion that this divine principle is generally occluded: that is to say that symmetries are everywhere, but they are rarely obvious. The intuition that beneath or beyond the confusion of the world as it is ordinarily perceived there might lie some inalienable ordering principle has always been potent. It is this belief that underlies not only the aesthetic and scientific impulses but also the spiritual; hence symmetry concepts have been prominent in all three areas of enquiry.

Different modes of thought have claimed the word 'symmetry' and the fact that each has put a quite different construction on it has led to the meaning of the term itself being somewhat obscured. Most dictionaries reflect this terminological confusion, presenting various definitions, often vague in themselves, and bearing an uncertain relation to each other. Generally definitions of symmetry seem to fall into one or other of two broad categories. On the one hand they are described in such terms as 'the right proportion of parts' and 'the beauty resulting from this', which one might call the aesthetic interpretation; then there are those more precise, or scientific, explanations whereby a symmetrical object is one that presents 'two or more identical parts that are systematically arranged'.

Even these generalisations are inadequate; we find hints that symmetry is not necessarily limited to matters concerning the arrangement of objects in space at all, but that it is a far more extensive principle. There are symmetries in the abstract realm of mathematics for instance, and they are also found in music and in colour theory. In a sense the entire social fabric, insofar as it is held together by the reciprocities of ethics and justice, depends on this same, ubiquitous, principle.

Perhaps the clearest, and most straightforward, pointer to the nature of symmetry comes from the notion of *self-similarity*, and we have to look no further than the left/right morphology of our own bodies to find an example. When we look around there are many objects that share this sort of 'mirrored' symmetry: chairs, tables, cars, cats, dogs etc. Like ourselves all of these things have left and right halves that are approximately equivalent, except of course that they are mirror images of each other. The

Cart-wheel, ladder and Rorschach blot – all are symmetrical, but what is it that they have in common?

Radial symmetries

list of these *bilateral* objects seems endless, and it is soon apparent that this is an exceedingly common form of construction. Another, and quite different, form of symmetry that we meet with almost as frequently is arrangements around a centre; such *radial* symmetries are found in many flowers, in the sections of various fruits and vegetables, in wheels of all kinds, and as the basic configuration of centred motifs.

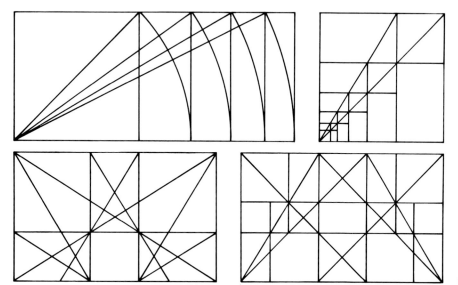

'Certain 'harmonic' relationships were noticed very early in the history of geometry; in the ancient worlds of Greece, Babylon and Egypt; these were gradually developed into various canons of proportion. Symmetry, in this sense, became synonymous with order and restraint in art and architecture.'

In addition to symmetries which can be characterised by their repetition of a particular element, the term has strong associations with the classical notions of *analogia*, those aesthetic principles of Greek origin that are concerned with ideal and harmonious proportions. This latter symmetry, though it has been variously interpreted, has played an important role in the theory of art, particularly in connection with architecture, sculpture and furniture. The concept of symmetry as the relation of various parts to a whole is, then, an ancient one. The sculptor Polyclitus used the term in a book on proportion in the fifth century BC, although the principle of a harmonious geometry was undoubtedly far older. However, as an expression, symmetry has tended to acquire new meanings without ever entirely discarding older ones. In more recent times, for instance, this already overloaded term has been subtly extended with further nuances. I am referring here to a usage that emanates from the world of physics; in this context symmetry, in the form of elegant algebraic equations, has become an important theoretical tool, one that is particularly useful, indeed essential, for the comprehension of some of the deeper and more abstruse aspects of particle theory. The keynote of this symmetry is not so much the notion of self-similarity, or of a transcendent harmony, but that of *invariance*.

'Symmetry results from proportion, proportion is the commensuration of the various constituent parts with the whole.'

Vitruvius

What do these different perceptions of symmetry have in common with each other, if anything? It is clear that nature is thoroughly imbued with symmetries of all kinds, but it is equally apparent that its forms are subject to change, so how are we to recognise symmetry and define its fundamental characteristics? Where does it begin and end? What exactly is symmetry?

At this stage, and before venturing to untangle the various strands of meaning implicit in the different interpretations of symmetry, it seems

'The whole object of maths is to create order where previously chaos seemed to reign, to extract structure and invariance out of the midst of disarray and turmoil, or in one word, to establish symmetry.'

Hans Giger

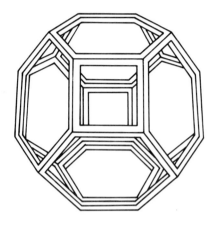

Leonardo produced a number of drawings of polyhedra for Pacioli's De Divina Proportione *and worked with this mathematician for several years.*

'Let proportion be found not only in numbers and measures, but also in sounds, weights, times and positions, and whatever force there is.'

Leonardo

appropriate to consider the related notion of *pattern*. Now pattern, in its primary sense, is nothing more than a category of symmetry, but it too has acquired rather a broad and indistinct range of meanings. In common usage the term probably centres on the sort of repeating design found in fabrics and wallpaper, but it also carries the meaning of a shape or form to be replicated or that of an habitual mode in the most general sense, for instance patterns of behaviour, patterns of speech etc. The common factor in these usages would seem to be the notion of predictability, but the term also extends to include decorative markings of various kinds, such as those of a snakeskin, or the marbling effect found in the endpapers of finely bound books. Here the problem of terminology arises again, for while we might accept such examples as patterns, or at least as patterning, we would not usually think of them as being symmetrical.

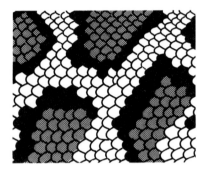 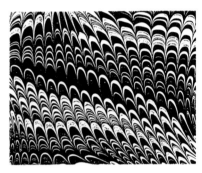

Detail of the markings on a python's skin (left), and a 'marbling' effect from the endpaper of a book. Both of these might be described as being patterned, but are they patterns?

The semantic niceties involved here are unlikely to generate high passions, but at the same time one is entitled to feel that these terms do refer to specific states, and that these represent precise qualities. We can begin to clarify the issue by drawing a distinction between that symmetry which is bound up with ideals of beauty and proportion, and those more mundane precepts that belong to the domain of exact science. The former refers to an ancient tradition based on a belief in the mystical and transcendent properties of numbers and ratios, whereas the latter conforms to the more exacting demands of the scientific method. From an historical perspective this distinction is relatively recent, and in a sense the different interpretations of symmetry have a similar point of origin. The western scientific tradition, as we have seen, traces back to the theories of the Pythagoreans, who also advanced the idea of the divine qualities of numbers, angles etc. (Euclid, the founder of geometry in its strictly mathematical sense, was himself a Pythagorean, and it is believed that his *Elements* was intended as an introduction to the five 'perfect solids'.) An analogy can be drawn between the divergence of these two broad interpretations of the notion of symmetry and that of the differentiation of the terms of reference in astronomy and astrology; in both cases there was a gradual differentiation of objectives from a common conceptual base and in both the complete separation coincided with the inception of modern science and technology in the early seventeenth century.[1]

The theories of the Pythagoreans represented the most complete and enduring expression of the Greek love of proportion and harmony. It was perfectly natural that the revival of classical science in the early Renaissance should have been accompanied by a rekindling of interest in Pythagorean doctrines involving number mysticism, canons of proportion etc. Many, if not all, of the most influential and creative minds of this period were affected by the revival of these ideas, including Leonardo, Dürer, Palladio and Pacioli. In fact the classical ideals of a 'sublime geometry' had never been entirely forgotten and, throughout the dark interlude between the decline of Greek science in the early centuries of the Christian era and its later revival, there was a continuous, though secret, tradition of *analogia,* which found its chief expression in architecture.

It is clear from its appearance in many parts of the world, in advanced cultures, that there is something very appealing to the human mind in the idea of the existence of hidden relations in number and proportion, and this perception is not without a basis in mathematics. But the Pythagoreans, for all their obsession with number, never succeeded in constructing a system that was able to provide a consistent explanation of phenomena in the ways achieved by later, more secular, science. In fact some aspects of attempts at a synthesis of science and mysticism appear positively eccentric to the modern mind. Pythagoras himself associated certain angles and plane figures with particular gods, and he and his followers were ridiculed, even in their own time, for some of their excesses of imagination. Their belief in the existence of an unchanging and pure world of abstract principles behind the mundane was, as I have stressed, of inestimable importance to the development of science as we have come to understand it. However there are many examples, from their time and later, where a belief in the primacy of pure form, without reference to observable facts, proved to be a major obstacle to progress. Probably the most notorious example of this concerns the erroneous but long-held belief in the spherical movements of the celestial bodies (the sphere being the most perfect of solids, and therefore divine). Aristotle's proposed cosmogony of concentric, transparent spheres was transformed into a rigid dogma that hindered speculation throughout the whole of the medieval period.

The emergence of a notion of symmetry that is simply concerned with the 'relation of parts' in a purely geometrical sense, without any mystical overtones, goes back to Euclid, who laid the foundation of geometry as a proper science of spatial relations. But curiously it was only with the development of crystallography, and the need to place crystal types in specific categories, that the symmetries of space division were systematically investigated. The orderly partitioning of space had, of course, long been a matter of interest to artists and designers as well as mathematicians; in particular the symmetrical relations involved in plane geometry became familiar over the centuries to those designers concerned with pattern. But a precise mathematical account of the possibilities and limitations of symmetry in the plane came only in a retrograde way, as a component of the greater complexity of three-dimensional symmetries, the uncovering of which was the principal objective of theoretical crystallography until the advent of X-ray diffraction analysis.[2]

Many religious traditions adopt symmetrical motifs as symbols or as meditation devices.

This notion of what might best be described as *geometric symmetry* is an extremely useful way of describing the world, for nature is both profligate and economical in her use of such regularities. The great variety of crystalline structures, as we have seen, are absolutely contingent on these symmetry principles, and in the macro-world we find every conceivable mode of the apportionment of space. There are however certain highly favoured forms. I have already remarked on the frequency of bilateral symmetries, and there are certain spiral, helical and polyhedral formations that occur with surprising regularity. The fact that the same kind of symmetrical formation is found in widely different circumstances often leads to the most interesting correspondence between otherwise unrelated areas, and it is this that gives the subject its particular fascination. The distribution patterns in a mass of soap bubbles can provide a useful model for the arrangement of cell tissues, or the molecular arrangements in a crystalline structure. The pentagonal dodecahedron is a figure chosen by many viruses, and is one that is also widely used by fungi; in addition it is the form adopted by many inorganic molecular 'cages'. The same sort of spiral can be found in mollusc shells, in the tracks of sub-atomic particles, and so on.

A butterfly is symmetrical because its wings are congruent, *and in an* array. *Symmetry is diminished both by the loss of congruence (above right), and by the loss of periodicity (below right).*

Clearly there is great diversity in types of symmetry, even within this more precise understanding of the term, but we can return to the original question of the nature of symmetry with rather more hope of an explicit definition. We find that a symmetry of this, as of any kind, concerns 'the relation of parts', but that this disposition of elements does not, in itself, constitute a symmetry. An additional factor, concerning mutuality, is required and this is probably best conveyed by giving an example. The wings of a butterfly are precisely disposed in relation to each other and, in addition, they are extremely similar in appearance, though mirror-reversed. Every feature on one wing has its counterpart on the other, to the most minute degree of detail, so that they are not only in *array,* but are perfectly *congruent.* This notion of congruence is an extensive one and is an essential component of a symmetry in the sense of the word that we are dealing with here. A geometric symmetry is determined by the criteria of *congruence* and *periodicity;* where either of these factors is disturbed the symmetry of the whole is similarly reduced. Reflection is a particular case of *isometric transformation* whereby one figure, or part of a figure, is related to another through their congruence.

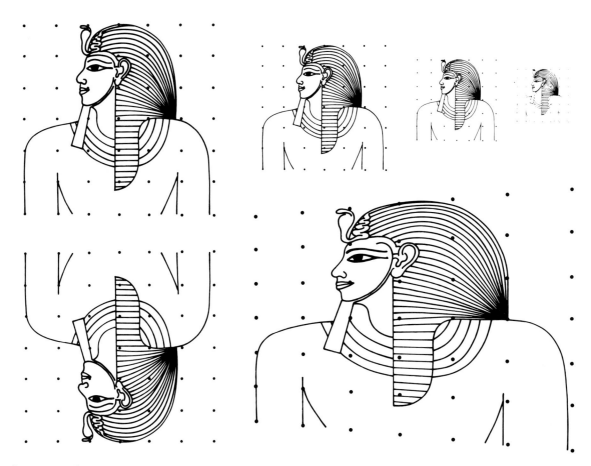

At its most elementary, symmetry is expressed simply as a regular repetition along the primary, uni-dimensional movement of a line.

Congruence implies a relationship between figures (or parts of figures) such that for every point on one there is a corresponding point on the other.

One can imagine such an arrangement extending to infinity; as long as these motifs and their interval remain the same their symmetry will be maintained.

It is an arrangement that is perfectly orderly, and therefore predictable, that is the hallmark of a symmetry. Something very interesting happens when this periodic array is extended from the simple single dimension of the line to the two-dimensional plane, for we find that a perfectly equidistant arrangement can be achieved in two distinct systems, each of which is capable of infinite extension.

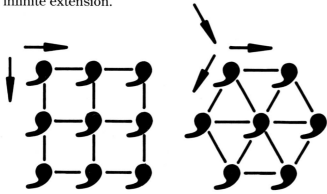

A motif can be laid out on a plane surface in two quite distinctive ways to form a regular (i.e. equidistant) array.

It is interesting too that these plane-filling arrangements, which are patterns in a quite specific, geometrical sense, reflect the configurations of Plato's 'basic triangles'. As may be imagined the variety of symmetry types becomes more complex with every additional dimensional factor, although there is no theoretical limit. While the notion of regularity, and therefore predictability, is essential to any symmetry, this can be maintained in a great variety of ways. The marking of a constant interval is, as we have seen, the simplest expression of a continuous symmetry, but a symmetry can be sustained if this interval is regularly increased. . .

. . .or if the component itself is regularly amplified. . . or both. . .

. . .and similar criteria apply both in the plane and in three dimensions. So long as the conditions of congruence and periodicity are fulfilled there will be a symmetry, and this arrangement can also be centred around a particular point both in the plane, as here, or in three or more dimensions.

By now, I hope, it should be possible for you, if you could not do so before, to distinguish the elements that go to create the symmetries in the earlier illustrations of the wheel, ladder and Rorschach blot, for all these, in their different ways, satisfy the necessary terms. On the other hand the 'patterning' of the snakeskin and the marbling effect, though they both present ordered arrays, would seem to fall short of the conditions for pattern in a strictly geometric sense. They, in fact, are cases that occupy the borderland between pattern and non-pattern and it is this quality that gives them their particular aesthetic appeal. Geometric symmetries are concerned with appearances, with the form of things, but symmetry in a more general sense is not always obvious. Even the snakeskin and the marbling have regularities that trace back to a symmetrical scheme. The coloration of most patterned snakes has an overall organisation that is laid out on the very precise arrangement of their scale systems, which act as a sort of regulating graph or grid. Similarly the consistency of the marbling effect is achieved by a 'combing' technique involving the use of a tool with regularly placed needles.

Although the world at large would appear to be characterised by its disorderliness it is in fact thoroughly permeated by abstract and non-apparent symmetry principles. Science, which in essence is wholly concerned with these underlying invariant principles, has appropriated and generalised the term symmetry so that it now applies to the notion of invariant relations of very many kinds. To understand this relatively new and extended meaning of the term we once more have to go back to basics and it is perhaps best to begin again with simple, graphic examples.

An all-over chequer pattern presents an elementary form of invariant relation, in that this arrangement remains absolutely constant even when its black and white squares are interchanged. A disc rotating about its centre provides another two-dimensional example of invariance. Here again the overall shape does not change; a disc is a disc even when it is moving. In a similar way a sphere taken through any movement about its centre will retain its shape in three dimensions. These are simple enough examples, but science, in effect, has generalised this notion so that it applies not only to objects, but to the the whole of space itself. When physicists speak of *translational invariance* they are referring to the symmetry that applies to the universal operation of the laws of physics. Newton's theory of gravity, probably the greatest single advance ever made in science, works in this way. Gravity refers to a force that applies throughout the universe, between the sun and the earth, the earth and the moon, and any one mass and another. In any equation dealing with such

Two elephants together are merely similar, but three or more regularly spaced form a geometrically symmetrical arrangement. Design from an Indian textile.

A chequer pattern remains essentially the same when its black and white squares are changed around.

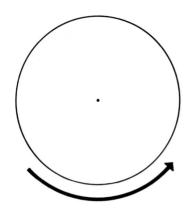

A disc remains the same shape when it is rotated.

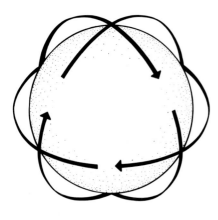

A sphere retains its shape in three dimensions when it is rotated about its centre. In scientific terms objects such as these that remain unchanged through a transformation present a translational invariance. *Science has generalised this notion of symmetry and applied it to the whole of space.*

masses this force can be changed from one side to the other without any effect. Newton's law is *invariant*, it applies to every part of the universe without fear or favour, and it is therefore symmetrical in the wider meaning of the term.

When, in the early years of this century, Einstein formulated his revolutionary new ideas of a space-time continuum, his achievement, in essence, was to advance the symmetries that were implicit in Newton's gravitational theory. It was, in fact, becoming clear that physical laws of all kinds were a consequence of symmetry; Einstein saw that Newton's gravity would be the same for a moving observer as for one who was still, and indeed for one who was accelerating, and his theory of general relativity stems from this realisation.

Physicists now consciously search for symmetries; it is their basic strategy. Where they discover a symmetry there will be an invariant relation of some kind, and the likelihood of a new conservation law. This process can also work the other way round. Abstract symmetry principles that have been developed in the first place as pure mathematical expressions have been found to apply to physical reality. The supreme example of this is the application of the elegant, algebraic symmetries of lie group theory to the problems of the interactions between basic quanta, *quarks* and *gluons*. In the words of the Nobel prize-winning physicist C.N. Yang 'Nature seems to take advantage of the simple mathematical representations of the symmetry laws.' The very basis of material reality cannot, it would appear, be understood without reference to the principle of symmetry. There is a definite sense in which the ancient ideals of the Pythagoreans have been vindicated; there *is* an order underlying the whole of the creation. Every imaginable interaction involves a symmetry, and symmetry, in the final analysis, is synonymous with order.

NOTES

1. The separation between what might be termed the numinous and the profane interpretations of natural phenomena was not complete until relatively recently, even in European science. Needham has pointed out that even in the sixteenth century science was known as 'natural magic'. It is interesting in this context that Kepler worked until the end of his life to uncover the harmonies that he believed governed the relationship between the planets, although he never succeeded in establishing the synthesis of mysticism and science that he hoped for. Newton himself has been called 'the last of the magicians', and like Kepler he had a wide-ranging interest in all manner of esotericism. Both, incidently, were convinced, and practising, astrologers.

2. In 1850 Bravais described the fourteen space lattices that came to be known by his name, and by 1890 all 230 space-groups had been designated by the Russian Federov, but though implicit in the latter it was not until the 1930s that the plane groups were specifically dealt with by Polya, Niggle and Speiser.

Reflexions and Rotations

> A geometry is defined by a group of transformations, and investigates everything that is invariant under the transformations of this given group. *Felix Klein*

The Gothic rose window (Chartres). Radial symmetry as a supreme aesthetic expression.

The notion of form is inseparable from that of symmetry. Ordinarily we think of an object that has no obvious symmetry as formless, but although nature is characterised by the enormous variety and complexity of its forms, its symmetries are often less apparent. Clearly this is partly due to the ways in which we perceive things. For a start we can only take in that which we can organise in our own mind's eye. The world, as we normally experience it, does seem rather a messy and uneven place; at least as disorderly and unpredictable as it is orderly and predictable. Although science assures us that symmetry principles are universal and that they keep the whole show together, their influence, more often than not, is

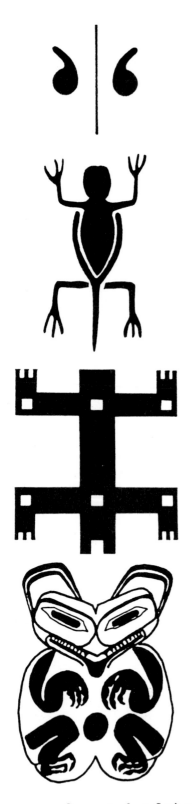

indistinct; symmetry, as it were, tends to be concealed within itself. It has always been the primary task of scientific enquiry to expose such hidden regularities, and in the course of this century symmetry has become important in several distinct and specialised areas. It is notable in biochemistry, quantum physics and of course crystallography where it occupies a dominant role, but although it has been thoroughly investigated at a higher technical level the literature dealing with this subject in a more general way is curiously limited.[1] While it is true that symmetry is now finding a place in most school curricula there is still a widespread unfamiliarity with even the most basic symmetry types, and it is possible that there are deep-seated cultural reasons for this deficiency.

Since it should be clear by now that symmetry concepts have a direct bearing on any investigation into the topic of order/disorder it seems appropriate at this point to throw a little more light on the subject, and to try to identify some of the more common symmetry types. We know that symmetry is not simply concerned with order in the spatial sense, but the conceptual framework of geometric symmetry is, I feel, as good a place as any from which to approach the subject as a whole.

Equal weights will balance in scales of equal arms. Archimedes saw in this simple case an indication of the more general importance of symmetry principles. Scales are also the symbol of justice, which is an indication of the place of symmetry concepts in society, or any other form of organisation, including ethical and religious belief-systems.

Symmetry by reflexion (along a line).

Any discussion of symmetry should begin with the image of balance-scales and the notion of equivalence. All symmetry involves a mutual correspondence of some kind, but perhaps the most familiar is that where the elements on one side of an imagined line have their equivalent on the other. This form is a *reflexion*, or mirror symmetry. Such a configuration is common in both art and architecture and also in the natural world where it is a most useful arrangement, since practically all species of living creatures that propel themselves about the planet are constituted in this way. Mathematicians describe the relationship involved in this, or in any other symmetry, in terms of a *translation*, or 'movement'. In a reflexion, which on a plane surface is arranged along a line, and in 3-space about a mirror-plane, there is a doubling up and also a reversal of images, so that this form of translation is held to be *indirectly*, or *oppositely*, congruent.

But there is another, equally fundamental form of congruent transformation that involves a movement of a different kind; this is *rotational* symmetry, in which the elements pivot about a central point (or a line in 3-dimensions). Rotational symmetries are held to express a *direct* congruence, because their components are equivalent and unreversed.

An example of rotation in its simplest form is to be found in the design of 'court' cards in an ordinary pack of playing cards: these are clearly symmetrical and if one is cut through the centre, in any section at all, it will be found that one half corresponds exactly to the other. But there is no reflexion here; instead the design repeats in an exact half-turn around the

(Left) triad rotation: the repeat element here is 'rotated' through three 120° turns. (Right) tetrad rotation: the repeat is 'rotated' through four 90° turns.

centre of the card. This particular arrangement, of two similar elements, is known as a *dyad* rotation; where there are three elements in a regular array around a point, as in the triskelion symbol of the Isle of Man, it is known as a *triad* rotation; a figure with four such elements, such as a swastika, is a *tetrad* rotation, and so on. It is worth re-emphasising here that rotational symmetries, in common with all others, require an equivalence in the disposition of their elements as well as in the elements themselves. If a particular component is out of place, that is to say out of regular array, the overall symmetry is that much reduced.

Symmetry by rotation (around a point).

129

Bilateralism in nature.

Bilateral symmetry in art.

Where a symmetry leaves a point unchanged, as in these rotated figures, it is said to belong to a *point group*, and its symmetry is described as *cyclic*. Point-group figures can also show reflexion in the lines that run through their centre, and this leads to one of the most familiar of all symmetry types, the sorts of radial configuration that can be found in flowers, in the cross-sections of fruit and in many other natural forms, particularly in the plant world. These *dihedral* symmetries, which combine rotation and reflexion are also well represented by decorative motifs from virtually every part of the world. Perhaps the supreme expression of this form is found in the magnificent rose windows of Gothic cathedrals, which themselves are a most potent metaphor for an omnipresent ordering principle and which, interestingly, are of an undoubtedly Platonic inspiration.

Point-group symmetry: (a) simple rotation (b) rotation plus reflexion.

The sort of patterns produced within a kaleidoscope also show both reflexion and rotation; the reflexion here, of course being literal as well as geometrical. But different effects are obtained when the mirrors of this device are set at different angles. In accordance with the strictures of symmetry a completely regular image will only appear when the mirrors are set at angles that are regular divisions of the circle (e.g. 30°, 45°, 60°). Two mirrors are sufficient to produce a point-group figure, but when a third mirror is added the extra element of reflexion produces an image with a series of centres, giving an impression of an overall pattern.[2]

The kaleidoscope. A centred (point-group) image appears with the use of two mirrors. (a) 45° (b) 30°. If a third mirror is added, (c) 60°, the additional element of reflexion produces an illusion of a series of centres and creates the effect of an overall pattern.

The procession of unique but orderly images produced by a kaleidoscope manifest the dual aspects of symmetry, that is to say, of its restraining power and its creative potentiality. It is evident that there is

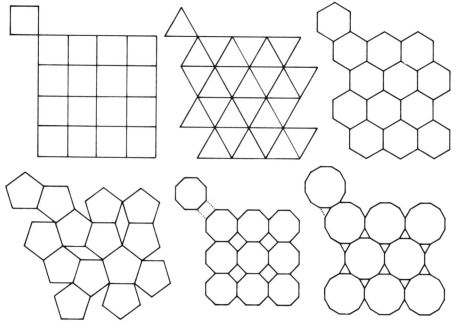

Regular polygons with three, four and six sides can completely fill the plane, but those with five cannot. Octagons and dodecagons contribute to the semi-regular tesselations, but need one or other of the basic three to finish the job.

131

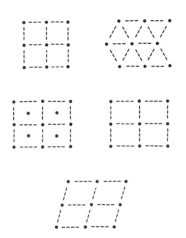

The seventeen patterns (plane groups) that are generated from the five basic nets (above) and the symmetrical movements of reflexion and rotation. These represent all possible variations of plane pattern.

both give and take in order, geometrical and otherwise; symmetry laws are not arbitrary, but they are compelling. A typical example of how these rules can appear, from nowhere as it were, involves the regular division of a plane surface; it is a curious fact that only three of all possible regular polygons will, in themselves, fill the plane. These are the square, the equilateral triangle and the hexagon, and the last two of these arrangements are closely related. There are, it is true, other regular shapes that can be used as plane-filling tiles, but they work only in some combination involving the primary three. For this reason arrangements such as the octagon/square and dodecagon/triangle are known as *semi-regular tesselations*. It is strange perhaps that regular polygons formed of five, seven, nine, ten or eleven sides, and upwards of eleven sides, cannot, in any combination, be put together to form an unbroken surface, but there it is... we just have to accept the fact.

This sort of delimitation is not restricted to plane division either. The classification of crystal types into their respective systems and classes was determined by precisely similar considerations of space division. In fact the whole field of symmetry is involved with such number games. If, for example, we take the simple matter of laying a given motif on a plane surface so as to form a regular pattern, we find ourselves restricted to just five possible configurations, formats that derive from the so-called *basic nets*. When we rotate and reflect these repeat elements about the points of

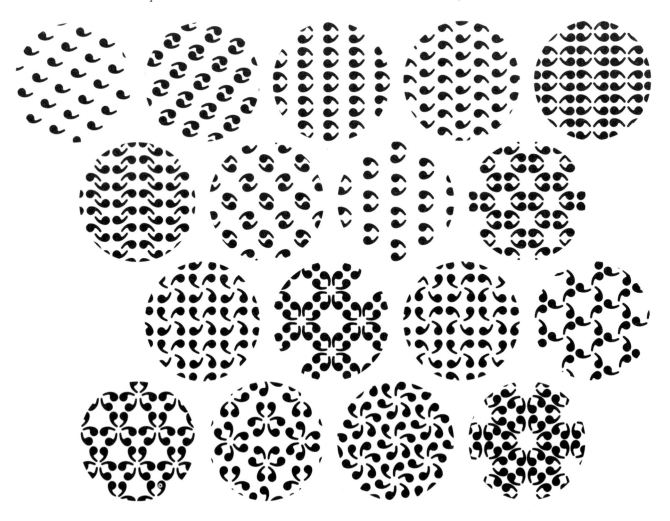

these nets we can, in fact, generate a total of seventeen kinds of plane pattern; but this is the limit. In pattern design these are all the possibilities available, and any attempt to uncover an arrangement that does not reduce to one or other of these is as futile as trying to square the circle.[3]

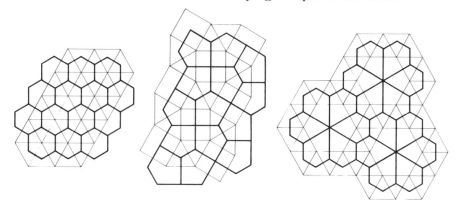

Symmetries implicit within others. These are reciprocal tesselations, a grid of irregular pentagons that emerge from one of the semi-regular arrangements.

Certain patterns may indeed give the impression of greater complexity than the rather stripped-down examples illustrated here, but this is usually because their repeat element is absorbed into an overall effect. Any pattern can be analysed by locating the lines of symmetry that form its supporting grid; the nodes of this grid will constitute the basic net of the pattern, and its repeating elements can then be located within this network as a series of cells and sub-cells. Symmetries in three dimensions can be analysed in much the same way, and of course most natural symmetries tend to occur in three rather than two dimensions. Solid objects, with the complication of an additional dimensional factor, present, as would be expected, a far greater variety of symmetry types, but the principles that apply in the plane extend out to this further dimension. Reflexions and rotations can be found in solid objects, and there are point groups, line groups and patterns in

Symmetries in three-dimensional space: (a) reflection about a mirror-plane (b) rotation about an axis (c) linear (d) point group about regular points in space (e) space-group patterns in space (f) dilation symmetries in space.

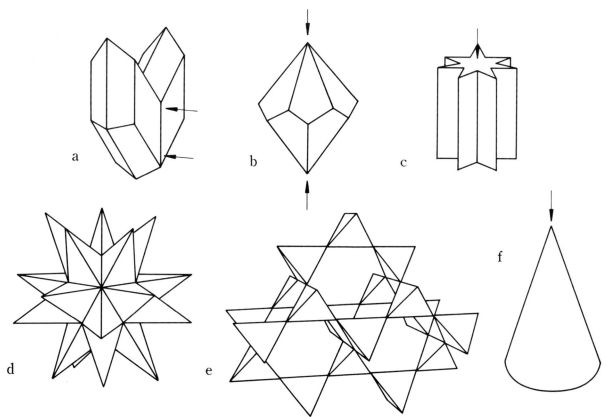

space just as there are on plane surfaces. Also there are three-dimensional equivalents of those symmetries that, at a uniform rate, increase or diminish the *dilation* symmetries.

Dilation symmetries.

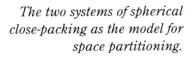

The two systems of spherical close-packing as the model for space partitioning.

When we look at the ways in which space can be regularly divided it is clear that the most elementary forms result from a simple extension of the regular plane figures, in other words prisms. Just as the equilateral triangle, square, and hexagon will fill the plane the prisms based on these

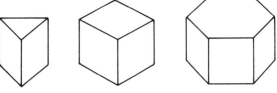

will completely fill space. But when it comes to dividing space so that it is regular in all directions the options are rather more limited. There are, in fact, just two basic systems of equidistant points in space These are the cubic and the hexagonal arrangements, and they can be represented as two modes of spherical close-packing. The regular partitioning of space is obviously an important criterion in the optimising of form, and because of

Space-filling solids:
(a) truncated octahedron
(b) rhombic dodecahedron
(c) twist-rhombic dodecahedron.

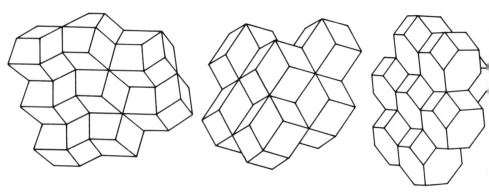

134

this it is treated most carefully in nature; although there are five regular solids that perform this task there is one that seems to be most favoured by organic forms. This is the *truncated octahedron*, which is able to section space with faces that meet with co-equal angles of 120°. Because it is the most efficient and economical system it is the one adopted by soap bubbles in a mass, and for similar reasons, is found as the basic structure of a great variety of cell structures.[4]

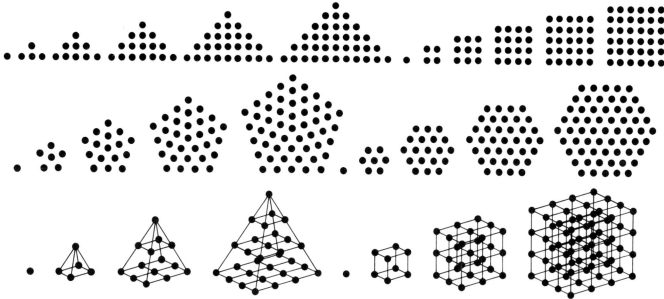

The isometries of all geometric symmetries, both in the plane and in three dimensions, can be described in purely mathematical terms. In this way it is possible to enumerate every kind of repetition and combination, and to establish in a rigorous way the various symmetry types in each of their classes. Historically it was the Pythagoreans who were the first to explore the connections between the successions of geometric terms and those of pure mathematics. Indeed by converting *shape* into *number* they could be said to have initiated the partnership between science and mathematics. Pythagoras and his followers were fascinated by the relation of numbers to real-world phenomena, by the concordant intervals of the musical scale for instance, and other 'predictive' qualities of the numerical series. As a result of their many, genuinely impressive, discoveries the Pythagoreans began to believe that they had found the key to the secrets of the universe ('all is number'). From a modern standpoint they can appear to have become almost intoxicated by their discoveries and to have wandered into far less fruitful areas, such as that of number mysticism.

The belief of the Pythagoreans in the near magical power of numerical series is perhaps more understandable when we realise that they saw number as the direct source of form, as a pattern of dots that created characteristic 'figures' (one of many of their terms that we use). The Pythagorean notion of figures began with relatively simple polygonal groupings of points, but they soon progressed to three-dimensional number series, in cubic, pyramidal and tetrahedral forms. All of these progressions were, of course, intensely symmetrical, and such successions of terms, which proceed according to a definite rule, are still very much a part of mathematical analysis.

Numbers were regarded by the Pythagoreans as patterns of dots, which formed characteristic 'figures'. Beginning with simple polygonal groups they soon progressed to cubic, tetrahedral, pyramidal and other three-dimensional series.

135

It is quite easy to understand how the more elementary of these symmetrical series should have lent themselves to both a numerical and a geometrical interpretation. For instance it is perfectly easy to visualise the *divergent* progressions (1,2,3,4,5 etc., or 1+2+3+4+5 etc., or $1^2+2^2+3^2+4^2+5^2$ etc., and no more difficult to imagine those series that increase by regularly diminishing quantities (i.e. $1+^1/_2+^1/_3+^1/_4$ etc. and $1+^1/_2+^1/_3+^1/_4$ etc.).

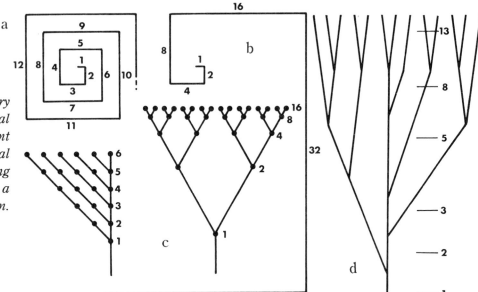

Representations of elementary progressions: (a) arithmetical progression as an equidistant spiral (b) the geometric spiral (c) arithmetical branching (d) the summation series as a branching system.

These latter *convergent* series, incidently, are integral to those theories that underlie the systems of tables of logarithms, sines and tangents. As well as these divergent and convergent progressions there are *semi-convergent* series, whose successive terms are positive and negative (i.e. $1+^1/_2-^1/_3+^1/_4$ etc.). This form like the others can be imagined in geometric terms, as a movement that progresses in alternate directions, left and right. While we are on this subject it is worth referring to that particularly interesting progression known as the *summation series* in which the progressed number is the sum of the two previous ones, often referred to as the *Fibonacci series*, (after the nickname of its discoverer Leonardo of Pisa). This incremental formula underlies some of the most attractive natural symmetries, those found in many shells, pine cones, cacti etc.

The Fibonacci series in pine cones, shells, flower-heads and phyllotaxy.

We now take the analytical and descriptive possibilities of mathematics pretty much for granted, and do not experience the same feelings of reverence for its intricate and abstract relations as did the Pythagoreans. In a sense this is because we are the direct heirs of their belief in the creative potentiality of pure number. In fact their instincts in this respect have been vindicated beyond their wildest imaginings. The Pythagoreans might well be surprised at the extent of the present scientific and mathematical understanding of nature, but they would be better prepared for it than any of their contemporaries. Indeed it was implicit in the teachings of this school, which laid the foundation of both arithmetic and geometry, that human understanding of all phenomena could be advanced to the very limit by means of number, that in the ultimate there was no part of nature that could not be drawn into the 'jewelled web' of mathematical

The symmetries of spirals, ellipses, waves and vortices: (a) the equidistant spiral (b) the equiangular spiral (c) a conformable system of equiangular spirals (d) the elliptic series (e) sine-wave forms (f) outline of a compound leaf based on composite sine-curves (g) vortex symmetries.

137

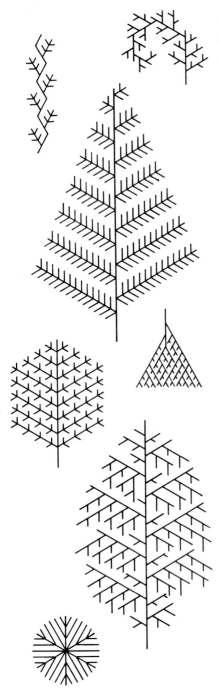

Varieties of symmetrical branching.

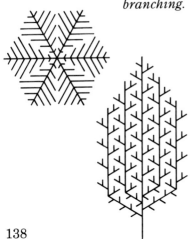

description.[5] Before leaving the subject of the formal, geometric aspects of symmetry I should like to remark on two further modes, both of which are very common in the real world, but perhaps not so generally recognised as expressing symmetry in the ordinary sense; these are the symmetries of regular curvature and of periodic branching. Like most of the other symmetries described in this section both of these can be expressed both in the plane and in three dimensions, and both are endowed with the universal and archetypal quality of all such symmetries.

A curve can be thought of as a point that moves along a continuous path, or locus, and it will be symmetrical when the direction of this locus is self-consistent. The simplest curves, such as the circular or those of the various conic sections, parabolic, elliptical and hyperbolic, are usually described as curves of the second degree, since they will intersect with a straight line only at two points. Spirals and helices are symmetrical by virtue of the regularity which which they wind around a centre, or a pole. Regular curves in three dimensions, the so-called tortuous curves, are measured by their changes of direction across three continuous points. Wave forms too can be symmetrical, in both their length and period; a simple sine-curve, for instance, can be thought of as a projection on a plane of the path of a point moving round a circle at a uniform speed; if this movement is regularly increased or diminished it will result in a characteristic sine configuration.

As with the symmetries of curvature there are an infinite variety of forms of symmetrical branching. Branching systems can be thought of as having a real existence, like those of actual trees, as mathematical entities, also known as trees, or simply as mental concepts that exist independently of any representation. Quite complex branching systems can be generated from fairly simple sets of rules or algorithms, and will remain symmetrical so long as they conform to the same principles of congruence and periodicity that apply to all other symmetries.

NOTES

1. See Bibliography.
2. For those interested in making their own kaleidoscopes the best effects, in my experience, are obtained from the arrangement of mirrored rectangular strips, in the ratio of 7:1 laid out on a triangular plan.
3. The decorative arts of most cultures do not usually avail themselves of more than a limited selection of these possibilities, but I have found examples of all seventeen plane group symmetries in two artistic traditions, namely those of ancient Egypt and Islam.
4. The truncated octahedron is one of the thirteen Archimedean solids, which have the distinction of being facially regular, and which can be inscribed within a sphere. As solids this group could be said to correspond to the semi-regular plane tesselations.
5. In fact all manner of 'strange' kinds of order have been discovered in the most complex and turbulent conditions – more about this in the next section.

Symmetries Seen and Unseen

Nothing in physics seems so hopeful to me as the idea that it is possible for a theory to have a high degree of symmetry which is hidden from us in ordinary life. *Stephen Weinburg*

In the two previous sections I have given a broad account of the nature of symmetry and an indication of some of its more familiar modes of expression, so we might now feel better placed to return to the question that was posed earlier concerning the limits of symmetry: where does it begin and end? Surprisingly, the more we delve into this subject the more extensive we find the principle seems to be, and in the final analysis, it would appear not to have any natural limits, nor are there any circumstances or phenomena where symmetry factors of one sort or another do not apply. There is a paradox here: symmetry, which is identifiable with every limiting, ordering and regulating process, is itself without limitation. Indeed by adopting a rather one-sided, 'crystalline', viewpoint we can see science as the principal method by which we extend our knowledge of the symmetries inherent in nature, and the whole of nature itself, from its very beginning as a grand process of diffraction, or symmetry breaking, from which there has emerged an ever greater diversity of form.

In the first instance we tend to encounter symmetry by way of its strong aesthetic appeal. The more obvious symmetries of such things as crystals, shells or flowers are universally recognised and appreciated, but the greater part of symmetry is concealed from view. Most of us will have seen

Computer-generated designs of this sort, which express one aspect of the new science of 'chaos', are extremely complex, but since they are generated from relatively simple algorithms, they are absolutely self-consistent and therefore 'symmetrical to an extreme degree'. (Mandelbrot)

fine specimen crystals, and we now know that their clean-cut regularity derives from an invisible, internal ordering. In a similar way we may have been struck by the complex symmetries of plant structures in micro-slides, or simply by slicing a fruit or vegetable, but the important point about these and all other examples of natural symmetry, is that although they might be unusual and striking enough in themselves the principle that gives rise to such formations is one of the most general in nature.

The ideal shape of the graded profile of a riverbed, which of course is never attained, is that of a hyperbolic curve.

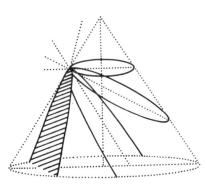

The hyperbola as one of the curves formed by the plane section of a cone.

Let me illustrate this with an example involving symmetries of a less familiar kind. When we stand on a river bank, particularly in the higher reaches where it is a fast-flowing stream, it is hard to imagine that symmetries of any kind have much part to play here, a river being more like a continuous process than an objective thing. Nevertheless it is the case that all rivers are deeply influenced by a whole range of symmetrical constraints. To begin with, every river is graded so that its general profile, from source to outlet, perpetually strives towards the creation of an ideal hyperbolic curve, which is one of the curves of conic section.[1] It is also the case that the lateral windings of a river, its meanders, tend to adopt the precise configuration of sine-generated curves. Although these ideal forms may seem far from apparent in actual rivers, all deviations from them, such as those caused by lakes or waterfalls, in the scale of geological time, have to be seen as no more than temporary dislocations; rivers are constantly filling in and smoothing out such irregularities. In addition to these greater symmetries the progressive cross-sectional profile of a river reveals a series of rhythmically alternating parabolae. The currents within this system have their own circulatory patterns that generate a helical path which reverses its direction of rotation with each successive meander. These are some of the principal regularities of form in rivers, but one could go on and on with this process of *reductio ad symmetrium* without ever exhausting all possibilities. In this, as in all other phenomena, the point will never be reached where symmetry principles no longer apply. In fact we might paraphrase the Pythagorean precept that 'all is number' with the assertion that 'all is symmetry'.

Clearly, though, this is not the whole story, otherwise everything would be perfectly symmetrical and it very obviously is not. The fact is that symmetry is a relative term and there is no *absolute* symmetry any more than there is an *absolute* separation of any phenomenon from the cosmic continuum. At the same time a measure of symmetry is essential to the very existence of matter of any kind: it is the 'invisible organiser' of energy. One of the most interesting and far-reaching notions to have come out of physics in the post-war era is that symmetry, at the very deepest level, implies *interaction*. Because the properties of fundamental particles are completely bound up with the ways in which they interact the symmetries involved in both particles and exchanges are identical. These invariant qualities are now seen to constitute conservation laws that apply to every kind of particle reaction, and which are therefore responsible for the fundamental structure of matter.[2] Such concepts, which in one sense are

The sine-generated curves of river meanders.

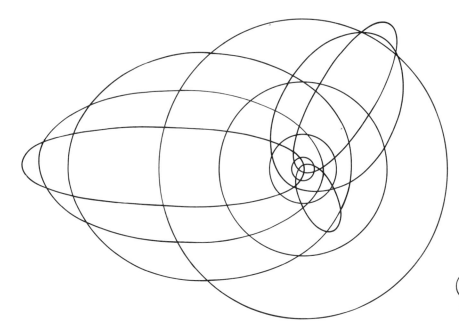

*In any atomic arrangement
the energy values of the
electrons involved compels
them to adopt specific orbits.
(Based on Bohr's original
model of a hydrogen atom)*

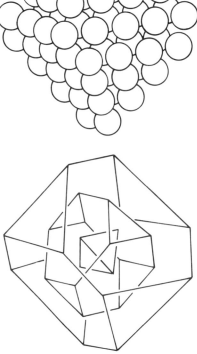

purely mathematical abstractions, are nevertheless essential for our deeper understanding of nature. The basic impenetrability of matter, for instance, is a direct consequence of the symmetries implicit in the Pauli exclusion principle. The arrangement of particles within the atom is, of course, intensely symmetrical. In response to quantum laws, and according to their energy values, electrons adopt quite specific orbits about the nucleus to form three-dimensional shells or 'clouds' which are electrically balanced with the protons in the central nucleus. The complex system of the nucleus itself, which holds most of the mass of the atom, is also highly symmetrical, having a structure similar to that of certain crystalline formations (face-centred cubic). The chemical properties of all elements are entirely determined by this internal, atomic structuring and by the number of electrons and protons involved. Just as symmetry is involved in the differentiation between chemical elements, so it is in the relations between them. As every schoolchild knows, chemical equations must balance; the number of atomic elements of a particular kind that enter a reaction must also leave it. Because quantum theory has been so successful in accounting for the internal structure of the atom, and in explaining the processes involved in the combination of one atom with another, chemistry now tends to be understood from the bottom up, as it were. It is now seen to be

*The structure of the nucleus
(of calcium-400) according to
the face-centred model.*

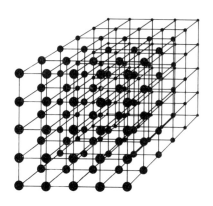

*A characteristic X-ray
diffraction pattern. It is
precisely because molecular
order is so symmetrical that it
can be exposed in this way.*

141

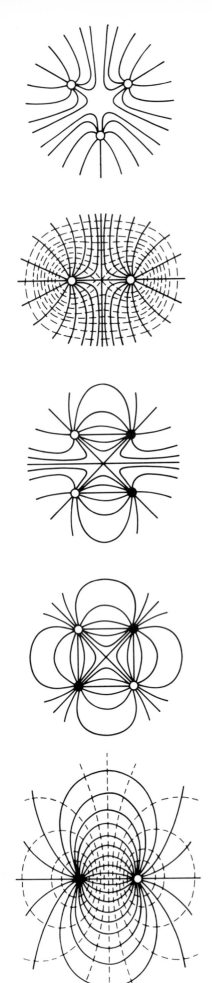

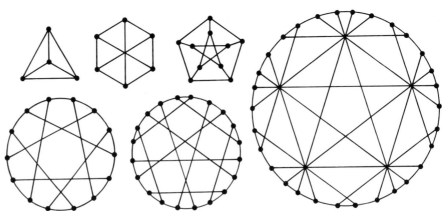

Chemical reactions, however complex, can be plotted on reaction graphs.

based on the intricate patterns of exchange between the constituent atoms of the elements involved, and this is an entirely symmetrical process.

Since the advent of relativity, science has viewed mass as a form of structured energy; according to Einstein's formula the energy contained in any particle is equal to its mass times the speed of light ($E = MC^2$). We have seen that symmetry principles are inextricably involved in this structuring, or confining, process, and that they are actually inseparable from the notion of form at this and all higher levels.

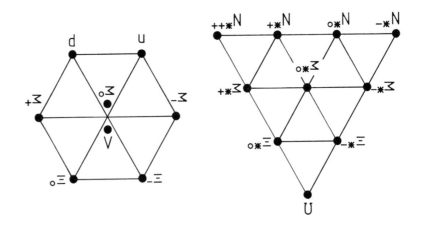

The elegant symmetries at the very heart of matter: The classification of hadrons as an octet and as a decuplet of baryons, a scheme that later came to be understood in terms of quark combinations (the so-called eight-fold way).

Symmetry is ubiquitous; indeed certain of its expressions are to be found at the very extremes of scale. One of the more memorable images of recent decades is that of the earth viewed from space; we have known that the planet is round for a very long time, but photographs that show it as a perfectly smooth sphere suspended in the isolation of space are still unfailingly impressive. The sphere, which demonstrates a perfect

The 'invisible organisation of energy' at its most elementary level: The symmetries of the lines of force produced by different combinations of positive and negative poles.

142

symmetry around a point in three-dimensional space, is an ideal shape in geometric terms and for this reason was an object of fascination to many early Greek thinkers. Xenophanes, who was the first philosopher to put forward the idea of a single, supreme deity, believed that He, or rather It, would have to be in the form of a sphere! It is not easy to see how one could test that particular hypothesis, but it is now felt that the cosmos itself, in the most general way, expresses a spherical symmetry.

It is not only our own planet that is spherical of course, but also all other large heavenly bodies. The sun and the moon, in common with all other stars, planets and their accompanying planets, adopt the shape of minimum surface area in response to the power of an attractive force; on a smaller scale soap bubbles and water droplets do the same sort of thing, though the force in these cases is molecular rather than gravitational. Scale is an influential factor here. The gravitational force that gives the earth its spherical shape has the contrary effect on most of the objects on it so that, at least on our own level, spherical symmetry is not all that common. Even those fruits and vegetables that incline towards the spherical tend to be polar, which means that their internal symmetry radiates from an axis rather than from a centre. Of course the sphere is an extremely useful shape for mechanical bearings, and a fairly essential component of a great number of sports, but it is not until we enter the world of micro-organisms that this form really comes into its own again. Many microscopic creatures, by virtue of their size and density relative to their surroundings, are symmetrical about a point, and some, including bacteria, algae and volvox, are completely spherical, a condition that they achieve by being fairly indifferent to the force of gravity.

In contrast the earth, and all other massive bodies in space, tend towards the spherical precisely because every part of their mass pulls towards a centre of gravity, so that this shape represents a maximum concentration as well as a minimal surface area. If the earth were still and of equal density, it might be a perfect sphere, but since it rotates about its axis its spherical symmetry is disturbed by centrifugal force. This causes it to bulge slightly at the equator, and flatten at the poles, creating a slight asymmetry which amounts to a difference of some twenty-seven miles between its polar and equatorial diameters. If we were pedantic we would have to describe the earth as an *oblate ellipsoid* rather than a sphere, though the deviation is very small. On the other hand the distribution of the land masses about the surface of our planet is highly irregular: less than 30 per cent of the surface of the earth is actually covered by land and 80 per cent of this is concentrated in the so-called land hemisphere (which has its pole in Brittany of all places). There is little indication of symmetry of any kind in the scattered and non-uniform distribution of land masses, though of course this sort of inconsistency is an extremely familiar aspect of the real world. But even here, as is so often the case in nature, there are underlying regularities. Quite literally underlying in this case, for the continuous lateral displacement of the major land masses of the earth is actually induced by large-scale, and highly symmetrical, movements of its interior. These movements are caused because the earth is hottest at its centre and cooler on its outside, which facts lead to the creation of massive convection patterns rather like those in a heated saucepan; these movements are sustained in great convection cells that partition up the whole of the

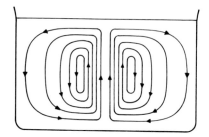

Convection currents in a saucepan.

143

interior in an intensely regular manner. (It is salutary, to say the least, to think of all our fields, forests, mountain ranges and deserts, in fact everything that we hold dear, as a sort of by-product of this and other grand processes.)

Perhaps the best picture we can form of the cosmos is that of a wavering equilibrium, or more precisely, that of a progressively disturbed symmetry. For example: our planet is rotating on its axis and is less symmetrical as a result, but since this rotation is itself uniform we do have a regular pattern of days and nights; also, because the axis of the earth is tilted by a constant 23.5 degrees relative to our path around the sun, our symmetrical relation to it is 'broken' into the lesser regularity of the seasonal cycle. When we add to these factors the differential heating of the surface of the earth between the equatorial and polar regions , the results, which we commonly refer to as 'the weather', are very complicated indeed. On a global scale the weather is inherently unpredictable, but of course within certain wide parameters it too maintains an equilibrium. The question of whether the universe as a whole is nearer to or further from a state of equilibrium is an exceedingly abstruse one since, essentially, we have nothing else with which to compare it. What we can be sure of is that there was just sufficient equilibrium on the surface of our planet, and just the right degree of disturbance to it, to give rise to the most complex symmetries that anyone has as yet detected, namely, living organisms.

The great majority of living things are symmetrical in their overall appearance and their cells, tissues and organs also tend to be symmetrical. All organisms adopt their characteristic symmetries in response to, and to take advantage of, their environment. Very simple creatures, such as the free-floating protozoa, achieve the most complete, that is to say spherical, symmetry since every part of their surface has the same relation to their environment. Ova are typically spherical for similar reasons. This invariance is also an indication that although they are highly symmetrical they are very simple-minded creatures. Where the influence of gravitation intrudes upon the existence of an organism, even very slightly, this is bound to bestow upon it a particular directionality, involving the process of symmetry-breaking again. The jellyfish, for example, is another fairly simple free-floating creature that has no 'left' or 'right' in its world, but it does have a sense of 'up' and 'down', so that although it has no sides it is quite definitely possessed of top and bottom ends. The same sort of symmetry applies to most plants; although usually anchored to a particular point plants do not, for the most part, have a back or front, though their top and bottom ends are well differentiated because, of course, most of them grow from the middle, both up and down. Nothing marks the distinction between plants and animals so much as the differences between their respective symmetries. Plants tend to stay in one place and animals to move about; this means that the gross symmetry of the former is arranged for them to take the greatest advantage of their sessile state, and that of the latter to help them get around. Plant symmetries, then, tend to be radial, in three dimensions of course, and those of animals bilateral or, to be pedantic again, *dorsiventral*.

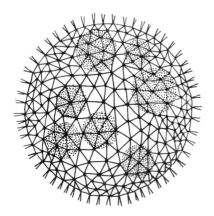

Only the very simplest creatures can aspire to spherical symmetry (Volvox).

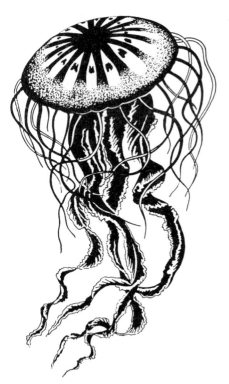

The jellyfish has distinct top and bottom ends, but no front or back, left or right.

In general terms, organisms are symmetrical for reasons of evolutionary advantage, and they are symmetrical moreover at every level of their being, from the molecular to the cellular and upwards. The whole point of the complexities of plant structure is to make the most efficient use of available resources, both above and below the ground. This involves the systematic occupation of available space. The adopted mode of 'space-invasion' of a plant gives it a distinctive morphology that is entirely hereditary. Each plant has a coded response to its environment that is unique to its own species, but as no two individuals of the same species will ever be exposed to exactly the same environmental factors, i.e. of light, temperature and soil conditions, not to mention their encounters with other plants, these already complex forms will be further influenced in ways that lead to the familiar, 'chaotic' differentiation of the plant world, and to the concealment of their individual symmetries. A tree that is exposed to a strong prevailing wind, for instance, will show a marked asymmetry, whereas one of the same species that grows in a more congenial situation is likely to be far more regular in its overall appearance.

The hidden symmetries of flowers: (a) types of placentation (b) sections.

'Among the peculiarities of flowers there is one really astonishing fact, viz. the numbers of their petals is in most cases conformable to the laws of geometry. You scarcely ever find a flower of seven or nine petals, for you cannot construct these according to the laws of geometry in a circle as isoceles triangles. The number of their petals is always three or four or five or eighteen.'

Al-Biruni. (b.973)

One of the most prominent features of the morphology of a plant is its mode of branching, each species having a distinctive system that is part of its genetic inheritance.

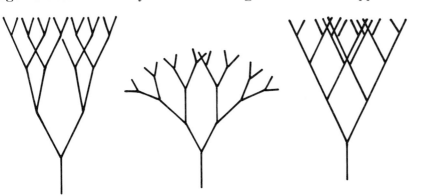

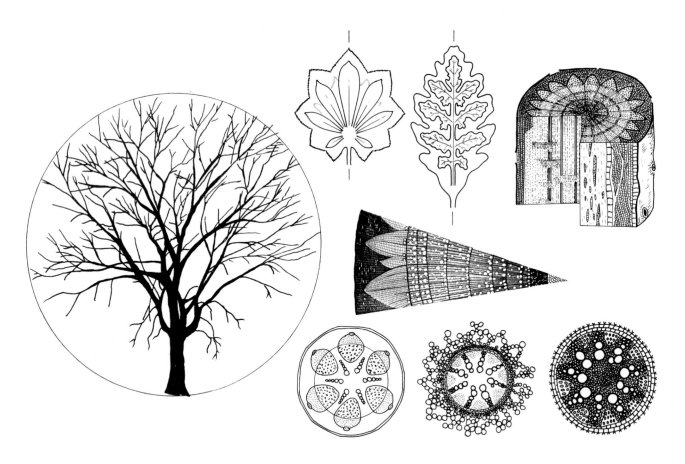

Other symmetries in plants. In trees where such external influences as shading, wind, gradients etc. are minimal there is usually a fair degree of overall, radial symmetry. Sectioning also exposes the symmetries of roots, trunks, flowers and fruits.

The major symmetries of plants, then, are 'internal', in the sense that their normal response to environmental conditions is largely predetermined. These primary responses are expressed in such important areas as the growth of stems (*nutation*), and the distribution of leaves on these (*phyllotaxy*). They also give rise to the characteristic spiral formations of the above. In addition each species has a distinctive branching system which, in flowering plants, also controls the arrangement of flowering branches and the systematic distribution of flowers upon them (*inflorescence*). The root systems of all plants are also structured according to similar, pre-ordained and algorithmic patterns. Most leaves and flowers are highly symmetrical, and the sectioning of almost any part of a plant generally reveals further symmetries.

One of the more surprising aspects of plant structure is the extensive occurrence of spiral forms, not only at the organ level, already mentioned, but also at the tissue, cellular and molecular levels. Surprising too that although this form is so extensive the spirality of one organisational level

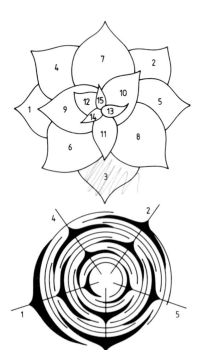

Phyllotaxy, the precise geometrical arrangements of leaf distribution, is determined by an interesting mathematical progression known as the Fibonacci series. This example shows a shoot with a 3/8 phyllotaxy, in which every eighth leaf is directly above another, the system having made three circuits of the stem; (below) section showing the spirality that derives from this particular series.

Section of Euphorbia Wolfanii *showing its 8/13 phyllotaxy* (after Church).

rarely has much to do with that of another. At the molecular level there are the well-known helical structures of DNA and the proteins; at the cellular level one finds that the cellulose fibres of secondary cell walls are frequently spiral, as is the structure of protoxylen and the streaming formation of protoplasm, and one could go on citing examples practically indefinitely. As with other organic symmetries the frequency of spiral and helical formations in the structures of so many different plant species, and across such a range of scales within them, has to be understood in terms of evolutionary advantage and efficiency. We can be sure that these are extremely useful shapes, particularly for plants, and that although they are frequently involved in highly evolved and complex systems they have the great merit that they can be generated from sets of relatively simple rules.

The correspondence between the functional requirements of a plant and the pure, abstract order of mathematical progression is particularly evident in the case of phyllotaxy. This, the spiral arrangement of leaves about their stem, is seldom obvious, but it can easily be demonstrated by winding a string around the stalks of successive leaves in growth order. There are various systems of phyllotaxy, but their numbers are closely prescribed, the limiting formula being tied to that of the aforementioned Fibonacci series (in which the third term of the series of the numerator is the sum of the two previous, i.e. 1 1 2 3 5 8 13 21 etc.). The fact that all leaf distribution systems are determined in this way has made phyllotaxy as much the subject of mathematical and philosophical as of botanical speculation. The simplest phyllotaxies occur where successive leaves fall at an angle of 180° to each other, so that the progression from one leaf to the next directly above it requires a whole circuit of the stem and the passage of two leaves; this is known as a 1/2 phyllotaxy. If the third leaf is directly above the first

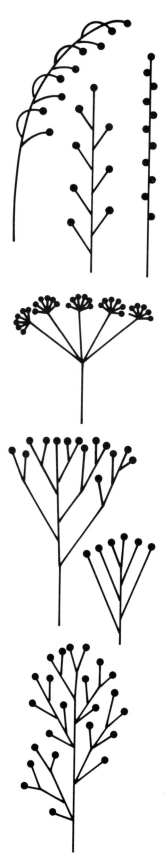

The symmetries of inflorescence, the arrangement of flowering branches, and of flowers on these.

147

Spiral symmetries can be found everywhere in nature, even at the very extremes of scale; they are the characteristic symmetries of dynamic systems, particularly those of living organisms.

The dynamic symmetries of spirals and helices: (a) the equable, or Archimedian, spiral (b) the equiangular, or logarithmic, spiral (c) double spiral (d) helix (e) dilated helix (f) double helix. All of these forms can be expressed in two distinct versions of 'handedness' (spirals in two dimensions, helices in three).

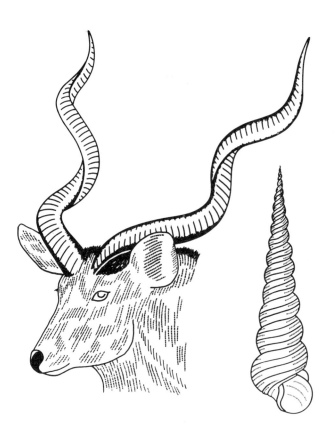

Enantiomorphism. Helical formations, of whatever kind, have to opt for either right- or left-handed forms, or both. This distinction also applies to those crystal types whose system does not present a bilateral symmetry. The quartz crystals shown here are perhaps the most common mineral with this trait, but single-handedness is also an important characteristic of the more complex molecular structures of living organisms (such as gene and protein material).

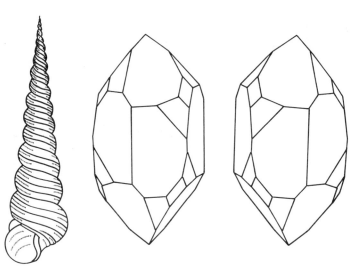

then a whole circuit of the stem and the passage of three leaves is involved, creating a 1/3 phyllotaxy, and so on.[3] The most complex arrangement found in any leaf system is that of a 5/18 phyllotaxy, but higher forms, such as 8/21, 13/34 and even 21/55 can be found in more compact systems, like those of pine cones for instance, certain cacti, and pineapples. The forms of spirals and helices, perhaps more than any other shapes, seem to endorse the separation, or even transcendence, of symmetry over scale, so that at one extreme we find beautifully etched spirals in the tracks of infinitesimal particles, and at the other the vast formations of spiral nebulae; in all their manifestations these symmetries seem to be associated with dynamic systems, which is the reason why they are so prevalent among organic structures. In the abstract terminology of geometry the symmetries of spirals and helices constitute a 'continuous movement'. In physical terms, of course, this usually results in discontinuous, discrete objects, but, interestingly, this movement gives these curves an objective directionality that has the effect of reducing their symmetry, so that they can all occur in two distinct forms, that is to say, in both right- and left-handed versions (although this only affects spirals as two-dimensional objects – think about it![4]).

There are plenty of examples of handedness, or *enantiomorphism*, in nature; the opposite helical twists of ram or antelope horns are a prime example. In these we have the seeming paradox of two objects whose symmetry is identical in every respect, but which, in one important sense, is utterly dissimilar. There is a great variety of other helical forms in nature. The majority do not appear in paired sets, but rather in one or other of two possible configurations. (They are obliged to opt for right- or left-handedness because helices are symmetrical about an axis, but do not have a plane of symmetry). We can observe this enantiomorphism in the elegant helical structures of sea shells, where one can find both right- and left-handed

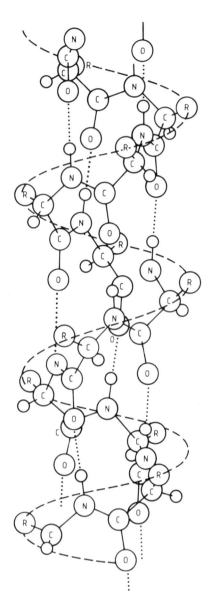

Part of the molecular structure of animal protein showing its helical form.

specimens. The shells of most species coil downwards in a clockwise direction, but a substantial proportion choose to go the other way. Some species do not appear to have strong feelings either way in this matter and so have a fairly random distribution of shells of both handedness. Others again are right-handed in one locality, and left-handed in another. To complicate matters even further all species seem to have the occasional 'sport', or awkward customer, which chooses the opposite handedness of most others of its kind. Another category is found in the familiar twisting formations of vines and climbing plants where, the situation is somewhat similar. Here we find that the majority of species opt for a right-handed existence, but that there is a substantial minority of left-handers. As in the case of mollusc shells it is clear that there can be no significant selective pressures at work here to force the issue of a particular handedness either way; indeed one can sometimes find both left- and right-handed varieties within the same species.

This appears to be the case in countless other helical forms in both the plant and animal worlds, where the choice of a particular enantiomorphism seems, in the great majority of cases, to be almost arbitrary. It would, for instance, be hard to tell in advance whether the coils of a bacterium, or those of a narwhal's tusk, or that of an umbilical cord or of an insect's flight-path will be clockwise or counter-clockwise, and in most cases it does not seem to be that important. This, at least, is true of most organic functions above that of the molecular; at this deeper level, however, the picture is very different, and highly predictable. For it is one of the outstanding facts of fundamental biology that the most vital substances in the chemistry of living creatures are helical in structure and that they are all committed to the same orientation. This applies to all the molecules that go to make up protein materials and to the twenty different types of amino-acid; all of which amounts to the fact that the chemical basis of life is right-handed. This, when it was uncovered in the early fifties, was an extraordinarily important discovery because it provided the most convincing evidence for the unity of life on earth, and of the singularity of its origin. Although it seems unlikely that we shall ever know the precise circumstances of the origin of life we can be sure that the earliest macro-molecules to master the art of self-replication opted for a particular stereo-chemical handedness, and in doing so determined the whole subsequent course of evolution. In effect life became possible by following the path of a 'reduced' molecular symmetry; although in the ultimate it was probably of no consequence which particular course was taken, just as it does not really matter which way a sea shell spirals.

Here we confront again the central paradox of symmetry, for it would appear that the progressively 'higher' orders of organic life became possible through, indeed are identical with, a progressive reduction of symmetry, and to the extent that we associate order with symmetry this seems contradictory and counter-intuitive. In fact the difficulty, which is posed here in a particularly sharpened form, concerns the precise point at which a symmetrical object becomes asymmetrical. This is not so much a problem in common usage where the latter term is almost synonymous with that of 'lopsidedness', i.e. it represents an aberration from a familiar, balanced arrangement. Also, in normal circumstances, we feel that it is perfectly adequate to apply a criterion of symmetry to one situation

without it necessarily being appropriate to another. For instance, a snowflake can be asymmetric even though it shows a clear plane of reflection, and this is because we expect it to be more 'perfect'. Similarly a begonia leaf, which for its own good reasons is developed more on one side than the other, is considered asymmetric because most leaves are bilaterally symmetrical; this is in spite of the fact that the points of similarity in its two halves far outweigh their differences. The same criteria apply to the fiddler crab, with its one highly developed claw; though it is unlikely that the crab feels itself to be unsymmetrical, any more than we do with our own right- or left- handedness. The term only applies then when there is an apparent disturbance to an apparent, or notional, reciprocity; where this sort of balance is not perceived, or expected, neither 'symmetry' nor 'asymmetry' are really appropriate. Even when we do use these expressions they have to be seen as absolutely relative, in much the same way that motion is relative in Einstein's theory. As far as 'asymmetry' is concerned semantic difficulties can only arise when the symmetry that it refers to is itself unclear, which can easily occur because, as I have stressed, symmetry is far more often concealed than apparent.

The business of uncovering symmetries has always been the essential task of science: indeed as science has advanced so has its perception of symmetry, and it is this, essentially, that has so changed our view of the world. The powerful new tools of modern science, such as giant telescopes and particle accelerators, have enabled it to probe further out and deeper into the cosmos than ever before, and the new kinds of order that have been discovered have had to be assimilated by the formulation of new laws. In recent years the whole notion of order, and therefore of symmetry, has had to be revised in the light of certain discoveries that have been made with that other and perhaps most important tool of science today, the digital computer. These discoveries moreover were as much to do with the abstract world of pure mathematics as with the external world of phenomena. The great advances in computer technology have ensured that they are useful to every branch of science, but they have also given rise, on their own account as it were, to a whole new set of ideas that have come to be known collectively as 'chaos' theories. Surprisingly, in view of

Asymmetrical, but in what sense? This untypical snow crystal can be seen as a symmetrical or an asymmetrical object, according to the criteria selected. In the same way these characteristically 'lop-sided' forms, a begonia leaf and a male fiddler crab, are congruent with others of their species and, in that sense, are symmetrical.

151

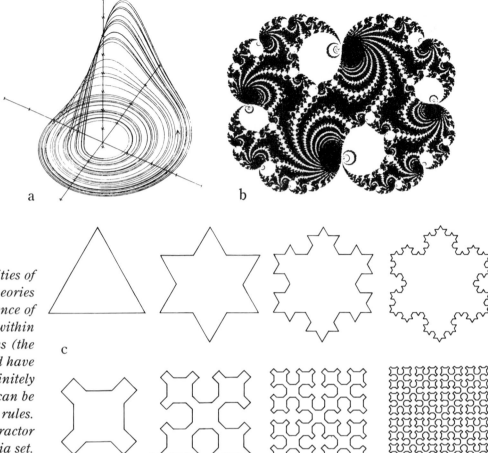

The complementarities of 'chaos'. These new theories have revealed the existence of novel types of order within utterly turbulent systems (the 'strange' attractors), and have also shown that wild, infinitely regressive patterns can be generated from simple rules.
(a) the Lorentz attractor
(b) a Julia set.
(c) the Sierpinski curve.

the fact that these theories are so firmly based in mathematics, they have had a most disturbing influence on many of the most basic assumptions of science.

These findings have two broad aspects: on the one hand they have shown that comparatively simple linear equations can produce extremely complex, non-linear results; on the other hand it has been found that a new kind of order, 'strange' attractors, exist in phenomena whose sheer complexity had previously been thought to render them virtually impervious to scientific investigation. The general subject of turbulence, for instance, which had been notoriously difficult to get to grips with, proved highly amenable to these new 'chaotic' interpretations: many kinds of turbulent phenomena are now recognised as possessing a concealed symmetry. The impact of 'chaos' theories has been considerable, and of two kinds: whole new fields of investigation have been opened up, but at the same time fresh limitations have been placed on the ability of science to make confident predictions. In essence, older, reductionist views that systems can be completely understood by breaking them down and studying each separate part, have been challenged. 'Chaos' has shown that small initial disturbances to a system, far from being 'dampened out', can be greatly magnified, and that the same criteria apply to very small errors of measurement. Since few measurements can ever be absolutely perfect there are serious implications here for science as a whole.

The relation of these theories to the notion of symmetry is perhaps best approached by way of their new concept of *fractal* (or 'dimensionally discordant') geometry, much of which gives a graphic expression to 'chaotic' notions of non-periodic order. Because so much of nature is worked on by what are now recognised as 'chaotic' principles this new geometry often provides a more appropriate description of the sort of 'regular irregularities' of the real world than conventional geometry can. Fractal geometry can be used to describe such 'fuzzy' configurations as those found in clouds and coastlines, in the markings of animals and the bark of trees. In fact many shapes that had previously been thought of as largely the product of random effects have been re-evaluated in the light of fractal theory and are now seen as symmetrical in its new and extended sense. Fractal geometry is far too extensive a subject to do justice to properly in this context. Suffice to say that much of it is *self-sensitive*, i.e. it involves feedback; and many of its forms are self-similar, i.e. they present similar sorts of configuration through an infinite range of scales. It should also be remarked that many fractals are highly intriguing and aesthetically attractive.

Complex 'squiggles' of this kind, common in geological formations, animal markings, plant structures etc., can be replicated by the computer using quite simple algorithmic procedures, a strong indication that nature itself uses fractal geometry.

The outstanding characteristic of fractal geometry, however, is that its highly complex forms have, with the aid of computers, been generated from relatively simple inputs. In fact the mathematician Benoit Mandelbrot, the originator of the term fractal, feels that living organisms exploit 'chaos' principles and that this helps to account for the prodigality of forms in nature, which in most other respects is extremely economical. Fractal geometry, and 'chaos' theories generally, not only demonstrate that great complexity can be achieved by simple means, but also provide a tool to probe for novel and concealed forms of invariance, and in doing so have greatly extended the notion of symmetry. There is something of a sense of *déjà vu* in these very modern ideas of an invisible and all-pervasive ordering principle. With our present, though very different, notions of symmetry we have almost come full circle, back to those ancient Greek ideas of *armonia*, of a great ordering harmony that operates between every part of the universe and the universe as a whole.

NOTES

1. In physics the hyperbola is found in any relation in which one quantity varies inversely with another. The most famous example is that of Boyle's law in which the volume of a given gas is inversely proportional to its pressure. The properties of conic sections in a purely geometric sense were thoroughly investigated by Apollonius of Pergo in the third century BC, but the first great realisation of their application to physical laws came when Kepler discovered planetary motion to be elliptical.

2. The principal laws of conservation in atomic processes concern their energy, momentum, orientation and electric charge.

3. The entire series of possible phyllotaxies is 1/2, 1/3, 2/5, 3/8, 5/13, 8/21, 13/34 and 21/55, this progression being made up of progressive alternate numbers from the Fibonacci series, which is itself essentially the expansion into a continuous fraction of the renowned golden ratio $(1/2 \, (\sqrt{5}-1))$. Because of this there can never be phyllotaxies of, say, 1/4 or 3/5.

4. A perfectly even three-dimensional spiral object coils about a plane and because it has a plane of symmetry separating its two halves it will not show a particular handedness. The shells of the nautilus and of fossil ammonites are like this.

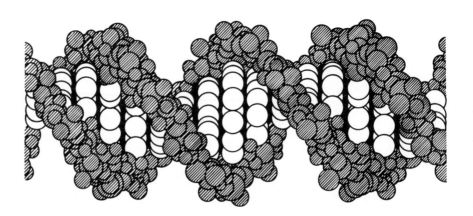

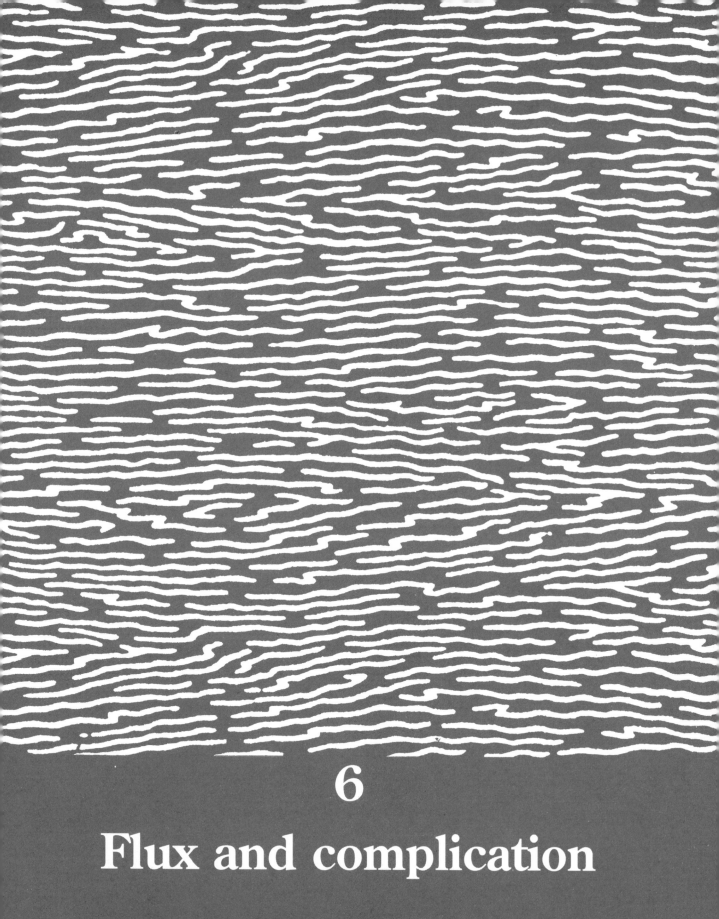

6

Flux and complication

Form and Force

Motion is the primary and most beautiful of nature's qualities, agitating her at all times. *De Sade*

Force, unlike matter, has no independent, objective existence. *D'Arcy Thompson*

It has been said that less was known about science at the time of the great revival of thought that occurred in Europe at the end of the fifteenth century than was known by Archimedes in the third century BC[1] The quickening of intellectual activity that came with the great thaw of the Renaissance led not only to the rediscovery of classical knowledge, but to a wholly new sense of purpose, particularly in the field of science. Science, with its origins in ancient Greece, had been in virtual stasis for a millennium and a half and was still primarily concerned with what it took to be the static and immutable aspects of phenomena. Up to this time its emphasis had been almost entirely on the *form* of things rather than on their *motion*, but the loosening of the shackles of thought at the end of the medieval period allowed a new breed of scientists to appear. They began to apply the

Leonardo's preoccupation with water currents, shown in his many drawings of the subject, reflect his attempts to grasp the fundamental principles of hydrodynamics. This particular drawing was made around 1507, probably in connection with a hydraulic project in Milan.

logical and analytical approach, characteristic of the Greek tradition, to problems that had never previously been considered, notably those to do with the transmission of force.

The Greeks themselves never formulated a theory of dynamics; matters such as the flow of fluids or the motion of falling bodies were simply not seen to be within the scope of scientific enquiry. Their greatest achievements lay in such fields as geometry and astrology. This focus on the fixed and substantive aspects of the world was retained throughout the whole of the late classical and medieval periods. From the time of the Renaissance however we see the scientific impulse towards the measurement and classification of phenomena, begun by Aristotle, extending to the realm of invisible and non-substantial forces. Gravitation was the first of these to be recognised, followed by the uncovering of thermal, electromagnetic and finally nuclear forces. Each of these revelations had a profound effect on science as a whole, and each, through its technological implications, has had an enormous impact on society at large.

Energy – 'the capacity to do work'.

In effect the great advances in science and technology over the past few centuries have involved us in a perceptual revolution. Although we can trace the evolution of modern science back to antiquity, our world view has been fundamentally changed in the process. The differences of outlook between older and more modern scientific attitudes are precisely those between a static and a dynamic perception of the world, and the whole history of science reflects the gradual transition from one to the other. On a social level we have yet to absorb completely the concept of an absolutely fluid, energy-charged world. The full implications of the latest, quantum, stage of the perceptual revolution are only gradually filtering through to the general consciousness. But science, as usual, is far more confident: as long ago as the thirties Heisenberg was insisting that atoms, which are after all the basis of physical reality, should not be thought of as 'things' that enjoy a separate existence from the space around them, and it is quite common these days for nuclear physicists to tell us to abandon our notions of material substantiality in favour of that of 'disturbances' in 'fields of events'. These concepts themselves are still somewhat disturbing to many of us, even though they are now well established as part of the new scientific orthodoxy, and it is strange too that such modern ideas, that regard matter as the result of the incessant motion of intangible forces, should find a resonance with far older concepts.

The atom as a 'disturbance in a field of events'.

In Chapter One I spoke of the rivalry between the early Greek philosophies of Heraclitus and Parmenides, which were utterly divided on the problem of permanence and change. Heraclitus, it may be remembered, identified change as the only reality, and tended to see the world simply as the product of dynamic forces in an eternal flux. His strange and somewhat mystical ideas came to be neglected in favour of the views of the Eleatics whose emphasis was on the fixed aspects of the world. Parmenides, who founded this school, taught that all apparent change was a mere delusion of the senses, and although this proposition also seems rather strange now there is little doubt that his school, with its emphasis on an analytical and reductive approach to problems, contributed greatly to western science, and to western attitudes in general. Pragmatic science was, in the end, successful because it offered satisfactory explanations to basic problems. It is all the more ironic then that science should come to hold views on the nature of the physical world that are so like those of the enigmatic Heraclitus, who asserted that there was no fundamental 'substance', that nothing exists statically, and that movement is the very essence of being.

Nothing illustrates the gradual change of perception in western science, from a Parmenidean fixity to a Heraclitean fluxity, so well as the evolution of its cosmological and astronomical views. Cosmological ideas, of course, reflect a state of mind as well as the state of science, and the history of cosmology in western Europe tells us as much about changes in social attitudes and beliefs as it does about advances in science. During the medieval period the positions of the planets (and those of the angels) were seen to be determined by a curious system of ten concentric crystal spheres that revolved, like some arcane machinery, in a perpetual, and perfectly uniform, circular motion.[2] This inflexible and intensely hierarchical scheme, which was actually a degenerate version of the classical Ptolemaic system, perfectly mirrored the rigid world of medieval scholasticism. The new spirit of enquiry that was engendered by the Renaissance however found men like Copernicus, Kepler and Galileo who were prepared to face the uncomfortable inconsistencies between the old theoretical ideal and the greater complexities of the real world. Their discoveries, which finally shattered the crystal spheres and removed their stifling influence, were part of a movement in a society that was itself in the process of becoming more complex and more dynamic.

With their powerful new tools for probing into space, scientists now have an incomparably clearer view of the cosmos than either the ancient or Renaissance astrologers; what has been found there has tended to support Heraclitus' vision of eternal flux. The picture that we get from the giant optical and radio telescopes of today is one of unlimited and unceasing cosmic activity. We see massive gas clouds that are gradually condensing into whirling galaxies, galaxies that consist of millions of stars that are themselves whirling and spinning in constant motion. We know that at the end of the life of a star it at first expands and then contracts in massive gravitational collapse, occasionally causing supernova explosions and giving rise to the now notorious black holes. All of these are continuing processes; every stage in the formation and dissolution of matter in space can be observed in some or other part of the heavens, but nowhere do we see stillness; every part of the universe is charged with activity. Also, it would seem, the whole show is expanding at a tremendous rate; every object in space is moving away from every other at a colossal speed. It is as if we were all part of a gigantic explosion, and of course this is precisely what is happening. The universe is still expanding as a result of the Big Bang of the original creation, and it will continue to do so for a very long time to come. It is possible that when it reaches the end of this period of expansion it will contract again, and it may well be that our universe has always oscillated between phases of expansion and contraction, though no-one is absolutely sure about this at present. What is certain is that the universe will never reach a state of quiescence, because if it did so, *ipso facto*, it would cease to exist.

The perception that the universe is not merely worked on by dynamic forces, but is actually sustained by them, is confirmed at the very opposite end of the cosmological spectrum, in the world of the infinitesimally small, where matter has been shown to be little more than movement. We now

'Matter, as such, produces nothing, changes nothing, does nothing; and however convenient it may afterwards be to abbreviate our nomenclature and our description we must most carefully realise at the outset that the spermatozoon, the nucleus, the chromosomes or the germ-plasma can never act as matter alone, but only as seats of energy and as centres of force.'

D'Arcy Thompson

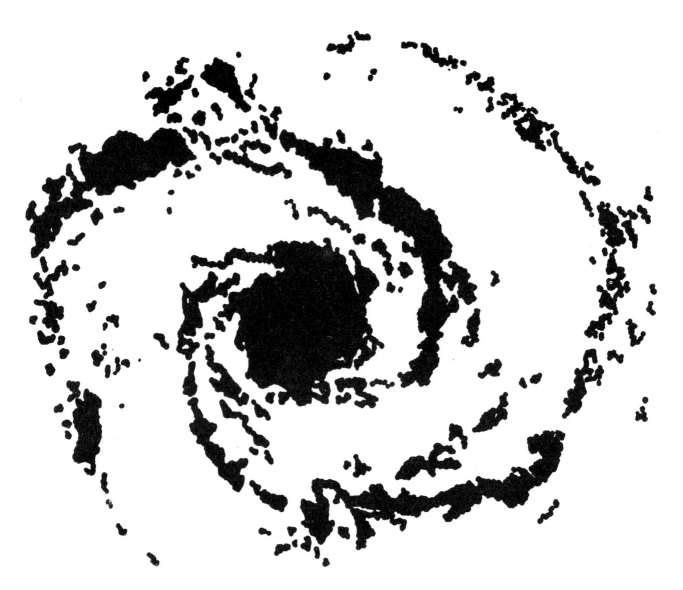

Wherever we look in the universe we find incessant motion, flux and transformation. The 'whirlpool' galaxy, NGC 5194.

know that atoms are not the irreducibly small billiard-ball-like objects that they were believed to be in the nineteenth century; quantum physics has shown that they are better characterised as so many levels of organised energy, of energy patterns within energy patterns. Most of the mass of the atom is contained in its central nucleus, which consists of protons and neutrons, themselves the foci of complex energy systems, bound together by immense nuclear forces in a tiny region of space. Around this ever-shifting alliance, and at some distance from it, the electrons whirl at unimaginable speeds, and it is this 'confined velocity' that gives atoms their extension in space, and matter its solid aspect. Just as the interior of the atom is characterised by a constrained dynamism so also are its relations to others in its molecular arrangements. Insofar as the conventional stick-and-ball models convey an impression of fixity, of static alliances, they are thoroughly misleading. Even in solid materials atoms are constantly dancing and vibrating about their equilibrium positions, and the intensity of their movements increases with temperature — in fact these phenomena are one and the same. When the temperature of a substance increases to a critical point this inherent restlessness leads to the break-up of the regular molecular array; the dance is then no longer an orderly, stately affair, but a more frenzied individual jitterbugging. At this point solid materials flow into the fluid state and energy, in a strictly local sense, eclipses form.

It seems appropriate here to recapitulate the central theme of this book, the complementarity of form and energy. We have seen that to exist at all an entity must possess form in some measure; but the acquisition of form, on any scale whatever, is bound to implicate the energy principle, since the attainment of shape involves motion. At the most elementary level then we can see that movement is necessary for the bringing together of the various constituents of a given form, and for keeping it that way for the duration of that form. Metaphorically speaking the 'crystal' principle must start to engage with the 'dragon' in order to realise itself; but there is a paradox here because the same principle of motion that is essential to the creation of form is also responsible for its ultimate destruction. The energy principle, though it can only realise itself through form, is actually indifferent to it, and is involved in its creation and destruction with equal disregard. As Heraclitus put it: 'All things come into being and pass away through strife.' To the modern mind the use of the term 'strife' in this context might seem somewhat incongruous; it may be that this was Heraclitus' intention, to give dramatic emphasis to the exposition of his theories. However we have to remember that in his time such concepts as 'matter', 'substance' and 'energy' had not been properly worked out or differentiated. The last of these, in fact, was not even to appear in the later and more advanced philosophies and sciences of the Greeks. As I have indicated, it was precisely this failure to conceive of the idea of energy that was to bedevil western science right up to the modern period. The basic reason for this one-sided approach to phenomena was that the foundations of science, particularly that part contributed by the Pythagoreans, were based on a visualisable geometry. The extraordinary advances of early Greek scientists in mathematics, astronomy and the mechanics of rigid bodies derived from this approach. By contrast the operations of *fluid* mechanics remained a mystery to them. The abstract notion of energy only gradually began to enter the scientific domain with the advent of the Renaissance.

'This world. . . is now, and ever shall be, an ever-living fire.'

Heraclitus

In his scientific work Leonardo da Vinci, the epitome of the Renaissance man, was one of the earliest to express interest in dynamics. Leonardo had an abiding curiosity with regard to fluid mechanics, an area in which he made some of his most original and enduring observations. He was drawn into the subject in the first place by way of his involvement in various large-scale hydraulic projects: the building of canals, diverting of rivers etc. His approach to the subject was characteristically thorough and systematic, and he actually anticipated many of the principles of hydrodynamics that were only fully worked out at a much later date. His achievements in this area were all the more remarkable because, as I have mentioned, there was little that he could have drawn on from either classical or medieval sources. Most of his ideas on the subject were based on his own observations of the action of water in rivers and canals and his subsequent experiments with hydraulics. These investigations, which are brilliantly recorded in a whole series of detailed drawings, represent the first theoretical and genuinely scientific approach to energy concepts in the western scientific tradition.[3]

Among Leonardo's drawings there are some, made during a stay at the coastal town of Piombo, that reveal his deep fascination with the effects of waves and currents on water. He observed in the accompanying notes that 'the surface of the water keeps the imprint of the waves for some time'. We can see from these and other thoughts of his on the subject that he had clearly intuited the essential point of both fluid mechanics and wave motion, namely that there can be diversity of movements and rhythms in one place. Leonardo was equally intrigued by the dynamic principles involved in fountains, jets and turbulence, and he refers to the *potenzia*, or force, within these as having the capacity to 'change the face and the centre of the world'. The age in which he lived was characterised both by its great new demands for energy and by its conscious recognition of energy as a resource. Leonardo, as the personification of the spirit of that age, was deeply involved in both its practical and theoretical aspects. From these first tentative appearances, in the wings of the theatre of science as it were, energy was rapidly to move centre-stage.

It was realised in time that force not only influenced form in a fluid medium to produce waves, fountains etc., but that it was involved in heat and light, and in all chemical and electrical processes. Furthermore it became increasingly clear that although these forces could readily be transformed from one manifestation to another they could be neither created nor destroyed; in other words energy was gradually recognised as an original and universal principle. By the middle of the nineteenth century Lord Kelvin, the pioneer of thermodynamics, was led to declare that 'the whole of physics has become the science of energy'. It was around this time, and through the work of Kelvin and others, that modern science received its first commandment, the law of the conservation of energy. Since then science has increasingly emphasised the role of energy at every level of being, and there is a sense in which our more general social ethos will have to catch up. At the moment we are at a stage rather like that of the late Middle Ages, still bound by the crystal spheres of older attitudes and beliefs. We have yet to admit to our wider consciousness the essentially pluralistic notions of modern science or to recognise the perpetual and reciprocal interplay of force and form.

NOTES

1. *Science in the Modern World.* Alfred North Whitehead.

2. 'We believe that the object which the astronomer should strive to achieve is this: to demonstrate that all the phenomena in the sky are produced by uniform and circular motions... because only such motions are appropriate to their divine nature.' Ptolemy in his *Almagest*. (I have taken this and the above quotation from Arthur Koestler's *The Sleepwalkers*.)

3. Leonardo's conclusions on the nature of the power of falling water clearly anticipated the law governing the speed of falling bodies (enunciated by Torricelli in 1642) and the basic theorem of hydrodynamics (formulated by Bernoulli in 1738). His theories on the action of waves predict the laws concerning these that were formulated by Huygens in 1673.

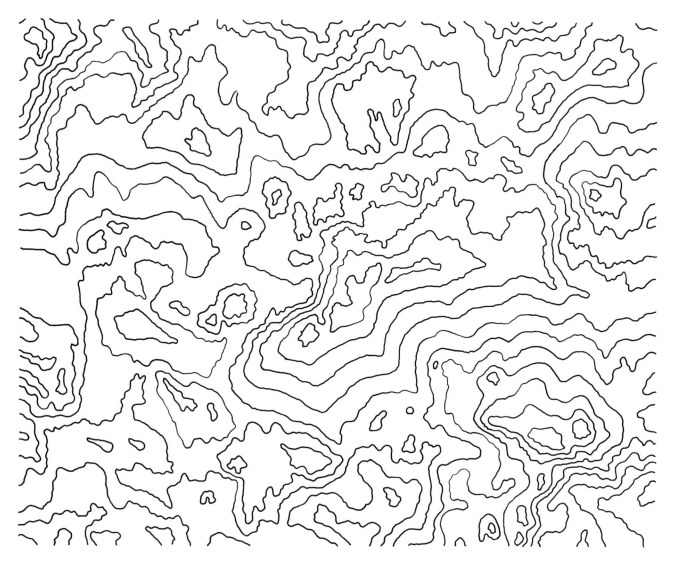

Energy and Fluidity

The complex contour lines of wave patterns over a 200-metre stretch of ocean.

What is of all things most yielding can overcome that which is most hard. *Lao Tzu*

You see the mountains and consider them immovable and yet they pass like clouds. *Qu'ran 27:88*

The essential difference between a solid and a fluid is that the former will move as a body whereas the latter flows under the slightest stress. This is to say that the fluid state, which includes liquids, vapours and gases, is more yielding, or receptive, to an applied force than a solid one. In physical terms the mechanics of a fluid medium are now seen to have a basis in the relationship between its individual constituent particles. The particles of liquids, vapours and gases, unlike those of solids, move relative to each other as well as to their surroundings, so that, characteristically, fluids readily deform in response to force and do not recover their original form when these external forces cease to act. Solids move 'as a body' because their particles have a coherent and *long-range* structure, in complete contrast to those of gases which, in a molecular sense, are utterly incoherent and structureless. Liquids occupy an intermediate position in this scale of molecular order, having a *short-range* structure, so that there are bonds

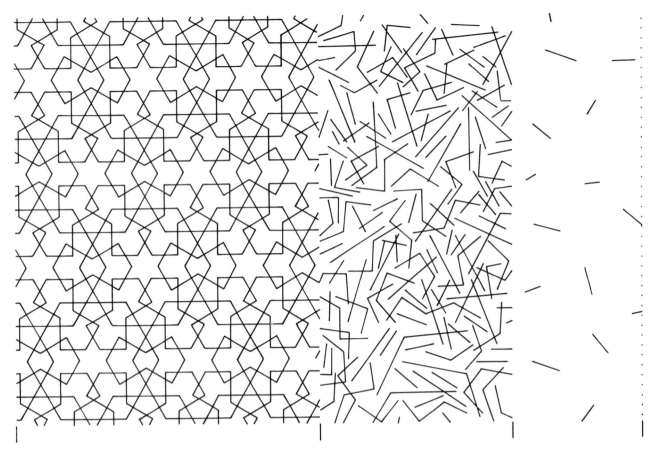

The disintegration of pattern as a model of the solid, liquid and gas states.

between neighbouring molecules, but none over greater molecular distances. The transient, short-range nature of liquid makes it the clearing house of both 'form' and 'force', and gives them a leading role in most vital processes.

Under normal conditions, that is to say those found on the surface of our planet, liquids are amorphous: they adopt the shape of their container. Of course simply by acting in this way they are responding to a force; under ordinary conditions the principal force acting on a liquid mass, whether it is an ocean or a glass of water, is that of gravity. It is gravity that holds a liquid within its container and prescribes its outer, surface limits. If we remove this familiar influence from a body of liquid, say by taking it aboard a space-ship to a point beyond the reach of the earth's gravity, it loses its more familiar physical properties. In fact under these conditions liquid tends to form into a sphere as a result of the attractive force of surface tension and the principle of least, or 'virtual', work.[1] This tendency is not entirely unfamiliar. We see it in oil suspended in water and in soap bubbles floating in the air. In both examples the influence of gravity is somewhat diminished.

The 'natural' inclination of water, of course, is to run to the lowest level, and while we are in a gravitational field this downward tendency can only be resisted by the application of a force that counters that of gravity. Nature undertakes this on the grand scale through that most important of natural processes, evaporation, but it can also be achieved mechanically – the simplest example being the jet of a fountain. A fountain jet will keep its shape just so long as there is sufficient force provided to overcome gravity; the moment this force is withdrawn the jet will collapse. It is obvious then

that the form of a fountain is not simply made up of water, but of water plus energy. The play of a jet, in fact, subtly traces the path of this squirt of energy as it strives against the prevailing flow of gravitational attraction. In today's physics this kind of dynamic form, which relies on a constant input of energy, is described as a *dissipative structure*. As we shall see later this is a term that is linked to concepts that have very far-reaching implications.

Perhaps the most remarkable feature of liquid is its capacity to respond to a whole range of influences in the same region and at the same time. This, of course, was the aspect of fluidity that so fascinated Leonardo at Piombo, where he observed not only the effects of currents and tides, but also those of conflicting wave movements, all acting simultaneously on the same limited stretch of water. Most of us will have noticed that even the action of rain-drops on a puddle can produce the most complex interplay of wave patterns. What Leonardo intuited, and what has since become the basic assumption of physics, was the possibility of studying force on its own account, without reference to the material that it acted on. In the event this development had to await the discovery of electromagnetism by Faraday.

It is as well here, perhaps, to remark on the intrinsic difference between the action of waves in a liquid medium and the action of the medium itself. In a steady liquid flow the particles involved are acting for the duration in a fairly coherent and concerted movement in a particular direction; water rotating in a bowl, for instance, moves as a body, almost like a solid. In wave motion, by contrast, individual particles oscillate in a tight circular motion, but are not themselves propelled in the direction of the waves. This is why we can find movement of waves that is quite independent of the general flow of a current; we have only to recall the relative motion of ripples caused by a stone thrown into a fast-flowing river, some of which are bound to go against the current. Perhaps the best analogy for the way that waves transmit energy through a medium, fluid or solid, is provided

Water waves do not in themselves cause a forward movement; instead each individual particle maintains its stability about a point by performing a circular motion.

In some of the more familiar forms that occur in a fluid medium, such as jets, vortices and waves, we see the clearest 'imprint' of energy.

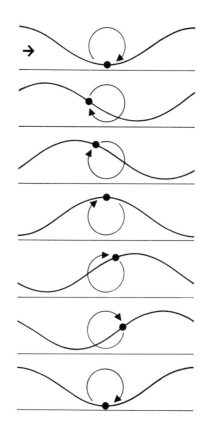

by the waves that can be created in a rope held between two people. If the rope is jerked at one end a wave travels along it in accordance with the amount of energy invested in the action. The rope goes up and down in a wave motion, but obviously it maintains its position between the people holding it. It a similar way a cork will maintain its position in water that is responding to wave motion; if there is no current it will bob up and down, but stay approximately in the same place.

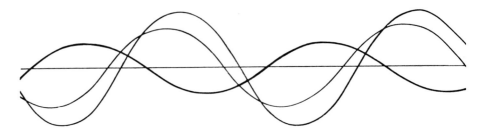

I have mentioned the phenomenon of co-incident patterns formed by the overlapping of waves from different points of origin, and it is in fact not uncommon in the ocean for longer waves, with a greater speed of propagation, actually to overtake other, shorter, waves that have come from the same general direction. Wave phenomena occur throughout nature in many different contexts, but whether they come in the form of water waves, sound waves or waves on the electromagnetic spectrum they have certain features in common, and the mathematical terms used to describe them are much the same. We can reasonably compare the action of wave motion on the surface of water to the flow of an electric current through wires. In each of these cases, and in all others concerning wave motion, it is *energy* that is transmitted in the direction of the wave and the medium itself retains its relative position.

Folds range in intensity from broad and gentle undulations to steep-sided, highly compressed 'wave-forms'.

The waves of geological folding are rather different in this respect, since the medium on which they are acting is quite definitely squashed and transported. But in many ways geological wave forms do resemble the waves of the sea. Folding is an almost universal feature of the stratified rocks of the earth's crust. In mountain ranges these folds tend to be tightly packed; in broader plains they are rather more gentle, but practically every part of the earth beneath us is folded to some extent. These wave forms are created in response to the immense lateral forces of continental displacement, which are themselves the result of the vast circulatory currents operating within the earth's mantle. Occasionally the enormous pressures that are built up by these tectonic forces are released as earthquakes, with devastating consequences, but usually these pressures are more gradually assimilated into geological formations. The rocks in the deeper levels of the earth's crust have a plastic flow that allows wave formations to occur; rocks at a higher level can also yield, but here it is the result of a process of microscopic fracture. The overall effect is rather like that of a table cloth that has been pushed to one side. Geological folding can be so pronounced that there is a toppling over of stratified layers which can result not only in horizontal strata being displaced to the vertical, but in cases where they are turned completely over. As with the waves of the sea, these folds are not simply made up of parallel ridges and troughs, but usually present a far more complex series of elongated domes and hollows

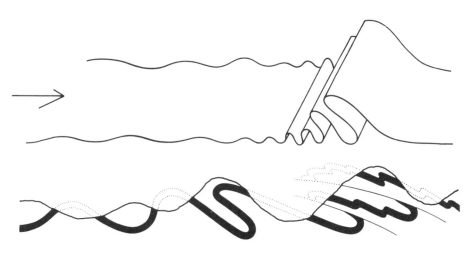

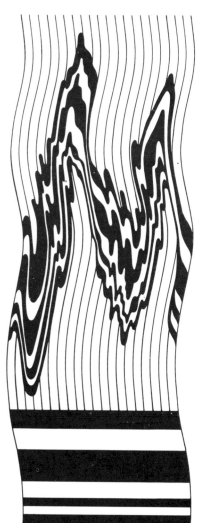

The 'table cloth' analogy for the formation of geological folding. In highly compressed folds the strata can be turned on end, even beyond the vertical; shearing can further complicate matters, leading to what are known as overthrust folds.

that rise and fall not only in front and behind, but also to the right and left. These formations should not, of course, be confused with surface features such as hills and valleys, which are caused by erosion, though both processes are part of a greater geological cycle. The slow but interminable movement of the land masses of the earth, known as continental drift, is caused by the action of circulatory currents within the mantle; the crust is being continuously dragged to *geosynclines*, the places where these currents meet and plunge into the interior, which induces a massive buckling effect that causes geological upthrust and the creation of mountains. The geological formations that we see exposed in a quarry or cliff face can give the impression of an arrested movement, and we might be forgiven for believing that these are a remnant of some past cataclysmic event, but the fact is that every part of the earth's crust, the solid earth beneath us, is moving. It is just that these formative processes take place in geological time, which in human terms is of an almost incomprehensibly long duration.

All the principal features that appear on the surface of our planet then, including those that we take to be the most stable and enduring, have been created by fluid processes. Even if we disregard the enormous contribution to its surface appearance made by organic forms there is an underlying cycle of purely geological events which endows the earth with an 'organic' continuity. In fact there is a sense in which our planet was a living entity long before life, as we now tend to think of it, made its first appearance. We can see oceans, mountains and rivers both as a part of its creative continuum, and also as so many focal centres of activity, as dissipative structures in fact. Earth presents the greatest range of surface conditions to be found in the entire solar system; none of the other planets, nor any of their satellites has the extensive palette of solid and fluid conditions that have endowed our planet with its unique capacity to receive energy and to convert it into enduring forms. Its gaseous atmosphere, liquid oceans and

Geological folding: original deposited beds directed by flow planes into convoluted configurations (above); the two ideal classes of folds, similar and parallel (below). (After Caret and Brown.)

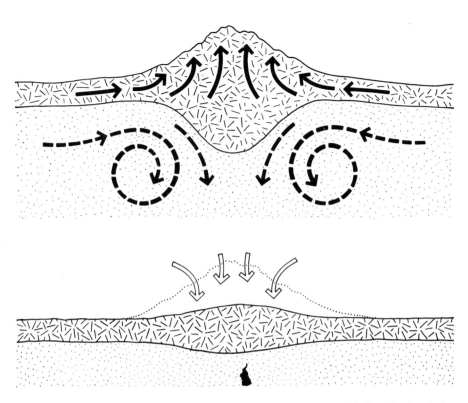

The mechanics of mountain-building. Subscrustal convection currents drag the earth's crust towards a geosyncline causing buckling and upthrust and the creation of mountain ranges. Eventually and inevitably these peaks are worn away by erosion and an isostatic balance is restored (the mantle being of far denser material).

floating land masses gave it the great creative potential that invited the evolution of ever more complex cycles of activity, and culminated in the emergence of biotic forms. The primary source of the energy that fuels the multifarious activities taking place on the surface of the planet is, of course, the sun. Ultimately it is the energy of the sun that sculpts our landscape, irrigates it with rivers, clothes it with vegetation and invests it with animal life. But it is the earth's fluid mediums that are the transformers of this extra-terrestial energy. Solar energy is carried across space, in the form of electromagnetic waves, but only begins to be converted to heat on entering the earth's atmosphere. The great fluid reservoirs of the oceans and atmosphere are the means by which this energy is first captured, and then converted into activity. The atmosphere absorbs some 17 per cent of the energy that passes through it, which serves to inflate it like a vast balloon, and which in itself creates a vast store of energy. But by far the most important component in this conversion process is that most essential liquid, water. It is water, in the form of vapour, that prevents solar energy, now in the form of heat, from being thrown back into space, and because

About half of the solar energy that reaches the earth is immediately reflected. Much of the rest is converted into heat on reaching its surface, but if there were no water in the atmosphere most of this energy would also be lost to space. Clouds and water vapour absorb considerable amounts of heat and in this way capture the solar energy that then drives the wind and ocean currents, which create the weather and bring into play all the geological processes of erosion and weathering. These processes, of course, create the basic conditions for all the complex cycles of organic existence.

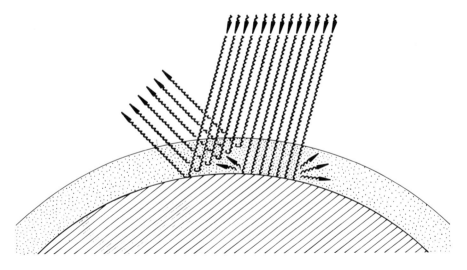

of this the temperature of the earth is kept at a higher level than it would otherwise be. This is the well-known greenhouse effect which provides the basic conditions for all the more complex deployments of solar energy, including every form of animate existence.

Water is so abundant on the surface of our planet (it is the most common and most widely distributed of all chemical compounds) and is critical to so many of its active processes, geological, meteorological and biological, that it might be more appropriate to name our planet 'water' instead of 'earth'. Quite apart from being the most abundant substance on the surface, water is the only one that is found in any quantity in all three states of aggregation i.e. as a solid, a liquid and a vapour. By virtue of its abundance and aggregational versatility water has the capacity to absorb and release vast amounts of energy: it not only prevents solar energy from being re-radiated into space, but also helps to distribute it, so that the earth is protected from extremes of temperature fluctuation. There is no place on the surface of the earth that water, in one form or another, does not reach, but wherever it is found it is rarely static; water is always involved in a cyclic process of some kind. These cycles can be of longer or shorter duration, but however simple or convoluted they might be, and of course some of them include ourselves, water always returns to its point of departure, the oceans.

The shortest water cycle is that in which it evaporates from the sea and falls directly back into it: since more than 70 per cent of the surface of the earth is covered by water this is also a very common cycle. A great deal of the water that is precipitated on to the land areas also evaporates fairly rapidly, but the remainder is the greatest distributor of the world's available energy. Because of this water is the principal agent of change; it is intimately involved in virtually every aspect of all the dynamic cycles of terrestrial existence. Water is an active geological agent and the most conspicuous evidence of the way in which it puts energy to work is the landscape itself. When it is brought to high levels the potential energy of water is converted to kinetic energy and it is able to carry off vast amounts of surface material, both in solid form and in solution. It is this force that

The systematic drainage patterns of rivers, which endow the landscape with form, can be seen to channel energy as well as water.

creates valleys and river systems, levels hills and mountains and deposits their mass as sedimentary rock on the floor of the ocean. This landscaping activity is an extremely gradual process, and it is only very occasionally, usually through some catastrophic event, that it impinges on human existence. However on a world scale the quantities of rock waste that are removed by the combined efforts of erosion and river transportation are truly prodigious, amounting to hundreds of millions of tons of material every day.[2]

To summarise then, practically all the free energy on the surface of our planet comes from the sun, and the fluid masses of the atmosphere and oceans provide the medium by which this solar energy is captured, distributed and put to work in creating the dynamic surface environment of the earth. Were it not for its gaseous atmosphere and liquid oceans our planet would be as arid and devoid of life as Mars or our own waterless moon. As it is, the constant supply of solar energy is transmuted into the dynamic continuum that constitutes our landscape and weather and into all the complex cycles of animal and vegetable life. Almost everything we see about us bears the imprint of solar energy; the rivers that irrigate its surface cannot be seen as mere waterways, but rather as vital channels of this energy, and virtually every other 'structure', from forests to thought processes, are modes of energy dissipation. As Heraclitus observed. every 'thing' is also a process, and all our forms, like the play of a fountain jet, are utterly dependent on a constant supply of energy.

NOTES

1. Surface tension operates by virtue of the fact that every molecule of a liquid attracts its neighbour; at the surface, molecules have neighbours at their sides and beneath, but none above and this creates an inward pull and a state of tension. It is this essentially molecular force that is responsible for the gravity-defying action of capillarity.

2. It has been estimated that weathering and river action account for the removal from the land areas of some 8000 million tons of material per year, about a third of which is in solution.

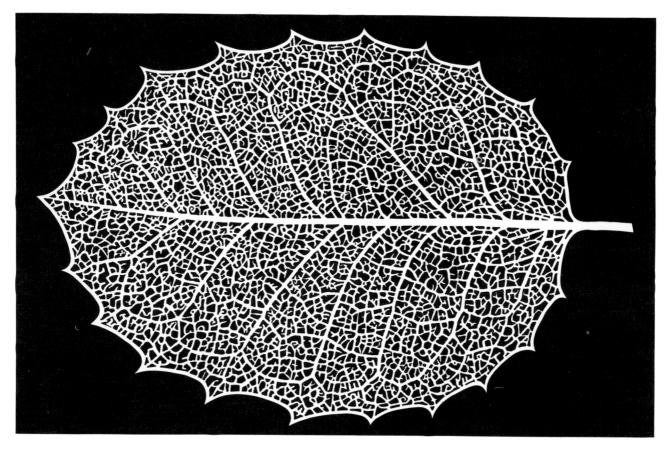

Energy Patterns and Dissipative Structures

The vein patterns of a holly leaf which provide both the basis of its physical structure and a vital system of distribution.

All the rivers run into the sea, yet the sea is not full. Unto the place from where the rivers come, thither they return again.
Ecclesiastes 1:7

Probably the greatest single advance in nineteenth century-physics came with the realisation that heat, like work, was a process rather than a substance, that it had no independent material existence of its own. Like all great conceptual revolutions this involved a change of stance and the abandonment of older ideas. Heat, before this, insofar as it had been investigated at all, was explained by the vague and rather improbable notion of a 'caloric fluid'. The conceptual framework for seeing heat and light as forms of energy, like that of motion, did not exist. It is rather difficult now, when the notion of energy is such a commonplace, to appreciate the enormous advance that this represented. Interest in the subject of heat, in a scientific sense, really began with efforts to improve the efficiency of the steam engine, that motor of the Industrial Revolution which had already done so much to transform society. Early in the last century the need was felt for a more complete understanding of the basic processes involved in the conversion of fuel to work. In the event, the energy laws that came out of these investigations had implications that went far beyond the original concern for the improvement of those primitive machines. It became increasingly clear that the flow of energy that was necessary to the continuing generation of work in an engine was equally essential to the continuity of all natural processes.

171

Once science had conceived the idea of energy it soon became apparent that it was dealing with an *original* force; while it could be used to generate work by a variety of means it could not actually be produced. However they might be expressed the various manifestations of energy were, in essence, conversions from one form to another. Without being consciously aware of it man had been involved in these conversion processes for millennia. In our use of fire for warmth and cooking we had long been using solar energy that had been stored up by plants, but the radical step that gave rise to the Industrial Revolution involved the more direct conversion of heat to *work*. The leap into industrialisation was made possible by the exploitation of the vast store of solar energy that had been locked away for aeons in the form of coal. The energy potential of fossil fuels like coal and oil traces back to the effort invested by plants, during photosynthesis, in separating the molecular combination of carbon and oxygen in carbon dioxide. Energy is released when these elements are recombined, the procedure being essentially the same whether it occurs in an open fire or in the engine of a jet aeroplane.

Until recently the sun was the indirect source of virtually every form of energy available to man. Our own muscle power, and that of the animals that we have learned to exploit, comes from the release of solar energy stored in the food that we eat. It is less obvious that water power derives from the sun, but of course water acquires its kinetic energy by the process of evaporation; it is the sun that lifts water to the highest levels, just as it is the heating of the surface of the earth by the sun that produces the winds and wind power. As, in the course of the last century, the universal nature of energy became clearer to science so it became apparent that the human use of power from these various sources was simply an extension of the process, in which living creatures have always been involved, of putting energy to work. It was not long before it was realised that every stage in the growth and maintenance of living organisms, and indeed every chemical transformation, involved the exchange of energy.

The capacity for *transformation* then is the primary characteristic of energy, but, as certain nineteenth-century physicists were the first to realise, this important property is bound up with another, that of *conservation*. The universe is thoroughly imbued with energy, and its power is readily converted from one form to another, but it can neither be created nor destroyed: in a phrase, 'energy is conserved'.[1]

We might for instance expend effort in lifting a weight, but if we release this weight its potential energy is also released, and it might even be made to 'do work'. In fact the energy principle used to be defined in just this way, as 'the capacity to do work', though this is a definition that rather betrays its Victorian origin and is somehow associated with the work ethic of that period. In reality energy is an essentially mysterious quality and is not concerned whether it does work or not nor, for that matter, whether it is 'creative' or 'destructive'; it just is, and there is nothing much that even science can say about it in the abstract sense. It was natural that science should have encountered energy in the way that it did, as a source of power, and in the form of heat, light and motion. Since the concept was first formulated, however, science has had to add other forms of energy to its list – chemical, electrical and nuclear. In fact the picture has so broadened

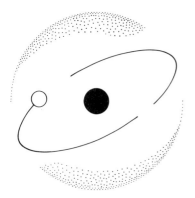 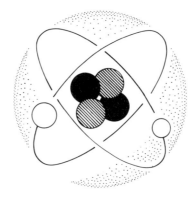 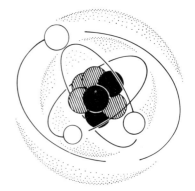

that we no longer see energy simply as a source of power, but as a *sine qua non*, an indispensable condition of every aspect of reality.

Because they originally dealt with the study of heat, the principles concerning the transformation of energy became known as the laws of thermodynamics. These theories, together with those dealing with light, as part of *electromagnetism*, were the last of the great achievements of classical physics. They laid the path to the later understanding of these matters as functions of the motion and distribution of particles, but so far as the public was concerned energy only attained top billing as a scientific theory with the advent of relativity. In relativity theory Einstein introduced the astonishing idea of the reciprocity of mass and energy, declaring that they were, in essence, different manifestations of the same thing. Since the concepts of mass and energy were, at this time, seen to be quite separate, this was a truly revolutionary idea, almost equivalent in its impact to Copernicus' heliocentricity or Newton's gravity. Because of the success of Einstein's theory, mass is now commonly perceived as a form of 'constrained energy'. Energy is extremely tightly bound in any arrangement of this sort, and a very small amount of mass can produce a very large amount of energy, which is what happens, of course, in an atomic explosion.

By installing this essentially mysterious principle as the cornerstone of physics there is a curious sense in which science has completed a cycle and returned to its point of origin. Science, after all, began with the differentiation of phenomena such as 'matter' and 'force', and by denying the existence of those spirit forces that were once believed to inhabit animate and inanimate objects alike. It is deeply ironic then, that by following its own path science should have found that the universe is indeed possessed of a vital spirit; ironic too that, in its dogged pursuit of certainties, it should have found uncertainty at the very heart of matter.

It has been pointed out by many commentators in recent times that the conceptual revolution that has caused science to modify many of its older deterministic and materialistic assumptions has steered it towards a view of the world that has common ground with certain far older eastern philosophical traditions. Perhaps the most extensive and interesting in this regard are those to be found in the more highly evolved streams of Chinese thought. Niels Bohr, who was one of the founders of quantum theory, was himself deeply interested in Chinese philosophy, and was fully aware of the parallels between his *complementarity* and the Chinese concept of mutually interdependent polarities. A tradition as ancient and

The 'constrained energy' of atomic arrangements. Layers of electrons 'orbit' around a nucleus of tightly packed protons and neutrons. As well as the individual electrons there are, at the deepest level known at the present time, the quarks which go to make up each proton or neutron.

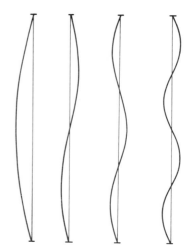

The ways in which electrons orbit the nucleus of an atom are intensely prescribed. These orbits are symmetrically arranged in the form of 'standing waves', so that they may only appear within quite specific diameters. This is to say that they occur where energy is contained within a specific region, like the waves of a stretched string, so that they exist in these particular orbits and nowhere in between.

continuous as that of China was bound to have thrown up speculation as to the ultimate nature of physical reality, but there is a fairly consistent stream of Chinese thought that offered an interpretation that is very modern-sounding indeed. We find, for instance, one of the most influential of the Sung philosophers, Chu Hsi, propounding the idea that matter depends on the ceaseless agitation of 'internal' forces. For this particular philosopher, whose ideas have distinctly Platonic undertones, the world was only made possible by the creative combination of the energy principle (*Ch'i*) with pre-existent patterns or forms (*Li*).

It is intriguing, in view of the position that energy now occupies in western science, that a comparable notion should have persisted in China from ancient times, when it was neglected for so long in the west. As a result of this difference of emphasis the arts and sciences of China were always predicated from an entirely different philosophical base than those of European traditions. A preoccupation with the flow of energy is quite evident in much of Chinese art (a matter that I shall return to in a later chapter) and is also central to its science. When Far Eastern art first began to appear in the west the looseness of style, delight in 'accidental' effects and deliberate asymmetry of certain of its productions were entirely novel to the European eye. Of course from the Chinese and Japanese points of view this approach was simply an expression of their very different, energy-orientated, view of the world.

'Dragon-lines': the crackle effects in ceramic glazes are, in essence, dislocation patterns, but were widely accepted in China as an attractive decorative feature of glazed wares (left); fault patterns in sedimentary rocks (right). Interestingly this kind of geological faulting, though it can occur in any tectonic setting, tends to appear in those rocks which are least affected by the action of folding.

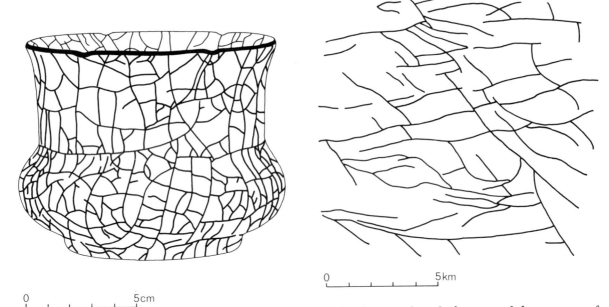

0   5cm

0   5km

With these terms of reference in mind some of the more unfamiliar aspects of Chinese culture begin to appear more comprehensible. The science, or art, of geomancy, for instance, has always enjoyed a high standing in China, and is widely used even today to determine the location of the most propitious site for a new building. The *feng-shui*[2] diviner is concerned to map the 'dragon arteries' of a locality, the lines of force that are seen to be acting upon and within the earth's surface, a consideration, incidentally, that has also been a strong influence on the art of landscape in China. Another example of this cultural affinity for energy patterns can be found in many traditions of Chinese ceramics where crackle-glaze effects were regarded not as unwelcome defects, as they were in the west, but as an interesting and sought-after form of decoration.

In the more prosaic terminology of western science the kind of faulting that is found in ceramic glazes represents the *critical paths* of energy flow. These crazed effects, like cracks of many kinds, are caused by shrinkage and appear spontaneously on cooling. The lines that are formed are rarely straight and make up an irregular network. Despite the great differences of scale these patterns strongly resemble geological fault-systems; the latter are different however in one important respect, in that they are active. Geological faulting continues to act as a sort of dissipative grid, a system that channels the enormous energies that are generated by tectonic forces. In fact analogies can be drawn between the lines of geological dislocations, which belong to the theory of elasticity, and the vortex lines of fluids in hydrodynamics, and both can be compared to the current-carrying wires of electromagnetism.

In those cases where electrical energy is transmitted without benefit of wires it inevitably follows the line of least resistance, creating its own pathways in much the same way that cracks do in a solid medium. The most dramatic example of this is of course the high-voltage discharge of lightning. Although we tend to think of the sudden and massive dissipation of energy in lightning as an 'event' rather than a 'thing', it is revealed by photography to have a quite complex form, one that bears a marked resemblance to the branching systems of a great river. These energy patterns, if we may call them that, are the very converse of those formed as fractures in a solid medium; lightning is intensely active but of limited duration, whereas dislocation patterns, such as crackle-glaze, are persistent but a mere vestige of the activity that caused them. In other cases, however, where there is a constant supply of energy to a receptive medium the 'paths of least resistance' can be converted into dissipative structures: the clearest example of this is a river system.

We have seen that the river, as an example of something that persists and yet is continually changing, was an important metaphor for that early theoretician of change, Heraclitus. Heraclitus realised that many other 'things' were actually 'processes', and it is these terms also that science, through thermodynamics, has come to accept. The essential form of a river derives from the coherent motion of its constituent particles, which means that the *work* that it performs is itself a *structure*. So long as the source of energy of a river, or any other dissipative structure, persists it will continue to impose a state of local coherence: the point being that so far as the constituent particles are concerned the term 'local coherence' is synonymous with that of 'structure'. Everything that exists is subject to change because, ultimately, all structures are dissipative; the real differences between the energy patterns of lightning and those of a river (or of a galaxy!) are their *rates* of dissipation.

The whole of nature, then, can be characterised as an infinitely complex release of energy; there is nothing in it that is not involved in this streaming process, but, like all unwindings, it is asymmetrical. This is because time itself is unidirectional. One of the most basic facts of existence is that the universe is using up its store of available energy: energy *is* conserved, but with the passing of time less and less of it is available for work.[3] As a result the universe as a whole, as many of us may have long suspected, is progressively running down. This is the ineluctable effect of the increase

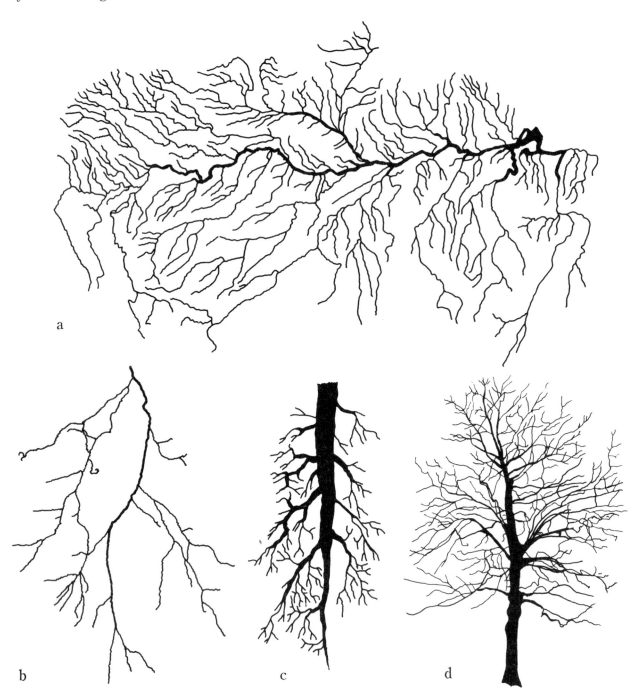

a

b

c

d

There are surprising similarities in a wide range of branching systems in nature: (a) the principal affluents of the Amazon, the world's greatest river system (b) a lightning stroke (c) the tap-root of a seedling (d) a sycamore tree.

of entropy; every movement, every exchange of energy since the original creative event of the Big Bang has contributed to this general unwinding. But to draw on the analogy of a river again, there are places where this current is so slow as to appear virtually motionless – some dissipative structures last for millions of years – and others where eddies and vortices create local disturbances that temporarily defy the main drift towards disintegration and build up temporary structures. I refer to the so-called 'morphic' processes.

These morphic, or integrative, processes, which tend towards an ever-greater complexity of structure, rely on a continuous inflow and outflow of energy. Because of this the forms that they create never achieve a perfect equilibrium but, at best, maintain a steady state, like the jet of a fountain. As we have seen, it was the steady-state conditions of the earth's oceans,

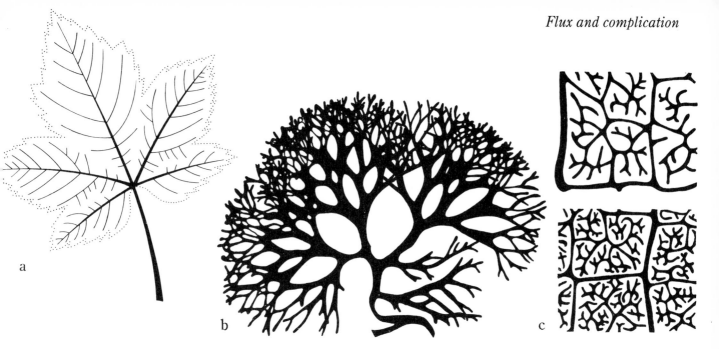

atmosphere and crust that set the stage for the emergence of living organisms. Even the earliest forms of life would have been the seat of activities that were far more complex than any of those in the conditions that gave rise to them, but one important aspect would have been carried over, namely the tendency towards ever-tighter cycles of activity, which

The 'energy paths' of plants: (a) the major vascular systems in a sycamore leaf (b) Irish moss seaweed (c) the minor vein patterns of a fig leaf.

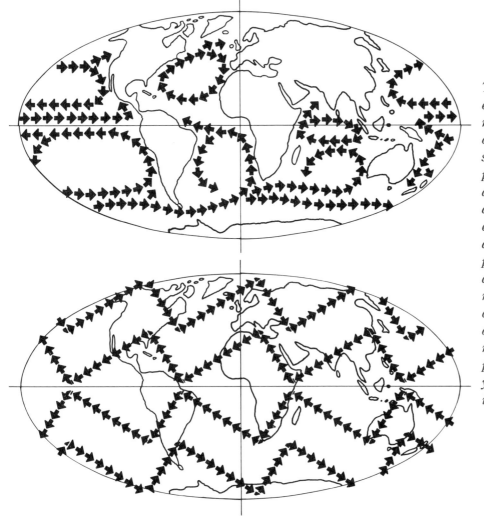

The dynamic systems of the earth's oceans and atmosphere might be likened to the blood-circulatory and respiratory systems of animals. Oceans play a vital role in the equable distribution of solar energy, and so help to regulate the earth's temperature. The atmosphere assists in this process of energy distribution, and is itself being constantly renewed. It has been calculated that every atom of oxygen in the atmosphere is recycled, by the action of plant photosynthesis, every 2000 years — a very short time indeed on the geological scale.

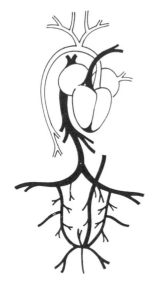

led inevitably to self-organisation. The great systems operating on and within the surface of the earth, the oceans, the atmosphere etc., act as vast dissipative engines that are continuously converting heat energy into work, but it was the inherently creative nature of these great cycles of activity that gave rise to the complex hierarchy of dissipative forms that make our surface environment such a rich one.

The mystery of the emergence of biological systems becomes clearer, or at least part of a greater mystery, once we accept the metabolic nature of the conditions in which they first appeared. A metabolism, whether it is that of an ocean, an organism or a living cell, might be characterised as a fluctuating, 'open' system that is sensitive to external conditions and which, as a result, is self-regulating. By definition a metabolic state cannot be completely identified with the matter of which it is constituted at any particular time, since this is being constantly replaced; it is rather determined by its tenure of a steady-state form that allows, and is sustained by, an incessant flow of energy. There is a sense then in which we can model all metabolic systems on that of a river. Rivers constantly receive and dissipate energy as part of the great water cycle, but they themselves become the conditions that give rise to a multitude of plant cycles, which in turn might become the conditions for animal cycles, and so on. Ecological complexity comes about precisely because its systems are open and allow for the evolution of ever more elaborate pathways by which energy may be diverted. Analogies between the operation of the universe and the mechanism of clocks are hardly appropriate in this post-determinist era, but there is one sense in which the comparison is still appropriate – like clockwork every aspect of the substantial world relies, finally, on the release or escape of energy.

NOTES

1. This is the First Law of Thermodynamics, the realisation of which, by Kelvin and Clausius, was one of the major achievements of physics in the mid-nineteenth century.

2. Literally 'wind and water'.

3. As a result of the Second Law of Thermodynamics, which was also uncovered by Kelvin and Clausius. This law is an essential qualification to the first law, declaring that the distribution of energy is an irreversible process.

The blood-vascular systems of animals are like an internal liquid environment. Animals need energy to maintain their life and growth and since the chemical processes that relay this take place in solution, every part of the organism must be reached by this system, which supplies it with food materials and oxygen and carries away waste products: The systemic circulation in man and, above, in birds.

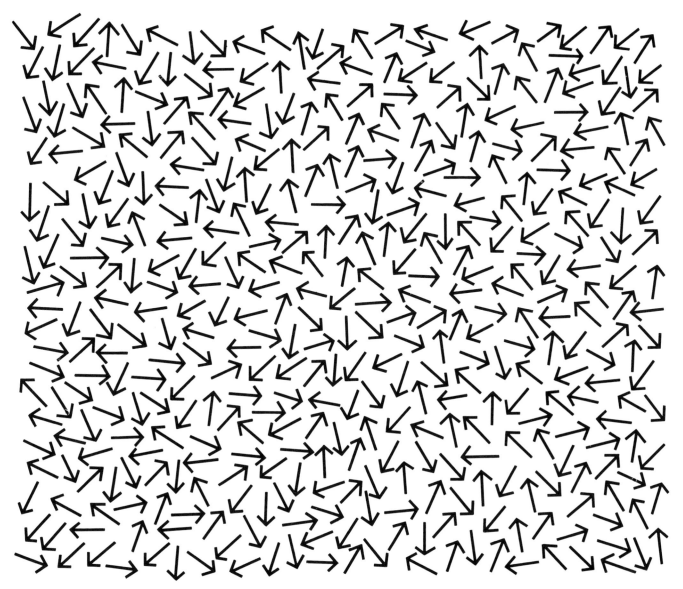

The Road to Complexity

Order and disorder are complicated notions. *Ilya Prigogine*

One of the most obvious features of the world around us is its sheer complexity, but what is far less apparent is the objective nature of complexity itself. Since practically everything we encounter is complicated in some sense or other it is clear that to analyse the reasons why things became so involved in the first place is to probe the very nature of being. Most of us are familiar with the way in which even the simplest tasks can involve unforeseen complication, but once we start to enquire into the mechanics of complexity, the how and why of the matter, we begin to trawl very deep waters indeed. In fact, when we get down to basics, our sense of personal and cultural identity is completely bound up with our idea of how things are, that is to say, how they came into being and how they are likely to continue. This being so it is clear that any examination of the process of complexity is bound to lead on to the more general matter of *causation*.

Is nature random, or does it have a purpose? How are we to equate the jostling, purposeless wandering of atoms and quanta with the highly structured and intensely complicated world at our more familiar higher level? Design from an Indian ritual textile.

179

There is an enormous diversity amongst the creation myths of the various cultures of the world, some of which see the universe as emanating from the void and others in which the divine creative power is personified, but practically all depict the primary state as one of elemental simplicity. This condition is variously described in such terms as 'a suspended calm', 'a silence', 'the darkness', 'the void', 'loneliness', and 'motionlessness'. The stages of creation, including that of the biblical Genesis, are invariably portrayed as a gradual advance from this primal simplicity to an ever more complicated state of affairs; a progression in which the notion of time is naturally implicated. All versions of 'the beginning' acknowledge one of the most basic facts of existence, namely that things tend to get more complicated with the passage of time. The most recent cosmological speculations see time itself as one of the products of this cosmic differentiation, so that the passage of time has no separate, eternal existence, but is part of, and in fact equivalent to, the unwinding of complexity. As Einstein put it, 'Time is what we measure with clocks.'

When scientists deal with the matter of causality they are of course concerned only with the phenomenal and not with any supramundane aspects; but since scientific attitudes have themselves come to exert a powerful influence on our general outlook, and because these are deeply rooted in European cultural monotheism, they have had to overcome certain older metaphysical problems attached to causality. I have already touched on the subject that constitutes the central problem of monotheism, that of Theodicy (Chapter One). Now the world of science may be indifferent to such purely theological questions, but in constructing its own cosmological view it has had to confront problems of a related nature, specifically those concerning the existence or otherwise of a universal causal agency – is there reason behind the universe, or is it driven by blind, purposeless forces? The question can be asked in even more direct material terms that are entirely within the province of scientific enquiry: how are we to equate the jostling, purposeless agitation, which appears to be the characteristic mode of atoms and quanta, with the highly structured, pervasive hierarchies of nature at all higher levels?

There has always been plenty of scope for argument around the topic of causality, because the cosmos seems to consist in almost equal measure of purpose and pure accident. In the complexity of the world there is plenty of evidence for the hand of a 'great designer', but unfortunately there is also a great deal for the contrary view; indeed there are now good reasons to believe that chance and randomness are essential conditions of existence. So the question of the exact nature of the forces which create order and disorder in the world is a perennial one. In cultural terms these have always been important matters since, as I have indicated, they not only provide the basis of belief, but also bear directly on the question of the relation of the individual to society. (The extent to which the universe is judged to be predetermined obviously relates to the degree to which an individual is deemed responsible for his own action.)

The question of the extent to which God exerted an influence over day-to-day events in the creation was a matter of constant debate within the early Christian community, and the problem of Theodicy was the underlying cause of the diffraction of Christianity into various schismatic and heretical

Brownian motion, which is due to the bombardment of dust particles by water molecules in thermal motion is the classic demonstration of randomness at the particle level; the path that is thus traced is inherently unpredictable. So how could order ever have arisen from *such chance collisions of atoms?*

movements. The problem of predestination in fact was never entirely resolved nor dispelled from Christian theology, despite the obvious difficulty that it presented.[1] If the destiny of an individual were predetermined in some divine scheme it would be hard to detect moral significance in any aspect of human behaviour; if, on the other hand, man were credited with free will the absolute sovereignty of the creator would clearly be diminished. This matter, however, became less pressing to the Church as it became a more completely established and central part of the social fabric. The problems never went away, but rather tended to be glossed over. However the whole argument as to whether or not the universe was pre-programmed by some supreme creative intelligence resurfaced in the seventeenth century with the ascendancy of the 'philosophy of nature', or as we now call it, science.

From the time that Newton published his *Principia* in 1687 cosmology entered the realm of science. It is interesting that Newton himself believed that the creation was the work of a single, divine agency, though he saw it as a piece of marvellous machinery which, once set in motion, was set to run its course for all eternity (although it might need some minor attention from time to time, like a clock!). As his admirer, Voltaire, put it: 'Everything is governed by immutable laws. . . everything is pre-arranged. . .everything is a necessary effect.'[2] This intensely mechanistic world view, with its assumption of absolute predictability, was to become the basic premise of classical physics. Newton's success in explaining the laws which govern movements of the heavenly bodies led him to believe that the interactions of all physical matter, right down to its constituent particles, might be similarly determined. This, of course, was an extremely powerful idea, and it fell to the French mathematician and proponent of Newton's theories, Laplace, to express the creed of determinism in its purest form. Laplace was to declare that an ideal observer, given the position and velocity of every particle of the universe, could predict the whole of the future, and, for that matter, the whole of the past; all phenomena were seen to be the sum of their parts, and every effect was linked to a traceable cause.[3]

These were powerful ideas. They were the dominant influence on scientific thought for well over two centuries, and, it must be said, they were enormously successful. However, if taken literally, the notion of physical determinism, like that of religious predestination before it, had some rather strange implications for the role of man in the world. If the universe were to be seen as either the working through of a pre-ordained master plan, or as the mere unwinding of some vast celestial machinery, then obviously there could be little place for voluntary action of any kind. If they were pre-determined, all the intentional actions of man in society would be illusory, and would amount to little more than an elaborate puppet show. Clearly there is something deeply unsatisfactory about this proposition because if there is one thing we feel in our natural state of self-awareness more than any other it is that we can determine our own actions, and make our own choices from moment to moment. We do not feel that our actions are pre-determined, and it follows that they are essentially unpredictable. After all even if some conjectural external intelligence, however all-knowing, were to predict some aspect or other of our future actions we could confute the prediction simply by doing something else, out of sheer contrariness!

On the other hand many aspects of human behaviour are predictable – indeed the whole coherent structure of society relies on this fact. Human activity is not determinable in the way that the future position of a particular planet or the outcome of a specific chemical operation might be, but it is hedged about with all manner of inescapable obligations, both of the more conventional and of the purely intuitive kind. We can draw a comparison here with the action of elementary particles: there is, as we know, a fundamental indeterminacy about the behaviour of an isolated particle, but the action of particles *in the mass* can be extremely predictable (especially in the form of planets or clocks). Similarly, despite a thorough familiarity with the usual circumstances, we can never be completely sure whether or not a particular individual will drink a cup of tea at a certain time, while market researchers are able to state with great confidence, and a high degree of accuracy, that so many hundreds of thousands of citizens *will* be drinking tea at, say, precisely four o'clock on any given day.

It can be seen from all this that there is no direct correlation between the polarities of order/disorder and those of simplicity/complexity; that in fact the processes that contribute to complexity can involve the tendency towards disorder, or the tendency towards order, or indeed of both. It is as a result of this that our complicated world has both predictable and unpredictable features at all levels; that there is evidence of both 'accident' and 'design', of a divine 'purpose' and the lack of it, in every part of its make-up. There are, in fact, two rather different modes of complication; there is one that we might characterise as a 'messy' variety, such as the tangle of string and the miscellany we occasionally encounter lurking at the back of a drawer, or there is the more orderly kind, like that of the complexity of a city street map.

There is a subtle nuance between the terms complication and complexity that turns on this distinction. Both words are of Latin derivation, but each has a slightly different root meaning: complication comes from *complicare*, which means 'to fold', whereas complexity derives from *complexus*, meaning 'to encompass, or embrace.'[4] In common usage there is only a shade of difference between the two, with perhaps a slightly negative connotation about the former: a tangled mess of string is certainly complicated, but is hardly complex. The latter term, although it also implies a degree of intricacy, has undertones of formality or regularity, as in a complex of buildings, or the complex structure of plants etc. There is, of course, a fair degree of subjectivity in these distinctions – one man's complexity is another man's mess – but in both cases what we are referring to is a situation that has progressed from a relatively simple state of affairs to one that is more involved.

It is no mere curiosity that the state of complexity, or complication, should be conduced by those two most basic, and yet seemingly opposite tendencies, towards order and disorder; in fact these apparently mundane transitions reflect natural laws of the most fundamental kind. The nineteenth century brought Darwin's theory of evolution and, as a result of investigations into thermodynamics, the uncovering of the principle of

entropy. Each of these momentous discoveries came to exert a considerable influence on the course of science and, subsequently, on our general view of the world. Each has established itself as an unshakeable principle, one might almost say as an article of faith in the scientific belief system, and yet, at least on the face of it, they would appear to be irreconcilable! According to the law of entropy the universe, from the particulate level upwards, has an inherent tendency towards *disorder*, whereas evolutionary theory is concerned with a completely opposite influence, one that seems bent on creating structural organisation of an ever higher *order*. Every aspect of the cosmos, down to the most minute detail, is subject to these conflicting influences, and it is precisely the interaction of these forces that makes the world the complicated place that it is.

So how is this explicable in scientific terms? It is a commonplace that things tend to become disorganised, that energy has to be expended just to keep things as they are. On the molecular level this increase in disorder is described as an increase in entropy; the laws that govern this effect point to a fundamental and irreversible asymmetry in nature. This means that although work can be entirely spent in producing heat, the reverse is not true. As a result of the wayward habit of the atom of bestowing energy at random, this energy tends to be dissipated, which means that in every part of the universe it is continuously breaking down from higher forms which can be converted into work, into lower ones where it is 'bound' and no longer available. In other words the universe is gradually running down.

But it is also building up. There is another force at work in the universe, one that operates through chance, that resists this slide into a deadly equilibrium. This is a force that is *convergent*, where entropy is *divergent*, and *agglomerative* where entropy is *dispersive*. It is a principle that is responsible for the building up of ever more diverse hierarchies of structure; moreover it is clear that this process, like that of entropy itself, goes back to the very origins of time and matter. The separating out of the elements, the formation of atoms and molecules and of crystalline structure,

Complication can be very messy or very orderly — more often than not it is a mixture of both: (left) a tangle of string; (right) a city street map.

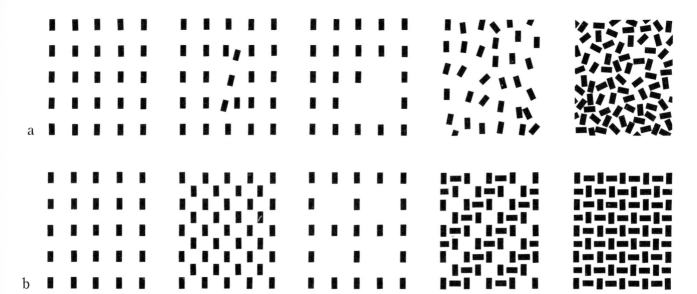

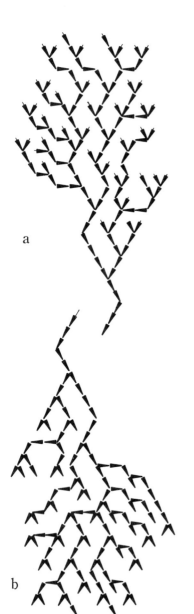

What is it that makes for complication? The series at (a) is intended to represent various stages in a transition from a relatively ordered condition to an increasingly disordered one, and that at (b) its opposite, namely a progression from a simple arrangement to one that is more organised. Both developments are extremely familiar aspects of the real world, and although they represent quite opposite tendencies both can be seen as a progression to a more complicated state of affairs.

the progressive assemblage of ever more complex molecular compounds culminating in the emergence of biological forms, are all manifestations of this universal 'morphic' imperative.

The reason why the random motion of 'atoms in the void' should have given rise to our intricately involved and fairly well-ordered universe, and why indeed they have not gone so far as to create a completely ordered state of affairs, is that the influences that were responsible for its creation at the outset are still in force. The general consensus that seems to be emerging from contemporary cosmological speculation is that of an inherently disturbed cosmic symmetry: to exist at all, in this view, is to be asymmetrical. The universe, it is now believed, originated in an event of cosmogonic dislocation, an act that disturbed the balance of a presumed primordial symmetry and which, in the process, generated a limitless store of energy. It was this original act of separation that brought the phenomenal world into being, and which provided the impetus that continues to sustain it. Because of this the cosmic process can be seen either as an intricate and infinitely protracted sequence of symmetry-breaking events (rather like the bifurcating patterns of a great tree), or as a vast dissipative mechanism, through which the primal energy is constantly streaming. Each of these descriptions, of course, is of the same dynamic process, which is that of a world that is in a perpetual state of 'coming into

The general plan of these two imaginary flow patterns is precisely the same, only the direction *of flow is reversed. They can be directly related in real life to many phenomena. One might, for example see (a) as a river system, and (b) as a genealogical tree. They are actually meant to represent the two great universal tendencies, towards concentration and dispersion .*

184

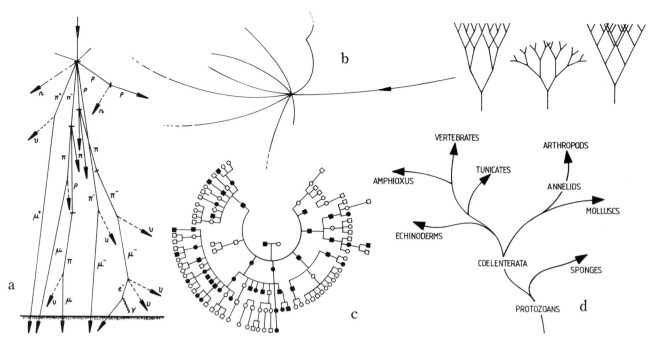

being'. All the complexities involved in the differentiation of phenomena, including time and matter, have resulted from the reciprocal action and reaction of the components of the original creative disturbance, and all, in some way or other, reflect the terms of a dislocated symmetry.

The universe then is a *creative continuum,* but in cosmology, as elsewhere, there is no 'free lunch'. The price of our infinitely complicated world, with all its predictability and unpredictability, lies in its essentially *irreversible* nature. The asymmetry of time is, for us, the most familiar aspect of this cosmic skew, yet it is this very imbalance that endows the universe with its great creative potential, for with the diffraction of the primordial symmetry there came the possibility of error and from this the opportunity for change and development and, ultimately, for life. We can, for example, see the whole process of evolution as relying on unpredictable factors. Life, like everything else, depends for its continuation on a high degree of stability, but springs ultimately from instability.

This seeming paradox brings us back to the question of complexity. We recognise that the general drift of events, whether they incline towards a higher degree of order or away from it, tends to an increased level of complexity, and because these processes occur within time they are inherently asymmetrical. It is clear also that the term complexity is absolutely relative; the very simplest of living organisms, for instance, are extremely complicated chemical entities. It is fairly obvious too that this is a thoroughly open-ended concept; things can get more complicated in a great variety of ways, and it is hard to imagine any object or circumstances which could not become more involved in some way or other. Since we humans are highly structured entities ourselves it is natural that our conceptual focus should be on the more 'positive', or orderly, aspects of the cosmos. However this has led us, particularly in the west, to take a somewhat lopsided view of nature. Western thought is thoroughly imbued with the notion of 'the creation' as a single, ordering event and, at least up until the modern era, has tended to disregard the equally fundamental *dispersive* force in nature, or to regard it as an aberration. It has been this

The dispersive tendency in nature, represented by these various branching systems, can be indentified with the principle of entropy, the universal tendency towards disorganisation: (a) the scattered paths of cosmic ray particles; (b) an induced particle collision; (c) the characteristic pedigree of a genetic trait; (d) a classical phylogenetic tree.

185

Self-organising configurations, like these magnetic-domain patterns, can arise spontaneously from the conjunction of two simple, linear elements. These complicated and essentially unpredictable forms are a characteristic product of 'chaos', the inherent self-generating complexity that operates in many systems to create uncertainty at many levels.

'Those reductionists who try to reduce life to physics usually try to reduce it to primitive physics, not to good physics. Good physics is broad enough to contain life, to encompass life in its description, since good physics allows a vast field of possible descriptions.'

Carl Freidrich von Weissacker (from *'Theoria to Theory'*).

somewhat one-sided attitude, of course, that has involved western thought in those metaphysical tangles to which I have already referred, concerning the older religious problems of predestination and the overly mechanistic views of scientific determinism. Our conceptual framework, however, has been utterly transformed by the acceptance of the discovery, made in the last century, of continuously active and progressive principles such as entropy and evolution. The radical effect of these revelations has, moreover, been compounded by more recent discoveries that point to a fundamental indeterminacy in nature *at all levels*; i.e. at the lower end of the scale Heisenberg's uncertainty principle, and at higher levels the 'chaos', or complication theories. These have combined to set new limits to the capacity of science for prediction, and have led to the recognition of the creative potentiality that exists in nature as a whole; it is now realised that structured behaviour can occur spontaneously and unpredictably even from random inputs. Among other consequences this has meant that serious deficiencies have been exposed in the traditional reductionist outlook, and there is a coming round to the more commonsensical view that there are many circumstances where the whole is far greater than the sum of its parts.

Although they are bound to take a long time to be absorbed, many of the more radical scientific discoveries of recent times seem certain to exert the most profound effect on our general belief systems. Already these days there is a considerable casting around for answers to basic philosophical questions other than those offered by traditional sources; however it is clear that although scientific explanations have supplanted religious ones in many areas this has not led to a widespread acceptance of atheistic 'blind-purpose' theses, and this, one suspects, is for intellectual as much as emotional reasons. There is, understandably, less of a sense of urgency about the whole subject than in the past, when such matters were implicated in the entire social and moral fabric. But, at the very least, the establishment of uncertainty as a fundamental feature seems likely to act as a modifying influence on our deeply ingrained monotheistic habits of thought, and to lead to the adoption of a more pluralistic outlook. There are many indications of this within science itself; the very notion of the cosmos as a disturbed symmetry is reminiscent of far older cosmological views that assume a manifest phenomenal duality. The very concept conjures up notions both of a primal symmetry and of a disturbing force, and a similar dualism attaches to the notion of matter as 'organised energy'. The realisation that the universe is not in any sense pre-determined, that neither order nor chaos can ever be entirely driven out of a system, and that each contains the seed of the other, would seem to provide a new point of departure and a much-needed new basis of thought.

NOTES

1. The doctrine of predestination is explicitly enunciated in Paul's Epistles to the Romans and to the Ephesians, and is a recognised element of many creeds, including the Anglican.

2. From the *Dictionnaire Philosophique.*

3. 'The present state of the system of nature is evidently a consequence of what it was in the preceding moment, and if we conceive of an intelligence which at a given instant comprehends all the relations of the entities of this universe, it could state the respective positions, motions, and general effects of all these entities at any time in the past or future.' Pierre Simon de Laplace.

4. Interestingly the English word 'fold' also once carried the meaning 'to embrace, or enclose', as in 'sheep fold'.

The notion of the Cosmos as constituting a 'disturbed symmetry' is reminiscent of older concepts that assume a manifest phenomenal duality.

photo: British Museum

7

Formalism and vitalism
in art

Magic, Religion and Style

> Seeing has a history of its own and the discovery of historically
> differentiated visual levels must be considered the most basic
> task of the art historian. *Heinrich Wolfflin*

It is not an easy matter to specify the precise role of art in any society, but
there is probably less agreement now than at any time in the past as to what
exactly constitutes art. Attitudes towards this subject, like so much else in
the modern era, have undergone unprecedented changes. Whatever one's
personal view it is clear that there is a general haziness as to what may, or
may not, be rightly regarded as an art object. There are two principal and
interconnected reasons for this: first we have experienced the vitiation of
our own European artistic tradition, and secondly, we have been thoroughly exposed to the arts of other cultures, at many and various levels of
civilisation, from every part of the world. The re-evaluation that these
contacts have brought about, and the resultant changes in our own
perception, are essentially a consequence of the Industrial and Technological Revolutions. The spread of manufacturing industry and the development of new and rapid methods of transportation and mass communication have utterly transformed society, but art, in addition to these
innovations, has suffered the impact of the invention of the camera.

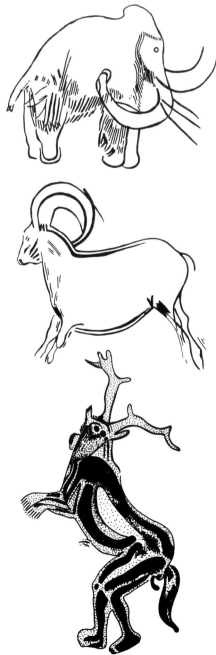

The mechanical processes of reproduction introduced by photography
had as devastating an effect on the painterly techniques of fine art as the
processes of mass manufacture had on the various craft traditions. All the
artistic innovations which occurred within the European traditions of art
and design in the mid- and late nineteenth century were a reaction against
this displacement. The moves towards 'primitivism' of various kinds in the
fine arts, and the rise of the Arts and Crafts Movement with its emphasis
on older craft traditions, were both essentially archaistic responses to the
new problems of style, a harking back to older and more vigorous forms
dating from a time when these problems simply did not exist.[1]

*The mural art of the Upper Palaeolithic was almost exclusively dedicated
to the larger animals of that time which were portrayed with a high degree
of naturalism.*

191

That the impact of the Industrial Revolution should have induced a crisis in the arts in the way that it did is, in itself, an indication of the important role that the arts play in social cohesion, at least in the wider sense of *style*. Art, it might be said, is the soul of society; the complexities and uncertainties of modern urban culture are perfectly reflected in the fragmented and indeterminate position that art occupies within it. The innovations of the various modern movements have become more or less established, if not entirely accepted by the population at large, and the traditional divide between fine and applied arts has lost much of its older significance. We are now becoming increasingly familiar with, and able to derive aesthetic satisfaction from, art forms drawn from virtually every part of the world, and from every period. Serious attention is also now given, quite rightly, to such previously disregarded forms as that of naive art, and the work of children and of the mentally disturbed. In one way and another we have learned to respond to a far broader range of artistic productions than past generations would ever have imagined we could.

So much art is available to us now, with such a range of artistic intention, that it is hardly surprising that there should be some uncertainty as to its ultimate value and present role in society. In fact there seems to be an unsettling question hanging over the whole subject, and it is this: what are the criteria by which we evaluate all the products of the creative impulse to which we are now exposed? Is it, in the final analysis, possible to define art in general terms at all these days? The first thing that can be said with regard to this question is that whatever the difficulties posed by the 'problems of style', they are not likely to deter people from engaging in artistic activity. The impulse to produce and respond to art, like the faculty of speech, seems to be a deeply ingrained human trait; and just as there are no genuinely primitive languages, so this sense of the aesthetic seems to be as evolved and consistent throughout all human societies. It is as natural that a social group (or an individual) should express its (or his) sense of identity or style in a distinctive mode as it is that this should be recognised as such by others. It is more likely than not that if we see beauty or a sense of style in an artifact, the effect was intended, however unfamiliar its aesthetic values.

All the products of human creativity are likely to carry at least some element of this extra-utilitarian quality, but for an object to qualify as a work of art it must, by definition, have qualities above those of mere necessity. Art in its very essence is a *communion*. We might pick up a leaf and admire its beauty, but that realisation remains a personal act; it is only when we communicate our experience that art comes into being. It is in this act of communion, or communication, that the necessity of art is revealed, since, ultimately, there is no clear distinction between art and style, and without style there is no social identity or cohesion. The art of a particular period, of a society or of an individual is, in essence, an expression of self-awareness, of collective or individual style, the maintenance of which is at least as important as any material consideration. As Oliver Sachs put it, 'Style is the deepest thing in our being'.

There are, I would venture to suggest, two essential components to a work of art: there are those features that make it a product of a particular period and place of origin, and from which it can never be entirely separated; but it must also possess a more universal quality, one that makes a direct, almost emotional, appeal to our sensibilities. These elements might be described, respectively, as the *formal* and *inspirational* aspects of art, and the possession of both, as far as I can see, is critical. Any work of art will have a formal or conventional intention, which may simply reflect the ethos of the social milieu in which it was produced, or project the creative intention of a particular school or individual artist; but it must also communicate these perceptions in a vital way. Any art that is purely conventional, and lacking this quality of vitality, is seriously deficient. On the other hand the weakness of much contemporary art lies in the fact that its intentions are often highly individual, and frequently obscure, factors that render much of it incomprehensible to large sections of the population. I should add though that it is clearly not necessary to understand a work of art completely to get pleasure from it.

Part of the fascination of the art of cultures remote from our own, particularly those that have now vanished, lies in the insight which we are given into utterly different and unfamiliar modes of existence. Of all the traces that might remain of a now vanished culture its art stands out as something that we can relate to in the most direct way. However exotic it may be an art object will always convey some flavour of its origin; but there are problems here, for without knowing the precise purpose or intention of an object or work of art there is always the possibility of misinterpretation. An art form of even the most minimal kind will always carry a vestige of artistic intention, since this is the very basis of style, but more often than not it will also have symbolic, magical or religious connotations with a specific cultural significance. Ultimately any art is bound, in some way, to reflect the beliefs and attitudes of the society in which it was produced; even the highly individualised art of our own time is ultimately rooted in conventional belief systems. Artistic intention, and style in general, will always be bound up with modes of perception, which themselves will always derive from a particular world view. Language and modes of dress are equally involved in this matter of style and identity; nothing places us so readily as our manner of speech and the clothes we wear, even though both are subject to fairly constant revision.

In the introduction to his classic work on primitive art the ethnologist Franz Boaz was at pains to emphasise that the mental processes of man are the same everywhere, that there is no reason to suspect that the intellectual capacity and skills of primitive man were in any way inherently inferior to our own.[2] If this assertion needed proof it is provided by the consummate skill and aesthetic sensibility demonstrated in that most ancient of artistic traditions, the cave drawings of the Palaeolithic. There is a fascinating quality in the very naturalism of this art which exerts a direct appeal, with none of the 'barbarous' qualities that we associate with some aspects of tribal art. Although these paintings are clearly imbued with magical intent, most aspects of which will probably always remain mysterious, its images are accessible to us in a way that a great deal of later primitive art is not.

The art of the Palaeolithic cave painters was entirely concerned with the animals on which their society was reliant; these paintings were probably the focus of an elaborate system of ritual, which may also have included ceremonies involving mime and dancing. The purpose of these rituals, if

In later Palaeolithic art images of the hunters themselves begin to appear.

we can judge by the practices of extant hunter people, such as the Bushmen of Africa and the Australian Aborigines, was to win a magical control over the animals that they were drawing. In other words this art was a form of sympathetic magic; the animals that were thus portrayed were 'caught' by this imagery; one is reminded here of the reluctance of some tribal people to be photographed for similar reasons, a likeness having a magical association with the original. So the art of the cave painters was both purposeful and direct; its images are representational and therefore easily recognisable. Whatever their magical intention, and whatever mysterious conventions they may have expressed, there is little that intrudes on our appreciation of their purely aesthetic qualities. Their power to move us rests on this ambiguity. We can respond easily and directly to their beauty and to their skilful execution, whilst at the same time feeling utterly distanced from their intended purpose which was clearly far beyond anything in our ordinary experience.[3]

Interestingly there is very little in the way of ornamentation or formal decoration in Palaeolithic art; it is almost entirely an art representing the animals on which the lives of the hunters depended, and later the hunters themselves. It was only at a later stage in human evolution that abstract and geometrical forms, with their indications of pattern and symmetry, began to appear. The underlying reasons for this are bound up with those changes that occurred in the prehistoric period, during the transition from the nomadic to more settled forms of existence. In the nomadic hunter/gatherer stage people were far more closely associated with nature. They followed the great herds of animals and, like them, led a mobile ranging existence. When, gradually, they began to settle and to involve themselves in the domestication of animals and the cultivation of food plants, their relationship with the natural world was utterly transformed. This was the time of the Neolithic revolution when humans, for the first time, were stepping out of the flow of nature, so to speak, and experiencing its forces in an entirely new way. It is, of course, difficult to be fully aware of the inner force of any current (a fact that will have impressed itself on anyone who has grasped an overhanging branch whilst drifting down a river).

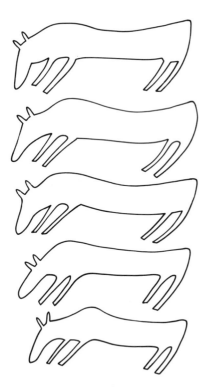

The magic of order. A frieze of oxen from a rock engraving in the Val Comonica (Late Palaeolithic).

In response to this new relationship with nature humans evoked the magical procedure of quantification; they began, in both senses of the word, to take stock. They began to count their animals and crops, and started to reckon the seasons; they also began to weave. Woven fabrics and basketry make their first appearance quite early on in this more fixed mode of existence, and pottery, another great innovation of the early Neolithic, begins to be decorated with abstract and geometric ornament. As humans gradually began to regulate nature according to their own needs, their art also began to reflect a new concern with order and regularity.

It is clear from a visit to any ethnological museum that there is a marked tendency towards pattern and symmetry in the arts of primitive people generally; the reasons for this can only really be understood by identifying with their particular view of the world. For primitive people the whole of nature was charged with *mana,* an animating principle that affected everything in their world, both material and immaterial. Rocks, rivers and mountains, as well as plants and animals, were imbued with this animate spirit. These were very real forces, very often of an uncertain disposition, which were likely to influence their every thought and action. Geometrical order is observable in nature, but is not a very prominent feature; such things as straight lines, regular curves, arcs and spirals are comparatively rare. To abstract these symmetries from the turmoil of nature, and to assert one's possession of them in a work of art, is a kind of magical power-stealing. By enlisting the agency of predictable form, whether in the service of art through pattern and symmetry, or in that of religion through ritual and ceremony, one gains a certain ascendancy over the unpredictable forces of nature.

It is, however, characteristic of forms that, once established, they should tend to endure. This is particularly evident in the art of primitive societies where certain motifs and patterns may persist for millennia with little change. Every manner of expression, in fact, can be found in this art, from direct, naturalistic representation to pure abstraction, and every degree between. In general though there is a pronounced tendency towards conventional forms, and a strong inclination to symmetry. Abstract geometrical ornament, sometimes of great complexity, is found in the art of tribal people from every part of the world; Boaz refers to this as the 'overmastering influence' of pattern. The symbolic significance of these forms can be highly variable, from those bearing a very high degree of symbolic content to others that have little or none. It is easy to imagine how regular, geometric designs may have evolved from such techniques as weaving, and having been developed in this medium, were easily transferred

Neolithic decorative motifs. In this period, which saw the establishment of more settled modes of existence and the domestication of animals and plants, there is a pronounced move towards more abstract, geometrical and symmetrical forms.

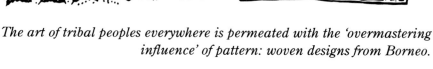

The art of tribal peoples everywhere is permeated with the 'overmastering influence' of pattern: woven designs from Borneo.

There is a marked inclination towards symmetry, specially bilateralism, in much tribal art.

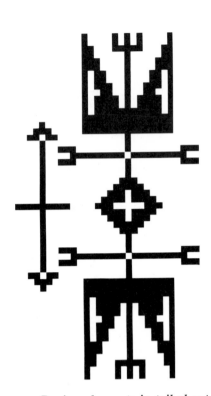

Design elements in tribal art that might appear to have a purely decorative or formal value may, in fact, carry quite specific associations. This Sioux design, for instance, represents an epic battle: the diamond-shaped centre is the body of a man, the large triangles are the tents of the village in which the battle took place, the pronged figures represent wounds and blood, and the straight lines supporting them represent the flight of arrows etc.
(After Boaz)

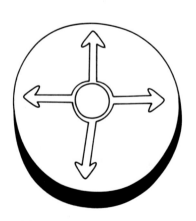

to others like pottery or woodcarving. On the other hand it is clear that there is a strong tendency towards pattern and symmetry for its own sake. The appeal of rhythmic repetition extends to the poetry, song and dance of tribal people everywhere; in fact it is fair to say that this great era of settled tribal society oversaw the emergence and development of man as the pattern-recognising animal.

Tribal society everywhere is 'prehistoric', in the sense that history proper begins only with the recording of dates and the invention of writing, and these innovations were only to appear at a later stage of social evolution. They came, moreover, as part of a wave of developments that were to transform the place of man in the world irrevocably. As was the case in all such major transitions this was characterised by both change and continuity. The so-called ancient mature cultures[4] that sprang from Neolithic tribal society are most obviously distinguished from it by being 'centralist'. Their social order was focused on a particular place, the city state, and on a specific personage, the divine ruler. Their cosmology was still entirely determined by what we would regard as magical principles, but their arts, their buildings, their whole social ethos were utterly different from those of the societies that preceded them. In fact the arts and artifacts of the mature cultures, wherever in the world they appeared, had at least as much in common with each other as with their precursors.

The common and outstanding features of these more advanced cultures include a flexible written language, systems of numeration and advanced calendrical and astronomical knowledge. These societies, whose economy was based on agriculture, were organised according to a religio-magical interpretation of the notion of order. The point of contact between the human world and the divine order was the sacrosanct figure of the ruler, the god-king. The pharaohs of ancient Egypt, for instance, were believed to control nature and were personally responsible for the continuing

The magical process of orientation. Shaman's drum with a design indicating the cardinal points.

fertility of the crops. In a rigidly hierarchical order descending from this figure of the god-king, there appeared a supporting structure of priests and administrators, amounting to a ruling class; beneath these there was a meticulous division of labour within the working population. Usually this rigid social order was mirrored by a pantheon of city and state gods, which themselves were organised according to an hierarchical system, and which also fulfilled quite distinct and specific functions.

The evolutionary progression by which loosely organised tribes were transformed into these far more complex and rigid societies can be viewed, as indeed it would have been experienced, as a thaumaturgical process, one that involved the acquisition, by an increasingly specialised coterie of priests, of new and potent magical knowledge. There is a similar formative pattern in each of these early city-state civilisations. The city began to emerge when fixed shrines became influential and developed into cult centres; the ensuing concentration of power and people in one place inevitably led to new kinds of economic and social organisation leading, among other things, to the large-scale exploitation of human energy and the formation of social hierarchies. The administrative division of labour allowed the priestly class to emerge and to uncover a succession of important natural laws; the regularities of the seasons and the movements of the heavenly bodies were found to respond to the magic of number. It is difficult for us to comprehend fully the impact that these discoveries must have made; what is clear is that their acquisition inspired a kind of cultural confidence that led to the remarkable achievements of these cultures, achievements that we still marvel at today.

It is evident from what we know of the way in which these societies were organised, and from the art and architecture that they left behind, that day-to-day existence in them was extremely prescribed; virtually every aspect of life was conditioned by magical-religious codes of behaviour. It has been said of them that 'everything that was not compulsory was forbidden'. It is no coincidence that in almost every place where these early civilisations flourished they should have engaged in the construction of vast 'crystal-line' and hierarchical monuments as the symbolic expression of their enduring power. The Great Pyramids of the old kingdom of ancient Egypt are, of course, the supreme example of this sort of massive structure, just as its society epitomised all those early city-state cultures in which magical-religious principles were the dominant and organising force. The art of ancient Egypt then was a magical art; its static, ritualistic quality reflected its orderly cosmological view, an outlook that was bound to be extended to its vision of society. All Egyptian painting, sculpture and architecture was bound by rules and rigid canons of design, and, as a result, it projects a measured and logical quality. The pyramids themselves were the highest expression of the Egyptians' veneration for this ordering principle. Their preoccupation with order and regularity, found in every aspect of their art and architecture, is shared to a great extent by all of the mature cultures, most of whom saw the city state and its inhabitants as subject to an all-

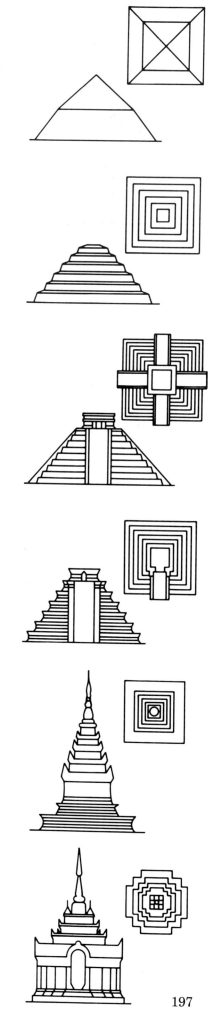

Sun temples, pyramids and ziggurats. Massive monuments of this sort are found wherever the ancient mature cultures flourished. They are the symbolic expression both of the enduring power of these civilisations and of their dedication to the principles of form and order.

illustration: Aris & Phillips

Egyptian art, the substantial part of which was never meant to be seen by mortal eyes, was a magical art. Its static, ritualistic quality reflects the intensely structured character of its cosmology and society. Its paintings always have a mathematical foundation, and are based on rigid and standardised canons.

embracing concept of the universe, one that for the first time placed the grid of logic on the bewildering phenomena of the earth, heavens and stars. Interestingly there is a tendency, common to all of these cultures, to adopt geometrical, especially rectilinear, formats in both their arts and architecture. Also their arts are invariably highly subject to convention, with rigid standardisation of design, particularly when dealing with sacred subjects. Typically the attributes of various deities were assigned according to a prescribed and familiar code, from which deviation was almost inconceivable. These are principles that are found to apply as much to the intricately painted codices of pre-Columbian civilisations as to Egyptian tomb paintings; but it is the tendency to associate the conventions of their belief systems with *geometrical* conventionality that marks the similarities between the arts of the mature cultures, and this also that sets them apart from their respective predecessors. The principles underlying their more formal approach to art are, however, still involved in the magical process of image-making, differing from Palaeolithic art in this respect only in their complexity. Indeed the canons of proportion to which Egyptian artists had to conform might best be compared to the complexities of more primitive taboo systems. In fact the history of this art is essentially the history of its conventions.

In time the mature cultures were eclipsed by the advent of more vigorous societies, from which there emerged a new sense of individual destiny. The activities of the gods became separated from those of man and religious thought began to be differentiated from other matters, which

meant that a level of cultural patterning that had once to be maintained by ritual observance was now simply assumed, and new formalities arose as the dominant organising forces in society. From this time on art was in the service of man, rather than of the gods; order in society and in art was no longer determined by magical imperatives, but was conceived in the terms of the new religious beliefs. These new attitudes of thought, in which magical principles were supplanted by ethical systems, oversaw the emergence of individual consciousness. There was a new emphasis on personal salvation and, of course, most ethico-religious systems were founded on precepts revealed by inspired individuals, in contrast to the mythopoic origins of the older magical-religious cultures. In art a division between the sacred and the secular became possible, but artistic style, as ever, reflected the prevailing ethos; the 'history of seeing' conformed to the branches of the major divisions of world thought. This meant that the objectives of the arts of say the Christian, or Buddhist, or Muslim spheres were as distinctive from each other as the aims and ideals of their respective worldviews.

The exploration of the possibilities of symmetry in decorative ornament that was begun by tribal peoples was continued and developed in later city-based societies: Pueblo pottery (left); Inca plate (right).

In conclusion then, we can see that all artistic productions are characterised by both formal and inspirational qualities. Each of the major areas of artistic expression to which I have referred had quite different and specific roles and different aesthetic conventions; each, in its own way, reflected the particular concerns and values of its own society. A more complete knowledge of the objectives and function of art in any society is essential to the deeper understanding of that society, but the fact remains that we can usually recognise art, of whatever period, for what it is; there is a universal aesthetic that reaches out to us across the centuries transcending the need for interpretation. This suggests to me that, if we have to define art at all, each of these criteria – the formal and the inspirational – are essential components of what is in itself an essential act of communion.

NOTES

1. The theories of the Pre-Raphaelite Brotherhood, which was established in 1848, were perhaps the earliest indication of this archaistic tendency within the European fine art tradition, but in reverting to a more 'primitive' and uncorrupted style they did not feel any need to abandon representational methods. Although the first photographs predate the formation of this group the impact of the new medium had not been felt in any serious way by mid-century. By the 1880s however photographic technology had greatly advanced: Kodak introduced their first snapshot camera in 1888, and by this time anyone that could afford it could produce a likeness. For art the implications of this invention then became obvious and devastating. In response to this challenge artists increasingly turned to primitive sources for inspiration. The term primitive then applied to virtually any non-European art form. Already at this time Gaugin was declaring the need to 'paint like children'.

2. *Primitive Art*, originally published in 1927 (see Bibliography).

3. Nowhere is the magical quality of Palaeolithic cave painting so evident as in the caves at Lascaux in south-west France, where they are sometimes located a mile or more beneath the surface and in some of the most inaccessible recesses. How difficult it is for us to identify with the compulsion that led these artist/sorcerers to work their skills in subterranean passages that might only be reached by climbing, crawling and swimming through submerged caves.

4. The most notable of these, of course, were the ancient civilisations of the Middle East – Egypt, Sumeria and Assyria – but there are striking parallels between these and the older civilisations of the Indus valley, those of the Chang dynasty in China and the pre-Columbian cultures of Peru and Mexico.

The Inca sun-god and god of darkness with their attributes.

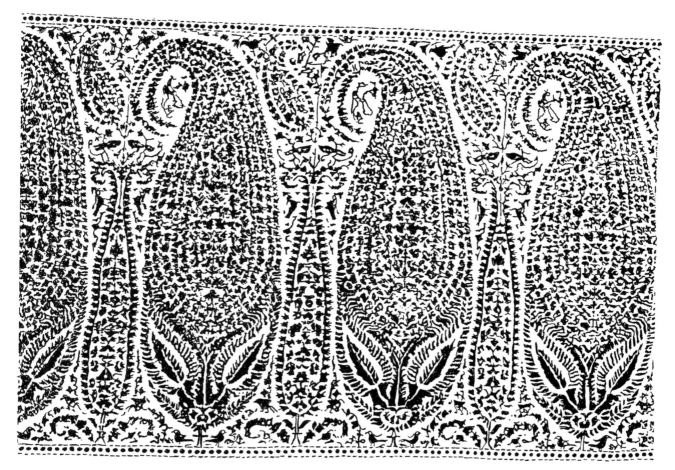

Pattern and Continuity

Ornamental pattern, to be raised above the contempt of reasonable men, must possess three qualities; beauty, imagination and order. *William Morris: Some Hints on Pattern Designing*

Detail of Kashmir shawl. Patterns of this sort were to inspire countless European imitations in the nineteenth century.

When we speak of pattern, in the sense of a decorative element of design, we are referring to arrangements that are formal and essentially symmetrical. Because pattern has a geometrical basis it is grounded in the realm of the predictable; this means that however complex a particular pattern might appear it will fall into one or other of the quite limited number of symmetry groups that are available (see Chapter 5). Or, put the other way around, from these constraints there arise all the possibilities of an absolutely infinite variety of designs. Pattern, then, can always be taken as a metaphor – within it the finite and infinite mingle – and of course the term itself has a very wide range of meaning. We talk of patterns of thought, of social patterns, of economic and weather patterns, the common thread being the notions of congruity and of a rhythmic constancy of some kind or other.

Our perceptions, and our cognitive processes in general, are deeply involved with symmetry principles; to a great extent we see and think in a patterned way. We might assume from this that the human mind has an innate predisposition, or receptivity, to pattern as an art form. This form certainly seems to have had a perennial appeal as an element of design. Since man first began his settled existence virtually every culture has used pattern to some extent though, interestingly, there is great variation in its

201

status. In general pattern is assigned a minor role, but there are many notable exceptions to this. There are technical factors that are conducive to pattern, and it is likely to arise quite naturally from any repetitive process – weaving or bricklaying for instance. It is fairly obvious also that pattern has an attraction of its own.

It would be easy, with the vast amount of evidence of its use as a decorative device, to assume that pattern is a natural, graphic expression of people as pattern-making and pattern-recognising animals. It is all the more surprising then to realise that the very earliest art, that of the Palaeolithic, shows little indication of symmetry of any kind, and certainly nothing that we would think of as pattern of a high order. Since it is clear from their paintings, engravings and carvings that Palaeolithic people had a highly developed aesthetic sensibility the lack of repetitive ornament in their art raises clear difficulties to the notion that pattern is an innate aesthetic response. It would appear that we have to learn how to make and to respond to pattern. When we examine the art of earlier prehistory we find that the emergence of symmetrical motifs was a very gradual affair, and one that was, naturally, charged with magical significance. It is interesting in this regard that children, whilst showing some feeling for symmetry in their art, have to be introduced to the notion of pattern; it does not occur to them to create patterns for themselves. It would seem

It is often difficult to separate the purely technical aspects of pattern from the aesthetic. Pattern arises quite naturally from many repeated processes whether the techniques are stone age or modern: basketwork patterns.

The magical potency of symmetry: an array of frogs on a shaman's cloak (British Columbia).

however that once the notion had been introduced into the human artistic repertoire it became established as a stock item. So far as prehistoric art is concerned this advance was probably an indication that a level of social consciousness had been reached that was not easily reversed. Humans were becoming more conscious of their special place in the natural order, and their society was becoming more structured. There is a sense in which pattern, as a design element, reflected the emerging patterns of fixed societies. Ultimately patterns are appealing, whether they are artistic or social, by virtue of their quality of reassurance.

There is a marked tendency towards symmetry and pattern in much of primitive art: A typical North American blanket design showing a characteristically bilateral arrangement.

As I have observed, the art of tribal peoples everywhere is permeated with pattern and symmetry, especially bilateral symmetry. It seems to be the case that where a 'primitive' craftsman has to make a choice in a design arrangement he is more likely than not to opt for a symmetrical solution, or for a consciously asymmetrical one which amounts to the same thing. This tendency is found in one example after another in tribal art; indeed it is in the field of applied decorative ornament that the best primitive work may equal, or even surpass, that of more technologically advanced cultures.

203

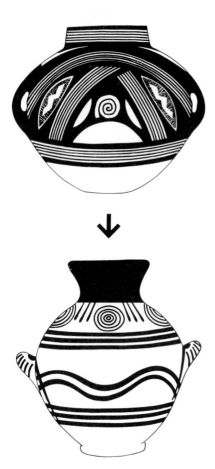

At the same time we have to be cautious in our assessment of the 'meaning' of pattern to tribal peoples; in these societies pattern, and ornament generally, may have carried a symbolic significance which can only be completely understood in its social context. For an uninformed outsider it is usually impossible to determine whether a particular design has any symbolic or ritualistic value or is purely decorative, or whether, as is most often the case, it contains something of both.

In short there is a wide spectrum of symbolic value in the decorative art of tribal societies, which extends from those forms which have a close association with specific natural or mythopoic phenomena, to others where such connections, if they ever did exist, are completely forgotten. The progression by which a design element loses its symbolic significance is a one-way process; in time the most highly charged symbols are likely to lose their meaning and to become no more than a decorative feature, but once a decorative style is established it shows a remarkable tendency to persist, and to be disseminated. Part of the reason for the consistency of decorative styles over great periods of time is that it is self-referring, unlike representational art which always has the standard of nature itself. It is also true that patterns of any kind tend to persist.

Artistic styles are a mirror to social styles, but as Boaz has pointed out, there are no instances where a mode of expression can be seen to have developed entirely from within the cultural life of a particular group; for an art to be unique it would have to be conceived in complete isolation and this has never been the case. Human artistic development has always reflected social evolution and the growth and spread of ideas generally, so that the divisions and subdivisions of artistic style correspond to the greater and smaller divisions of cultural influence. Because of this it is usually quite easy to detect the underlying characteristics of such major stylistic tendencies as African, Oceanic or pre-Columbian, despite the enormous variety seen in their productions. A sense of cultural identity can adhere to even the most elementary components of design; the simple counterchange pattern shown below, for instance, is unmistakably of pre-Columbian origin.

Even the most highly charged symbols will, in time, become completely conventionalised. The earliest form of pottery decoration, as in this example from the late Neolithic (top), consisted of spirals and bands and symbolised the principle of renewal, but in later times these potent motifs became decorative elements with no symbolic significance (below: Attic amphora).

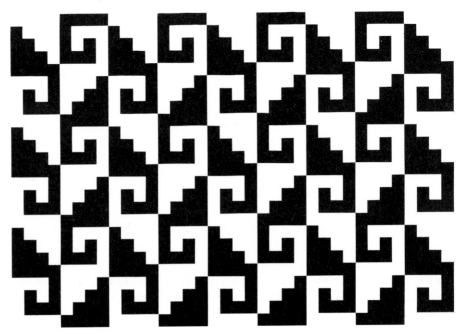

Pattern from a Peruvian textile, circa 1000 AD

When we examine the art of tribal people in detail it soon becomes apparent that some cultures are more inclined than others towards formal modes of expression and, as a result, have a greater affinity for pattern; a point that would seem to indicate a far wider range of 'ways of seeing' than is generally assumed. In the 1930s this notion was reinforced by an investigation which tested the responses of various West African tribal groups to representational drawings and photographs. Among the different ethnic groups involved considerable variation was found in the ability to interpret these pictures.[1] Some tribespeople were able to understand them perfectly easily, whereas others, whose own art was far more inclined towards the formal and decorative, had some difficulty in this respect. This latter response might appear to most of us, who are so familiar with realistic imagery, as somewhat incongruous or even more unkindly as the result of intellectual inadequacy, but this is not at all the case. What is involved here are differences in basic modes of perception. Perception is not a mere accumulation of visual data; the information that our eyes receive, in common with that from all other sensory receptors, has to be processed. We have to learn the techniques of perception, and we are bound to be influenced in this by basic cultural assumptions. A person who has been blind from birth and whose visual capability has been restored in the physical sense will not, as a result, be able to see immediately; in fact he or she may never attain full sight. To learn how to see we have to go through

In pre-literate cultures pattern is sometimes imbued with symbolic content: These relatively simple South American designs are held to represent a whole range of creatures, including bats, snakes, fish and bees.

205

a gradual learning and interpretive process. The West African investigation was important in that it seemed to have demonstrated that humans have evolved different modes of interpretation, and, by implication, different modes of perception.

All of us, from the time we are born, are influenced by specific cultural alignments, but in common with all learning processes this involves a profit and loss account. One of the demands of literate cultures, for instance, is that we learn to interpret images 'the right way up', that is to say from a particular orientation, but in assimilating this technique we forfeit our innate capacity to recognise an image in whichever way it is presented. Our ability to detect symmetries of various kinds is an important part of the mechanism of perception, but it is fairly clear that there are wide cultural variations in this aspect of visualisation. The best evidence for these variations, of course, is in the creative output of different cultural groups; in European art, for instance, pattern has tended to occupy a rather lowly position, at least since the medieval period, whereas other cultures, notably those of the Islamic sphere, are far more pattern-conscious. In a similar way African music is renowned for its rhythmic complexity, in marked contrast to the tonal basis of most western music.

The creative potentiality of symmetry principles is such that they can never be entirely ignored in art; the 'conventionality' of pattern is still recognised today, even though so many other conventions have been abandoned. In the field of contemporary fine arts for instance it might be felt that absolutely anything goes, that no subject is too obscure or any medium too outlandish; art can now be based on comic strips or be made of squashed beer cans, but there remains one important area of taboo. Fine art cannot concern itself with pattern. To do so it would have to cross some unspoken line of demarcation and fall from grace into the realm of the 'applied'. These days it is considered quite legitimate to 'apply' fine art – a scarf bearing a Matisse painting, for instance, is perfectly acceptable; but the reverse procedure, the use of pattern in fine art is not.

The present feeling that pattern is 'all right in its place' is in itself an affirmation of the potency of symmetrical arrangements but at the same time is indicative of a certain reluctance to admit them into much more than a peripheral role. This attitude clearly reflects deeply held cultural values, which are however like so much else these days, in a state of transition. In fact the process of upgrading the worth of purely decorative art that has taken place in the modern period has a history of its own which traces back to the theories of people like Ruskin and William Morris. It is significant too that the aesthetic movement of which these two were leading figures was as concerned with the need for social change as it was with artistic renewal. Indeed they saw the two as being inextricably involved. The remedy for the 'oppressive influence of industrialisation' was sought in an aesthetic revitalisation, and their hopes were that this would be accompanied by, or at the very least exert influence on, changes in social attitudes in general. The Arts and Crafts Movement, which began in the 1880s, can be seen as part of a more general re-evaluation of the role of the applied arts, and this in turn was part of the broad response of art to the impact of industrialisation, and to the invention of photography. It is natural that the massive social upheavals that occurred in the past century should have been reflected in

The perennial appeal of these designs is partly attributable to their very predictability. Taken from a Kashmir shawl.

art; and interesting that, in the face of such unprecedented change, pattern, as a decorative form, should have retained its appeal. The essence of pattern is order; William Morris refers to this, in one of his many essays and lectures on the subject, as an absolutely necessary quality of art; in his words it is a 'wall against vagueness' and 'a door for the imagination'. But perhaps he best defines the reasons for the perennial appeal of pattern when he observes that it can remind us not only of that part of nature that it might represent, but also of much that lies beyond it.[2]

NOTES

1. A Field experiment in Racial Psychology. *Brit. J. Psychol.*, 1937. Mentioned in *The Psychology of Perception* (M. D. Vernon, Penguin Books, 1962).

2. From his lecture delivered to the Workingmen's College in 1881, entitled *Some Hints on Pattern Designing.*

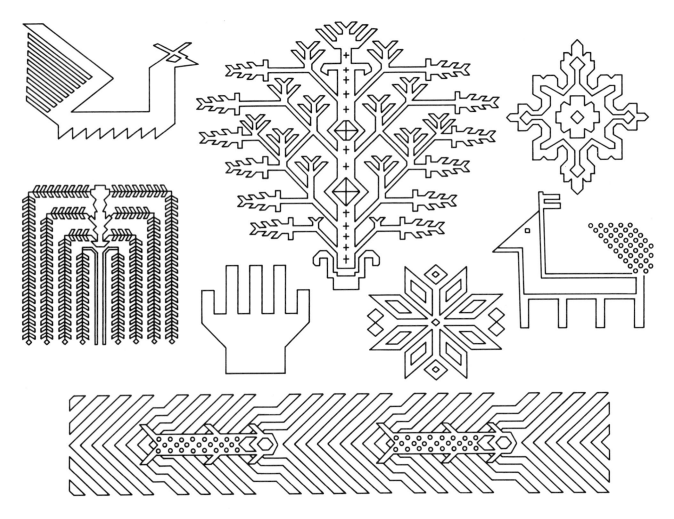

The crystal garden. There is a conventional symbology attaching to many of the motifs in oriental carpets but underlying this there is a more general, less easily defined, tendency towards the crystalline.

Motif and Metaphor

Since these forms are significant they must be representative, not necessarily representative of tangible objects, but sometimes of more or less abstract ideas. *Franz Boaz in 'Primitive Art'*

Art has a special value for ethnologists since it constitutes one of their principal means of understanding the complexities of social and intellectual evolution. The earliest forms of art are particularly interesting and important in this respect because they provide the main evidence of the modes of existence led by man in the remote past. I have already mentioned the fact that decorative and symbolic motifs play a far smaller part in the art of the Palaeolithic than in that of later, more settled peoples, and that the main subjects of the cave paintings of that period were the animals on which the hunters were dependent. This art, early though it was, demonstrates a highly developed aesthetic sense and the beginning of the use of symbolic imagery. In the caves at Lascaux many of the animal paintings are accompanied by enigmatic rectilinear figures that have become known as 'traps'. It is unlikely that these diagrams were meant to represent traps in any literal sense, rather that they had a specific magical intention that was probably concerned, in advance of the hunt, to ensnare the soul of an intended prey. Whatever their intention these simple designs clearly had a special significance for the Palaeolithic hunters. It requires an effort of imagination on our part to appreciate their potency since our world is filled with far more complex graphic imagery, and with symbolism and geometries of all kinds. In their context, however, these devices are as intriguing as the highly accomplished paintings of the animals themselves, for they represent the emergence of the most important of all human faculties, that of abstract, systematic thought.

Palaeolithic cave painting is mainly representational. Where symbolic motifs occur they are thought to refer to the animals that are depicted. Many of the paintings in the caves at Lascaux are accompanied by enigmatic rectilinear figures known as 'traps', but these are clearly not traps in any literal sense.

What we have to remember when we look at the combs, squares and odd rectilinear partitioning of the 'traps' and other geometric figures of the Franco-Cantabrian caves is that they were produced by a culture which had no permanent dwellings or artifacts such as weaving or pottery, was innumerate and had no written language, yet these petroglyphs seem to point the way to all of these attainments. They are clearly abstract, are unlike anything in nature, and though simple are carefully considered and formal. There is, in fact, an enormous variety of such symbols in the arts of hunter cultures generally, and there is little doubt that they have a great range of meaning, most of which is likely to remain obscure. We can perhaps get the best indication of their intended purpose by comparing them with the magical diagrams of Chinese Taoism. These doodle-like compositions, which originated in the shamanistic past of Taoism, have managed to survive into the modern period. They were, and are, used as charms and talismans and were the means of a symbolic contact with the psychic energies of nature and the supernatural. It is interesting that symbolic as well as representational art should have preceded that of pure decoration, but of course the distinctions between representation, symbolism and decoration are not easily made in any art. We have seen that in time symbols tend to lose their charge, and that decoration itself can be invested with all manner and degree of symbolic intent. The fact is that no art is entirely devoid of symbolism; the very act of artistic creation itself is symbolic and is bound to involve the intuitive faculty. It is for this reason that the enduring appeal of particular forms in decorative art can suggest a significance beyond that of aesthetic conventionality, and would seem to indicate a subconscious awareness of important natural principles. Wave

'Traps' and other geometric petroglyphs from the Franco-Cantabrian caves.

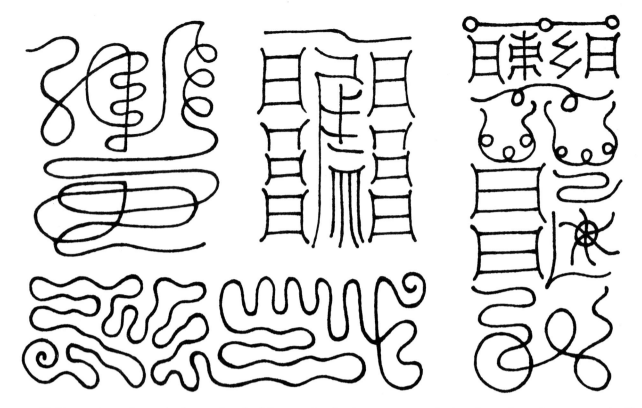

Talismanic and magical diagrams from popular Taoism.

and spiral forms, for instance, are archetypal modes of response in the physical world, so it is not altogether surprising to find such configurations featuring quite extensively in early and primitive art. These motifs, which seem to have occurred independently in many different parts of the world, are often associated with the renewal and continuity of life. Designs of this sort were felt to evince a magical potential because they 'fixed' *mana* in a recognisable symmetrical form.

Art as a response to, or as a restatement of, a perceived reality is bound to be concerned with matters of form and energy. Artists have always been fascinated by the basic structure of matter, by the grain and texture of materials and by the principles of flow and movement. Even amongst the cryptic symbolism of the earliest art there are many examples that appear to represent notions of formality and regularity on the one hand, and energy and fluidity on the other. Primitive art in general is rich with graphic expressions that seem to combine these elements; one frequently

Spirals and wave forms are common motifs in many parts of the primitive and ancient worlds. These examples are from Ireland, Japan, New Zealand, New Guinea and North and South America.

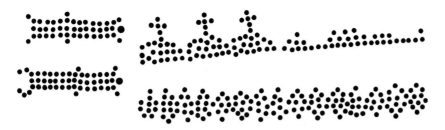

These enigmatic markings, somewhat reminiscent of punched card patterns, were found on a reindeer's antler in Denmark and have been dated to the Neolithic period (c. 7000 BC). They are believed to be 'ancestor patterns', genealogical trees, with the squatting figure (bottom left) representing the clan mother.

Art mobilier: *Decoration on bone from Isturitz, Magdalanian period.*

encounters adventitious asymmetries and permitted accidents, for instance, effects that are often mistaken for poor workmanship. Pattern in itself of course provides a far-reaching metaphor, not only for similar observable regularities in nature, but for the whole symmetrising and ordering principle. However patterns are quite often allowed, subconsciously or deliberately, to be disturbed, an effect that can make for a more interesting composition and one that can also be taken as a metaphor for the interplay of form and energy.

Primitive art is full of semi-deliberate accidents and asymmetries.

An impression of the turbulence of surf as captured on a Maori canoe paddle.

The depiction of the dynamics of fluid flow in primitive art is an interesting field of study in itself. As is the case with other natural phenomena this can be found in a whole spectrum of stylisation, from that of simple imitation to more formal and abstract modes of expression. The swirling designs on the Maori canoe paddles (above) convey a marvellous impression of the turbulence of surf and are clearly based on close observation of and familiarity with the action of waves and foam. In con-

Mexican frieze based on the action of waves.

trast to this treatment the Mexican frieze, which is based on the same subject, has a far more static and 'crystalline' feel, although it is still perfectly recognisable. The incursive, interpenetrating New Guinean design (left) shows another and quite different approach to the subject. Here again we have a formal and traditional style, abstract and freely rendered, which does not appear to be related to any natural formation, but which achieves a striking sense of balanced tension, combining dynamism with a certain underlying, latent symmetry. The effect is somewhat reminiscent of computer-generated fractal designs. Like so much in primitive art this piece seems to work on various levels. At the most superficial it is an attractive piece of decorative, applied ornament. It almost certainly has mythological and symbolic associations, but underlying these intentions there seems also to be a fine intuition of the principles of vortical and laminar flow, and of the sort of exchange interaction that occurs in the so-called domain patterns of magnetic anisotropy.

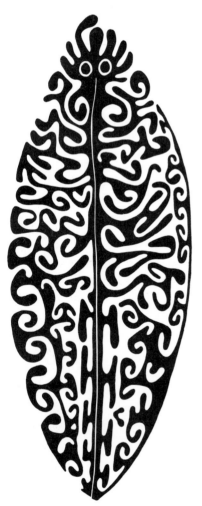

Mask from New Guinea. This intriguing design is comprised of the interpenetration of two domains, conveying the distinct impression of the interaction of two forces.

The use of knots involves conceptual skills of a high order.

It was, of course, precisely this ability to recognise the subtle workings of invariance in nature, and to turn it to advantage, that underlay human intellectual evolution. The skills that led to the development of tools and weapons naturally conferred enormous advantages on man the hunter. We can imagine that there would have been a natural progression from the concept of magical grids that were intended to capture the souls of animals to the making of actual grids, in the form of corrals, nets etc. which could have ensnared the animals themselves. The use of cords, and particularly of knots, involved conceptual skills of a high order and must have greatly enhanced the tool-making repertoire of humans. The power of knots to bind, restrain and ensnare would inevitably have held magical associations for primitive people, and in fact the use of knots in magical ritual was widespread throughout the primitive world. Knots were used for the control of malignant spirits, disease, death and even the weather, and for early people there would have been little separation between such ritual use and that which we would regard as purely utilitarian. Most cultures have traditions that reflect this primordial belief. It was still the practice in Elizabethan England for instance for witches to sell 'wind knots' to sailors to ensure safe passage on a sea journey. Traces of the belief in knot magic still persist in our language; when we are fascinated by something or someone we are 'spellbound', a term that originally implied the constraint of magical knots.

The knot and plaited interweave are universal motifs in decoration.

Knotted and interwoven designs are used extensively in the arts of both primitive and mature cultures in virtually every part of the world. As is the case with all such widely distributed motifs the degree of symbolism involved, and its meaning, vary considerably. In the case of knots there are often talismanic undertones. In China, for instance, the double knot is still

Qu'ranic inscription in knotted Kufic. Thirteenth-century Turkish.

In virtually every part of the primitive and ancient worlds there is a marked tendency towards geometric stylisation in textile design: a spiral motif from the Congo (above); a crystalline figure from Peru (below).

widely accepted as the sign of good luck, and in the Islamic world ornate knotted devices and intricate interwoven patterns have always been popular, to the extent that the words of Holy Scripture are often presented in this form. The very fact that these decorative devices are so universal would seem to indicate that they are in some way representative of some general abstract notion, and it is interesting that the woven and interlaced patterns that are used to decorate textiles are frequently transferred to more enduring mediums such as wood, stone or pottery. It is easy to appreciate the appeal of such patterns; they engage our interest because we can respond to them as if they had a spatial quality and were not simply flat images; our eyes tend to trace the path of an interlace and there is a certain satisfaction in the process of unravelment. Maze patterns, which also enjoy wide distribution, are engaging for the same reason. But I suspect their real attraction lies rather deeper than this; knots and weave, whether actual or simply graphic images, represent the intelligent organisation of effort and materials into a useful form, and are therefore symbolic of the basic perceptual skills and creativity of people.

It is not certain when and where woven fabrics first came into use. It has been suggested that it may have occurred when people were driven into a more settled mode of existence by the reduction of the great herds which began to decline, either because of climatic changes or through over-hunting. According to these hypotheses woven fabrics came in as a substitute for the animal skins that had been freely available, but it has to be said of speculation of this sort that it tends to disregard the sheer complexity of social evolution. Unfortunately, because of the perishable nature of textiles, hard evidence of their earliest use and development is non-existent. It seems reasonable to assume, however, by extrapolation from other surviving artifacts (pottery and so on) that even the earliest fabrics would have been decorated, and very likely that their decoration would have been influenced by the weftage of the fabric itself. Weaving, by its nature, involves a disciplined approach, and is a process that tends to evoke regular and geometric expressions. In virtually every part and in every period of the primitive and ancient worlds there is a tendency towards geometrical forms of decoration, particularly in textiles, and this tendency has to be taken as one of the more obvious representations of the developing awareness of man with regard to the power and value of the principle of order.

Central motif from a Chelaberd (Caucasian) carpet, showing characteristic crystalline growth patterns.

Woven fabrics are such a familiar product of our industrialised society that it has been a long time since we have felt any real sense of the symbolic values that they once held. The only area in which textiles that could be said to have retained something of an aura of respect and mystery is that of oriental carpets; the rich colours and dense ornamentation, particularly of older examples, gives them as much appeal now as they ever had. Part of the attraction here, of course, is the appeal of the exotic. Most of us are conscious that these carpets are the product of a society whose values are very different from ours and which has long-established and rich traditions of its own. There are considerable regional variations in the design of these carpets, but we would expect to find certain common features; these include rather dense designs, which might be highly geometrical and strongly patterned, but will almost certainly show a high degree of symmetry. These carpets are, in fact, produced in regions within the Islamic sphere, and the stylistic values that they express are those of Islamic culture.

Carpets have always been highly regarded there; in nomadic society in particular they always represented an eminently useful and portable item, and an important commodity of exchange. In the Islamic world they have long been admired for their aesthetic value and have attracted the sort of critical attention that we in the west have applied to painting and sculpture. Oriental carpets have also, for many centuries, been well received in the west, and there has never been any difficulty in our accepting them as beautiful and somewhat exotic objects. The possibility of misunderstanding the aesthetic intention of these art objects only arises if we attempt to interpret them in terms of our own cultural values, particularly in over-emphasising their symbolic content. In fact the general tendency in Islamic art is away from symbolic imagery, just as it shies away from the art of representation. In short, when we attempt to 'analyse' eastern carpets we encounter the same problems of interpretation as with a great deal of primitive art with its many levels of meaning. There is, quite clearly, both meaning and significance in Islamic carpet design, but it is not easily

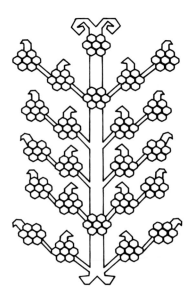

Highly stylised 'Tree-of-Life' motif from a Persian carpet.

215

defined; if we make any worthwhile generalisation about the essential qualities of style in these works it is that they tend towards a 'crystallisation' of form, and in this they are reflecting aspects of both Islamic and older nomadic cultural attitudes.

We encounter similar difficulties of interpretation if we try to analyse the appeal of that most familiar of Islamic motifs the *boteh* or 'paisley' device. This motif and the rich, complex patterning with which it is usually associated, seems to have originated in Persia, where they have long been featured in both carpets and woven textiles. There are a great number of supposed derivations of this figure; amongst others it has been taken to symbolise a flame, a teardrop, a cypress tree in the wind, a fir cone or the windings of the River Indus. It is also frequently pointed out that this shape resembles the constituent parts of the Chinese *yin-yang* symbol. In reality it is extremely unlikely that this device is derived from any of these things, but rather that it is representative of a far more abstract notion and that it was evolved gradually and intuitively. *Boteh* patterns were first introduced to Europe in the form of fine Kashmir shawls, were well received from the very beginning and soon became widely imitated. Since its introduction this kind of patterning has never been entirely out of favour; at different times it has become high or low fashion, but it seems to have established itself as a hardy perennial of design. Clearly, if we are to believe Boaz, for forms to persist they must be representative, and naturally there must be some underlying reason for this continuing popularity. The variety of these patterns is seemingly endless, but however they are presented they are characterised by two distinct features, apart from their usual intensity of colour and intricacy of design. These are the flowing, liquescent form of the primary motifs and the strictly symmetrical grid on which these are laid out. In my view it is the integration of this symbol of the fluid into the regulating formalism of pattern, common to all these designs, that gives them their significance and which accounts for their enduring appeal.

In the magical art of the Palaeolithic there was always felt to be a mysterious connection between a representation and the object itself; and art, with its power to move and inform, has always retained something of this quality. Our perception of the greater world has enormously changed and extended in the modern period, and we can see the unprecedented waves of experimentation that have taken place, and which continue to affect art, as part of coming to terms with these new visions. The attempt to find new 'ways of seeing' is a necessary accompaniment to the adaptation to change; in the past century or so the extent of social and technological change is so profound that it is bound to have involved not only an overturning of older aesthetic standards, but also a re-evaluation of the whole of the art of the past.

Archetypal swirling form created by circular motion in a liquid medium, and the yin-yang *sign that is derived from it.*

The boteh-i-mir *in regular array. Detail from a Persian (Mashadi) carpet.*

Imagery and Intentionality

People used always to reproduce things seen on earth –
things that had been, or would be seen with pleasure. Today
a new reality of visible objects has been revealed, and we
know that, in relation to the universe, the visible is only an
isolated case, that other truths exist latently and are in the
majority. *Paul Klee*

Despite all the transitions through which the western artistic tradition has
been in the past century or so it is still characterised by a division between
its 'major' and 'minor' aspects, or the 'fine' and 'applied' arts. This distinction, it is true, has been somewhat eroded by these changes, and it is clear
that there will always be a separation between those aspects of art that are
primarily concerned with decorative effects and others whose objectives
go beyond this. Nevertheless it is true to say that this demarcation has long
been a prominent feature of western art, and it still applies; naturally there
are good art-historical reasons for this. In fact the process of the separation
of the fine and decorative arts in Europe traces back to the adoption of the
'methods of illusion' in the service of representational art. Prior to this
development there was a common regard for the constraints of formality
in both ornamental and representational art; one only has to recall the
serried ranks of saints in the art of Byzantium. But in the pursuit of greater
naturalism this sort of formalism was abandoned. The portrayal of real
objects, figures and scenery through the techniques of illusion worked

*Form and energy in European
art. The art of the Middle Ages
was characterised by a high
regard for the constraints of
symmetry, an objective that
was gradually abandoned in
the pursuit of greater
naturalism. The advent of
photography impelled art into
many new directions,
including those which seem
concerned to invoke the energy
principle: 'Black and White' by
Franz Kline, whose vigorous
brushwork is somewhat
reminiscent of the art of Zen.*

against geometrical formality; these approaches tend to be irreconcilable – one must, it seems, opt for one or the other, and western European artists chose the former.

European schools of painting were to be extremely successful in this art of illusion but there was a price to it; as Goethe pointed out, any gains in the visual arts are bound to be accompanied by a loss. The elevation of the standing of the fine arts saw a reduction in the status of the decorative arts which led, inevitably, to a lowering of expectations and standards. From the late Middle Ages on, the problems of figural representation became the focal point of creative energy, and this field was marked by progressive innovations in the techniques of illusion. There was of course far more to the totality of this art than the evolution of mere technique, but there is little doubt that its central and continuing preoccupation was the concern to render a three-dimensional appearance on to a plane surface. An interesting aspect of these developments in the western artistic tradition is the fact that they were synchronous with the great advances in science and technology also taking place in the west. In particular there was the convergence between the achievement of an ever greater degree of realism in painting and developments in optics, such as the *camera obscura*, which culminated in the perfectly representational images of photography. The irony was, of course, that when this ideal of perfect representation was finally realised the effect on the fine arts was devastating. The skills of the art of illusion were confronted by an automatic and vulgar technique requiring little or no artistic proficiency, and they suffered in the comparison. Representational art has made something of a recovery since that initial impact, but, after its introduction, no art concerned with naturalism could ever ignore photography; it represented a new and permanent criterion.

In spite of being relieved of its commission by the techniques of photography, fine art has demonstrated a remarkable ability to retain its position. On the face of it this is rather surprising, but it is clear that the spirit of aesthetic enquiry and innovation that had characterised European art over the centuries endowed it with a momentum of its own. It was this spirit that carried it forward to produce the extraordinary range of experimentation which occurred in the post-camera era. At the present time, however, fine art occupies a somewhat rarefied and unconnected position, with the population at large being fairly bemused by the range and variety of its productions. Despite this, and whatever one's own feelings towards the general course of art in the modern period, this process of fragmentation has brought undeniable benefits. To reverse Goethe's maxim, with every loss in art there is likely to be a gain. If they have achieved nothing else the artistic experiments of the past century have succeeded in opening our eyes to the qualities of art outside the European tradition; this has meant that our perception of art is no longer limited to the simple values of imitation on the one hand or decoration on the other. Our taste has become far more catholic. It is almost certainly the case, for instance, that the work of ancient and tribal peoples is more meaningful to us than it was to our grandparents. Without necessarily

It is entirely in keeping with the perception of a divine and cosmic unity that the rose windows of medieval Europe should have been laid out on an intensely symmetrical plan.

grasping the original significance of the arts of unfamiliar cultures we have at least some critical sense of their value.

There is, however, a negative aspect to this great awakening, and it is one that has left art with certain central and rather disturbing problems. All art must be possessed of an aesthetic *intentionality*, however vague, but the range of artistic intentions to which we are now exposed, both from contemporary sources and from the whole of the past, are so diverse that no simple criteria could possibly be expected to deal with them all. This raises the spectre of 'required pre-knowledge', the notion that certain art forms (perhaps all!) cannot be fully appreciated without instruction of some kind, an alienating idea that has met with understandable resistance. There is a feeling that art should be able to stand on its own feet, that we should be able to understand it without the need for any involved explanation. In fact the necessity for exposition and interpretation, characteristic of so much of the art of our time, is a manifest weakness. The problem for art, and it is essentially a modern one, is that there is a deficiency of objective criteria. The difficulties posed are obvious: how are we to judge the artistic merit, or otherwise, of a given work of art without any indication of its provenance, or any clues as to its artistic intentions, if any? For instance, if we are presented with a piece of graphic imagery, which we take to be abstract painting, is its value suddenly diminished with the realisation that it has actually been generated by a random input to a computer, or that it is a false-colour microphoto of the intestines of a mosquito?

Clearly our response to art of any kind, even that which is purely representational or purely decorative, relies on an appreciation of its intention; we have to know what it is meant to do or to be. In our culture the terms of both representation and decoration are assimilated at an early age, so that we tend to take these intentions for granted, assuming that they are a natural, innate aesthetic response – which in fact they are not. Nevertheless these are clear and fairly universal artistic objectives; we can understand the purely representational and decorative aspects of art of whatever provenance. Representational art, of course, always has the standard of reality itself for comparison, and we can evaluate decoration on the basis of its 'internal' organisation, colour arrangements, etc. Other aspects of art however, such as those involving its magical, symbolic or religious intentions, have an 'external' point of reference, whose objectives may or may not be accessible to us. Our reaction to both these 'primary' and 'secondary' attributes will be conditioned by our more general attitudes, which themselves will be grounded in a particular social context. In other words art is a social activity and if its function can be simply stated it is surely to reinforce, and at the same time to extend, our perception within this limitation. This being the case it is clear that one of the principal tasks of art now is to respond to the new and unprecedented visions of reality that have been revealed by science. We may yet witness the emergence of an entirely new and broadly based aesthetic that is neither representational nor ornamental in the older sense, but which will refer, in the words of Paul Klee, to 'those other truths that exist latently'.

Our dual sense of personal identity and of external reality is sustained by the images that we receive of the world and of the ways in which we interpret them. The great technological revolution of modern times has

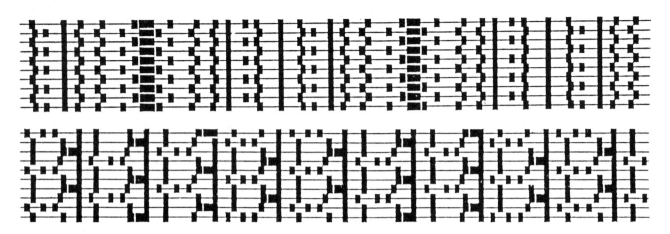

Not an example of tribal bead-work, but band patterns of collagen, the protein found in animal tissues. Since the advent of molecular biology it has been realised that a great deal of organic material is built up from repetitive elements such as these.

'Today a new reality of visible objects has been revealed.'

vastly increased the range of imagery at our disposal and we now have views into realms whose very existence was inconceivable not so long ago. In a paradoxical way our ability to adapt to these new visions of reality testifies both to our sense of imagination and to our lack of it. There is little doubt that the revelations of contemporary physics, with all their implications for technology, are deeply affecting the way that most of us are seeing the world. The present era is most frequently characterised as the atomic age, with practically every aspect of science now referring to the bedrock of quantum and relativistic physics, but it might equally well be described as the age of the image. In fact these terms are more closely connected than may be immediately apparent; the uncovering of the realities of the atomic micro-world was the first incursion by humans into a realm whose existence was indubitable, and indeed the basis of our own,

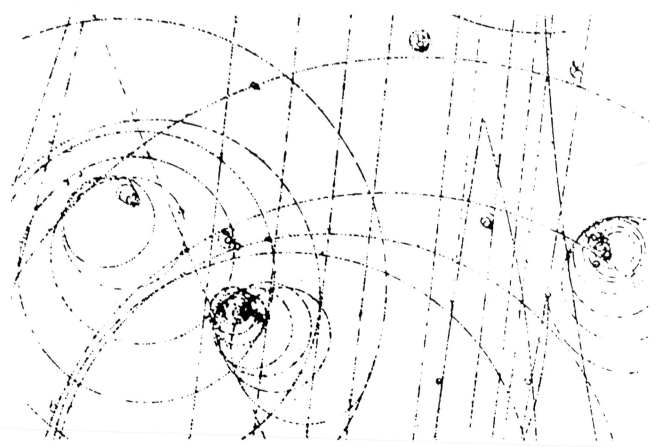

but one that was quite beyond direct sense perception. This was a reality that could only be reached indirectly, through the medium of instrumentation, which is to say, through imagery.[1]

Our understanding of the nature of the physical world has greatly deepened in the past century and virtually every aspect of this vast accumulation of knowledge has been accompanied by images. We are now presented with views of the microscopic, of the miracles of plant and animal structure, of the swirling weather patterns of our own planet and of the mysterious beauties of others. Much of this imagery, in contrast to that of the pre-photographic past, is, from an aesthetic point of view, ingenuous; it is a direct sampling of reality and little of it can be regarded as art in any traditional sense. But it is the nature of man to interpret and represent the perceived world, actions which are the very basis of identity and style. Although we are deluged with imagery, for one purpose or another, it has all been selected and, in the final analysis, selective representation is the essence of art. Moreover it is clear that many of the older boundaries within art itself are becoming less relevant; the differences between the art of the imagination, of description and of decoration are far less apparent than in the past. Of even greater significance perhaps is the extent to which the aims of science and art are themselves converging.

Descriptions of the absolutes of reality which are now being presented are of incredible elegance and beauty, a complex theophany of symmetries and energies, but ironically these new cosmologies are facing scientists with a dilemma that has never been confronted before. In the past, experimental verification of a proposition was absolutely imperative, but it seems that, in some areas at least, science is going beyond this. New visions of the origins and ultimate structure of the universe are proving to be increasingly difficult to verify so that, at the sharp end of science, it is getting unnervingly close to a position where fundamental beliefs have to be based on such unfamiliar values as faith and aestheticism. Whatever significance more recent scientific revelations might hold for the future of society, it is clear that they will continue to exert an influence on art. Such things take time, but once the implications of these new perceptions of reality are generally absorbed, art will surely minister to whatever conversion of the collective imagination that the situation may demand.

Design in nature: The micro structure of wood (Cymbopetulum).

'If art succeeds in creating a general language so that it surveys the whole range of forms, and can juxtapose and imitate various characteristic ones, then the highest level it can reach is style, the level on which it is equal to the highest achievements of man.'

Goethe

NOTES

1. The first images of the atomic world were produced by Von Laue in 1912, when he passed X-rays through a crystal of zinc blende on to a photographic plate. Soon after this Rutherford put forward the results of his 'deflection' experiments, in which he also used photographic plates, and so began the opening up of the interior of the atom.

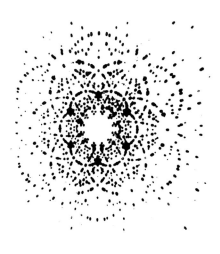

8

'Crystalline' form in the art of Islam

This chapter is dedicated to an examination of a particular aspect of Islamic art, namely its tradition of purely geometric designs. In my view, these provide one of the clearest, and certainly the most graphic, representations of the ordering, symmetric principle that is half the subject of this book. In common with most great artistic traditions a great deal of Islamic art has a direct appeal and has, therefore, little need of interpretation, but to appreciate its underlying motive, and the reason why it should have appeared where and when it did, we must place it in its cultural context.

It is a curious fact of history that Islam, admittedly at an early stage in its evolution, was regarded by certain fathers of the Church as a Christian heresy. This may strike us as rather surprising now because the image of Islam in the Christian west has long been the epitome of all that is exotic, forbidding and impenetrable; however mistaken an idea it may have been to have seen Islam as some kind of deviation from Christian orthodoxy it would seem to indicate an unexpected degree of cultural or religious proximity. Islam, as we shall see, is indeed closely related in its beliefs to both Christianity and Judaism, but it represented a genuine departure from both and, as is almost invariably the case in history, this separation became greater with the passage of time. There is, after all, always hope for those who are entirely ignorant of the 'true word', but little for those who wilfully persist in its misinterpretation.

In time, of course — in a very short time in historical terms — Islam developed its own cultural identity and became a serious rival and threat to both eastern and western Christendom. This was the beginning of a long period of mutual enmity, with each side regarding itself as the defender of the faith, and its opponents as infidels. During this period the whole basis of Islamic culture – its social customs, its art and architecture, etc. – became increasingly unfamiliar to the western observer. Even now there is a strong sense of rivalry and mutual suspicion between the Islamic and western spheres of influence, but the modern period has also seen a breaking down of older prejudices and an awakening of interest in the arts of unfamiliar cultures, among which the rich Islamic heritage must surely rank among the more brilliant and intriguing.

The Emergence of Islam

Once the spirit of the Islamic revelation had brought into being, out of the heritage of previous civilisations and through its own genius, the civilisations whose manifestations may be called distinctly Islamic, the main interest turned away from change and 'adaptation'. The arts and sciences came to possess instead a stability and a 'crystallisation' based on the immutability of the principles from which they had issued forth. *Sayyed Hossein Nasr*

The art and civilisation of Islam have frequently been characterised as possessing a crystalline quality, a generalisation which, in itself, provides an interesting line of thought. Is it possible that so narrow a description has any real meaning when applied to a cultural influence as great as that of Islam? Can the art of any culture be so easily defined, when it is bound to encompass a great variety of attitudes and modes of creative expression? Are there sufficient common features within the arts of those lands that profess the Muslim faith to give the term 'Islamic art' any real meaning? Certainly this could not be the case in a Christian context. If the term 'Christian art' were used as the title of a book we could not, on that basis alone, form any clear idea of its contents; for this there would have to be a more rigourous definition, such as Byzantine or Gothic art. The art of Islam is rather different in this respect, in that it developed certain modes of expression at an early stage of its development, and persisted with these forms with a dedication and respect analogous to that which it felt for the

An ornamental version of the Shahadah, *the fundamental testimony of Islam. 'There is no god but God, and Muhammad is the messenger of God.' Square Kufic script.*

The Word and the Place. The Qu'ran, the holy book of Islam, was believed to consist of a pre-existent 'heavenly scripture', that was revealed to Muhammad by God. The Ka'ba, *which itself is a simple, regular structure, symbolises the permanent and immutable character of Islam. It is the focus of prayer for the whole Muslim world, and is always veiled with a covering (Kiswah) to indicate its essential mystery.*

qu'ranic revelations which form the basis of its belief. In historical terms Islam developed its characteristic style very rapidly, and indeed displayed as much confidence in establishing its artistic priorities as in founding its distinctive social structure. So perhaps it is not too far wide of the mark to apply the 'crystalline' analogy to the Islamic ethos as a whole. From the time of its inception in the seventh century AD Islam experienced a steady, exponential growth, and it consolidated its advances with entirely original social forms, modes of existence which, once having been established, were to show remarkable powers of endurance and stability, with successive generations conforming to what was felt to be a pre-ordained and divine order. The supreme symbol of this social crystallisation is the *Ka'ba* (Cube), the plain rectilinear edifice to which all Muslims direct their prayer and which acts, in a quite literal sense, as the focal point of the Islamic world.

The term 'Islam' has various meanings; when we speak of the emergence of Islam we are referring to a set of principles that were at first a religious, then subsequently an imperial, and finally a cultural force. At each stage Islam was marked by a vigour and confidence that gave it a unique standing in the history of those ideas, religious, political or philosophical, that were to influence the destinies of entire dominions. There had been spectacular expansions of nomadic peoples before, and subsequent to, the rise of Islam, but these had invariably been absorbed by the less energetic but more advanced civilisations on which they imposed. The Arab conquests of the eighth and ninth centuries were different from all such previous expansions in that they were reinforced by a religious zeal. The early Muslims were able to consolidate their hold on their newly acquired territories, and to absorb the cultural influences that they encountered, by virtue of a confidence that derived from their newly acquired religious convictions. This sudden expansion of power, then, was at the same time a religious and an historical event of the greatest magnitude. It still seems remarkable that within a century of the initial revelations, received by a middle-aged prophet in an isolated and somewhat backward corner of the civilised world, that Islam should have extended its dominion from Spain and Morocco in the west to India and the borders of China in the east. It is extraordinary, too, that the vast area that was captured in those initial conquests should still, by and large, constitute the Islamic sphere.

An 'internal' perception of Islam, that is to say one taken from the perspective of a believing Muslim, is bound to see it as the 'one, true religion'. For Muhammad it was a revival and restoration of the monotheistic prophetic traditions of the Old Testament. In fact Islam sees Muhammad as the last, and greatest, of a line of prophets that included Moses, David and Jesus; he is 'the Seal of the Prophets'. In Islamic terms the Qu'ran is the word of God as revealed to Muhammad by the Angel Gabriel. At the time when Muhammad received the call he was living in Mecca, which was then a small town in the Hijaz, western Arabia, a place of no great significance to the outside world, lying on the very margins of civilisation; though it was connected through trading links to both the Persian and Byzantine empires. The bulk of the population of the peninsula at this time was nomadic, with no overall political order, and the commonly held beliefs were varieties of paganism. Muhammad's mission was to establish, or as he saw it to re-establish, the monotheistic tenets of Judaism and Christianity in a third and final manifestation. There is little doubt that

Muhammad's ambition was from the very first towards a universal acceptance of this creed. It is recorded that at a very early stage of the Islamic mission missives were sent to the rulers of all countries known to the early Muslims declaring that they would only be safe if they converted to Islam, a communication that must have seemed strange at the time, given the lowly status of the Hijaz. But although this burgeoning force met with some initial opposition it steadily gained an ascendancy that led to its first great success, the capture and control of Mecca itself. This and other early triumphs tended, of course, to affirm the righteousness of the Islamic cause. Significantly, Muhammad's first action on the acquisition of Mecca was the destruction of all the idols in its main temple, the *Ka'ba*, which up till then had been a pagan shrine. This was a symbolic act of cleansing which conformed perfectly with the iconoclastic streak that Islam had inherited from both its Judaic and Christian precursors. Interestingly the rise of Islam was almost synchronous with the major iconoclastic crisis in Byzantium, in which all images were taken out of their churches and destroyed.[1] The roots of Islam lie deep in the Semitic tradition of uncompromising monotheism which originated in the harsh climate of wastelands and deserts; the disciplined values of nomadic existence were to remain an important feature of this religion, which went on to become the dominant creed of the vast arid reaches of Asia and Africa, the 'lands without water'.

There is a real sense in which the artistic productions of Islamic culture are as representative of the essential spirit of Islam as its more purely devotional or social aspects. Islamic art, in all its variety, has a consistency and a purity that stems ultimately from the central doctrine of *wahdat al-wujud*, the 'unity of being'. This transcendent unity which is the underlying theme of so much of its art is, it must be admitted, far less apparent on the more temporal level of Islam, or, for that matter in its multifarious theological doctrines. The basic teachings of the Qu'ran itself are relatively simple, but to deal with the exigencies of ever more complex societies Islam was drawn into elaborate systems of law and custom. On the social level the vigour and clarity of the qu'ranic revelations were, inevitably, obscured by these complexities; holy texts themselves may be incontrovertible, but their interpretation is another matter. It was unfortunately the case that Islamic theological doctrines gave rise to as much rancour and disputation as those of any other religion. There is a terrible irony in the Islamic constitutional division of the world into the *Dar al-Islam* (the abode of peace), and the *Dar al-Harb* (the abode of war), since the Islamic sphere has itself been riven by disunity almost from its inception. But the noble aims of Islam, and its perception of a divine unity, are brilliantly reflected in its art. 'It is not surprising,' says Titus Burkhardt, 'that the most outward manifestations of a religion or civilisation like Islam should reflect what is most inward'.[2]

No art is original in any absolute sense, and there are elements in Islamic art that are clearly derived from earlier traditions, in particular those of Byzantium, Persia and central Asia. But once they were encountered by the vigorous, emergent culture of Islam these influences were rapidly assimilated and put to use in entirely original ways. The particular genius of Islamic culture gave its art a characteristic singularity of purpose; with its aim as the expression of the divine ordering and

Islam soon produced its own original and enduring art-forms: an 'arabesque' border from a Qu'ran.

Islamic art has a purity and consistency that stems ultimately from its central doctrine of the unity of being. Interlacing pattern in ceramic mosaic, Spain.

unifying principle it manages, at its best, to be the most abstract and transcendent of all arts, and at the same time to pierce to the very heart of matter. Above all else Islamic art is the art of pure form.

NOTES

1. *Iconoclast* = Image breaker. The iconoclastic tendency in both Islam and Christianity traces back, of course, to the Judaic interpretation of the second commandment, which forbids the worship of graven images. There was a strong feeling in the early Christian Church against religious imagery, since it savoured of idolatry, and this was revived in its periodic puritan reforms, including that of the seventeenth century. The Islamic interdiction on images was practically the same as that of the Jewish; that is to say that it prohibited the portrayal of living creatures, but permitted that of plants and other objects.

2. *The Art of Islam* (see Bibliography).

This border, formal, but not at all severe, is a typical detail of Islamic architectural decoration. From Egypt.

The Greek Connection

Islamic research has to raise the fundamental question of which creative ideas were basic to Islam, how the Muslims dealt with the Greek heritage, how they harmonised it with the other cultural elements that were theirs by innate genius or tradition and, finally and most important, what was the new original thing that evolved out of their creative endeavours. The indisputable fact remained, though, that Islamic civilisation as we know it would simply not have existed without the Greek heritage. *Franz Rosenthal*[1]

The ornate mosaic patterning on the floor of this fifteenth century Cairo mosque shows a direct continuation of the classical tradition of fine marble paving in public places. In fact the institution of the mosque itself is, to a great extent, the successor of the Roman forum *or Greek* agora.

The rise of Islam as a civilisation, as distinct from its purely religious aspect, owed a great deal to the heritage of the older civilisations that were

Geometrical ornament from the Byzantine Middle East. A precursor of the Islamic geometric style.

brought within its compass in its initial phase of expansion. The first of these civilisations to be encountered, and the one that was to exert the greatest influence, was the remnant of the classical world that it found in the Byzantine Middle East. While they were not lacking in religious fervour, the Muslim conquerors were still essentially unlettered nomads and were quite overawed by the superior culture of the Byzantine provinces that had fallen into their grasp. It is now generally acknowledged that

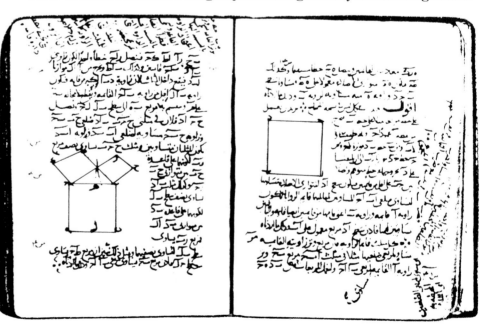

The entire scientific and philosophical literature of the Greeks was translated into Arabic. The theorem of Pythagoras from an early manuscript.

photo: British Museum

the impact of this civilisation, so much in advance of anything in their experience, made almost as great an impression on the minds of the early Muslim invaders as had the qu'ranic revelations themselves.

As Islam consolidated its hold over the thoroughly Hellenised dominions of Syria and Egypt it became increasingly clear that to maintain its position against a culture that was more advanced in almost every respect it must assimilate the civilised attainments of that culture. A growing familiarity with the values of Greek culture and Roman government gradually led the new Arab rulers of these Mediterranean provinces towards a distinct enthusiasm for the acquisition of classical knowledge. There were, moreover, no serious religious obstacles to this ancient learning; indeed, according to tradition, Muhammad had actually urged believers to 'seek knowledge, even unto China'. In fact there was a great deal in the classical tradition that accorded, or at least did not conflict, with Islamic precepts. The desire for a better understanding of this great body of knowledge culminated in the establishment of brilliant schools of translation that very soon brought the entire scientific and philosophical literature of the Greeks into Arabic, a language that proved to be particularly well suited to this purpose.

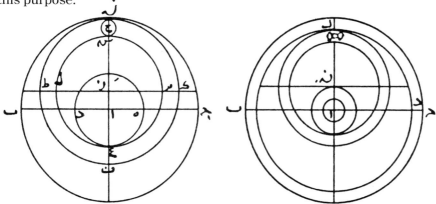

Theories of both planetary motion and atomism were among the many important scientific ideas passed on from the Greeks to Islam. Ptolemy's Planetary Hypotheses, from an Arabic translation.

© British Library

The outcome of this great process of cultural transference was that Islam, like Christianity before it, became thoroughly imbued with Hellenistic influences; the ancient Greek schools of philosophy, medicine and the exact sciences, which were still flourishing in the conquered territories, were taken up by Islam and became the basis of its own science, medicine, philosophy etc. It was not, however, entirely coincidental that Islam should have found so much in this ancient heritage that was in accord with its own spirit and objectives; both its religious precursors, Judaism and Christianity, had themselves felt the powerful leaven of Greek thought; Islam itself had been nurtured in the margins of the Hellenistic sphere of influence without really being aware of the fact. The Greek culture that Muslims encountered in the eighth and ninth centuries of the Christian era had however under-gone considerable transformations in the millennium since the golden age of Greek thought. Little remained of the classical traditions of drama and poetry, for instance, and the emphasis was now almost entirely on matters scientific, but of the knowledge that had survived into this late Hellenistic period virtually all was taken up by Islam. It was this rich heritage that was to give Islam an intellectual direction, and which was to form the basis of its own cultural identity.

The enthusiasm of Islam for Greek culture was such that it was soon seeking it out from much further afield than its own territories. Missions were sent to Byzantium to acquire works that were not available closer to home, and a great deal of material came in from centres of Greek culture further east – those of Persia, Bactria and India. The early Muslim scholars were not content simply to assemble this great range of learning, but were soon making original and important contributions on their own account. In fact the Greek tradition was to have a continuing life of its own in an Islamic setting. The Islamic genius responded particularly well to the mathematical sciences, which were still essentially those of the Latin *quadrivium*, i.e. mathematics itself, geometry, astronomy and music. There was less interest initially in Greek philosophy, since religious constraints were a tempering influence; however those philosophies that affirmed the divine unity, such as those of Plato and Aristotle, presented the least difficulty. In time the works of these philosophers came to be highly respected and at a later stage they were to inspire many worthy Islamic commentaries. The most influential school of philosophy at this time was the Alexandrian neo-Platonism that had, centuries before, made such a profound contribution to early Christian thought. The Gnostic teaching that this school propounded was readily assimilated by Islam, particularly by the followers of its more mystical branch, Sufism. There are many other examples of this cultural transference; Islamic medicine, which was destined to make very impressive advances, was largely based on the legacy of such great classical physicians as Hippocrates and Galen. In a similar way the great tradition of Islamic music relied heavily for its theoretical base on the precepts of Pythagoras and other authorities of ancient Greece.

The geometric abstraction of Islamic decorative art is in perfect sympathy with Platonic notions of beauty. It can also satisfy the Platonic stipulation for geometric proofs, in that its construction involves the use of compass and straight edge only.

The neo-Platonist school, which was to contribute so much to Islamic cultural attitudes, regarded itself as the direct heir of the Pythagorean and Platonic streams of Greek thought. This influence is apparent not only in the range of scientific disciplines that Islam took over from the Greeks, but also in the characteristic forms of Islamic art. The concerns of this art, its abstract nature, emphasis on symmetry and fixation with geometrical forms, can be seen as an expression of Platonic notions of ideal beauty, and are thus one of the more obvious and enduring manifestations of the Islamic adoption of Greek ideas. In fact Islam was particularly receptive to this stream of thought, not least because although it had made extremely important contributions to the rational sciences it had never, in the process, lost its quasi-religious sense of mystery in its contemplation of the universe. For the upholders of this tradition mathematics and geometry were held to possess a transcendent quality, and were felt to hold the keys to the secrets of the universe. In their new Islamic setting the Pythagorean/ Platonic numerical sciences, to quote an eminent Islamic scholar, 'became vehicles for the expression of unity in multiplicity. The Muslim has therefore always been drawn towards mathematics, as may be seen not only in their great activity in the mathematical sciences, but in Islamic art as well.'[2]

The neo-Platonists were fond of tracing their ideas back to Pythagoras who was, by this time, a semi-legendary figure. We tend now to think of Pythagoras as important in two ways, as the founder of mathematical physics and as the master of a school of philosophy which had many of the appearances of a religion. This distinction, however, is not one that would have been recognised by the original, or the later, followers of his school, who felt that they were in possession of a unifying vision of the world, one that embraced the concerns of the body, mind and spirit together. The essence of Pythagorean teaching is contained in the notion of *armonia*, or divine harmony, which was regarded as the ruling principle of the universe.

Pythagoras was reputed to have been a master musician, and his first great discovery concerned the rationalisation of the musical scale; the mathematical relations that were found to be the key to the problems of musical harmony were then applied in other fields – to the relation of figures in plane and solid geometry, and to astronomy (hence the 'harmony of the spheres'). On the basis of their undoubted successes in these fields Pythagoras and his followers built up a complex cosmology which managed to combine genuine scientific enquiry with an attitude of almost religious respect. Some of the beliefs of the Pythagoreans seem strange, and even absurd, today, but their notion of the purifying effect of scientific enquiry is a fact of great historical importance since it marks the starting point of the western tradition of a detached and rational approach to natural phenomena. There is a passage in Plutarch which epitomises their philosophical approach. 'The function of geometry is to draw us away from the world of the senses and of corruption, to the world of the intellect and the eternal. For the contemplation of the eternal is the end of philosophy, as the contemplation of the mysteries is the end of religion.' This description that might be equally well applied to the finer achievements of Islamic art.

'Pythagoras is the presiding genius of mathematical study in Islam. Greek and Indian elements are mingled in it, it is true, but everything is regarded from a neo-Pythagorean point of view.'

T.J. De Boer from *The History of Philosophy in Islam*

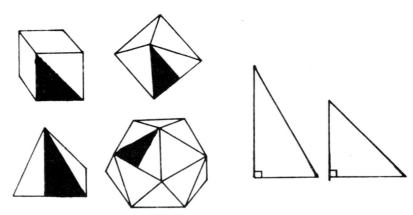

The Pythagoreans believed that the structure of the universe was to be found in mathematics and ascribed mystical properties to both numbers and geometrical figures. Plato was deeply influenced by their ideas and proposed a correspondence between the four elements (which the Greeks believed to constitute all matter) and four 'basic solids', which themselves derived from two 'basic triangles'.

'In view of its origin, carpentry needs a good deal of geometry of all kinds. It requires either a general or specialised knowledge of proportion and measurement, in order to bring forms from potentiality into actuality in the proper manner, and for the knowledge of proportions one must have recourse to the geometrician. Therefore the leading Greek geometricians were all master carpenters. Euclid, the author of the Book of Principles, *on geometry, was a carpenter and was known as such. The same was the case with Appolonius, the author of the book on* Conic Sections, *and Menelaus, and others.'*

Ibn Khuldun, *The Muqaddimah*

The Pythagorean leanings towards the purity of mathematical concepts, and their conviction of the important role of symmetrical relations in the order of things, inclined them to regard the gross material world as a place of corruption and illusion. This perception was later taken up by Plato, many of whose theories have their origin in the ideas and attitudes of the earlier school. Like them, Plato was deeply interested in geometry and felt that its method, which produced clear and definite proofs, could be more generally applied. Since the world of our sense-experience does not display much of the purity of mathematical figures he was led to suppose the existence of a super-sensible realm that was superior to, and quite separate from, the fluid world of ordinary experience, or, as he would have put it, of illusion.

Panel of a door in a fifteenth century Cairo mosque.

This proposition, the existence of a place of timeless perfection, colours the whole range of Plato's thought, including those of his ideas concerning art and the nature of beauty. Plato had a very low regard for the art of representation, referring to it in such disparaging terms as 'a copy of a copy' and 'a third removal from the truth'.[3] In another passage, by contrast, he makes it clear that 'the best part of the mind is that which places reliance on measurement and calculation'. From these and many similar statements, we can adduce that for Plato the truly beautiful could not be conveyed by any work of representation or imagination, since these, at their very best, were only conditionally beautiful; in the final analysis beauty had to convey some of the eternal quality of his separate 'world of ideas', the terms of which he seems to have found only in geometry. We can now see the characteristic modes of Islamic art as a product of the synthesis between the natural iconophobic tendencies of Islam and these Platonic ideas of perfect form.

Islam, as an original cultural force, was able to absorb the various influences that it encountered, and to convert them to an outlook that was uniquely its own. Greek science and medicine became Islamicised and went on to have an important existence of their own within this new setting. In historical terms this event was of the utmost importance since not only were new and significant advances made in many fields, but an intellectual tradition was maintained, one that was to be re-transmitted, centuries later,

Islamic art was deeply influenced by Platonic notions of pure form: Moroccan ceramic mosaic.

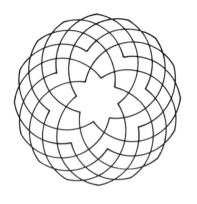

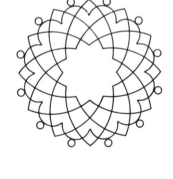

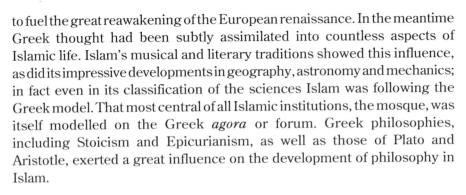

to fuel the great reawakening of the European renaissance. In the meantime Greek thought had been subtly assimilated into countless aspects of Islamic life. Islam's musical and literary traditions showed this influence, as did its impressive developments in geography, astronomy and mechanics; in fact even in its classification of the sciences Islam was following the Greek model. That most central of all Islamic institutions, the mosque, was itself modelled on the Greek *agora* or forum. Greek philosophies, including Stoicism and Epicurianism, as well as those of Plato and Aristotle, exerted a great influence on the development of philosophy in Islam.

In summary then, many of the attributes of Islamic civilisation can be traced back to the original religious inspiration of Islam, fired by the revelations of the Qu'ran, in combination with many of the features of late classical culture. If we seek for an explanation of the basic aims of Islamic art we must refer to the world view that evolved from this synthesis of cultural and religious sentiments, an outlook that was to become a permanent feature of Islamic life and thought. Islam is an all-inclusive religion, so that in a sense all its art has a religious dimension; the neo-Platonic concepts that contributed to its philosophical and aesthetic attitudes further inclined this art towards other-worldly, and also geometric, modes of expression. The underlying objectives of Islamic art are perhaps best epitomised in the writings of one of the more brilliant schools of philosophy to emerge in this formative period, the Ikhwan al-Safa, 'the faithful brethren,'[4] who incorporated neo-Platonic, neo-Pythagorean, Gnostic and Sufic influences into their cosmology. For them this world was simply 'a shadow of another world, more real than it'; they reasserted and developed the Platonic notion that 'the idea of everything in this world actually exists in the other'. In their scheme the phenomenal was simply 'a bridge to the real', a perception that is perhaps the best summary of the Islamic view of the role of art.

NOTES
1. *The Classical Heritage in Islam* (see Bibliography).
2. *Science and Civilisation in Islam*. Seyyed Hossein Nasr.
3. *The Republic*. Plato.
4. *Islamic Cosmological Doctrines*. Seyyed Hossein Nasr.

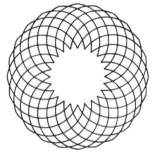

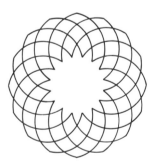

Compass-generated motifs such as these, which evoke notions both of planetary motion and of atomic structure, were very popular with Islamic ornemanistes. Similar designs can also be found in mosaics of the late classical period.

The Inspirational Canon

One would enquire in vain for the masters who brought this system to its flowering or those who later opened up new ways for its development. This art is totally anonymous and it would contradict the artist's noblest charge, which was the liberation of the spirit from the transitoriness of worldly ties.
Ernst Kuhnel, The Arabesque.

The art of Islam, taken in its entirety, has characteristics that make it as distinctive and as impressive as that of any other major artistic tradition. Its modes of expression are as instantly recognisable as those of, say Buddhist or pre-Columbian art, and like these it has certain broad objectives and priorities of taste that stamp its character on an enormous range of artistic productions. The assuredness of Islamic aestheticism stems, of course, from a deeper, cultural confidence, and has to be seen as the expression of a particular and original world view. The term 'Islamic art' conjures up a picture of the exotic architecture of domes and minarets, of elegant arches and richly decorated walls, of fine carpets and brilliantly illuminated Qu'rans. Not all Islamic art is impressive by its sheer magnificence, of course; in fact its styles range from the simple, and even the austere, to the extremes of ornateness; but there are consistent themes. The Islamic predilection for complex patterning and brilliant colour schemes is well known, and there is also, though it is less easily defined, a certain preoccupation with the dissolution of matter. This is an extremely orderly art, but one whose underlying intention is to turn the mind away from the mutability of the mundane world and towards the perceived perfection of the supernal realm.

Islamic art, to a very great extent, is the art of decoration. Within its chosen modes of expression, of which these are typical, there is a remarkable consistency of style: The example on the left is from Fez in Morocco, that on the right from Konya in Turkey.

Islam saw itself, as indeed it proved to be, a profoundly revitalising force; it managed to absorb many of the older cultural streams that it encountered within its vast newly acquired domains, and reconstituted many aspects of these older civilisations in new and original ways. In the eighth and ninth centuries of the Christian era this new cultural entity rapidly developed its own religious and social norms, and at the same time evolved entirely new art forms and aesthetic conventions that accorded with its emerging world view. In this way Islam was able, in a surprisingly short time, to found an artistic and architectural tradition whose achievements rank among the greatest in the world. There is much in this tradition that has a direct and universal appeal, and which has little need of interpretation, but there are some aspects that have been persistently misunderstood, particularly in the Christian west. It is, for instance, well known that Islam has a strong inclination towards pattern and abstract decoration of many kinds, and a corresponding distaste for representational art; these preferences have frequently been attributed by non-Muslims to the influence of religious prohibition. This interpretation does indeed have some basis, but is in itself a gross oversimplification of the determination of Islamic aesthetic attitudes. This is, perhaps, a point worth clearing up.

The fact is that representational art, as such, was never actually banned in Islam, except in a specific and very narrow religious context. There is no foundation in the Qu'ran itself for any prohibition on the representation of living forms; figural paintings were not allowed in mosques, but this was out of respect for the injunction against idolatry. On the other hand it is clear that Islamic culture in general has a distinctly iconophobic streak. As is the case with many of the more basic aspects of Islam this tendency derives from the severe monotheism of the 'Abrahamic', i.e. Judaeo-Christian, tradition. At its most elementary this impulse can be interpreted as a recognition, and a rejection, of the magical power of imitation. There are certain *hadith* (holy traditions) that support this ancient taboo.[1] To copy nature was construed as an act of hubris because the artist was seen to place himself in competition with God. Also, in qu'ranic usage, the term *sawwara*, 'to fashion or form' is synonymous with *bara'a*, 'to create'. The effect of these misgivings, however unspecific, was that neither painting nor sculpture have ever enjoyed a widespread popularity in the Islamic world. It is worth noting, as an aside, that the early Christian Church was equally touchy about this matter. The art of the painter was condemned as unlawful by Tertullian, 'the greatest of the church fathers'[2], and at one point in the history of the Church it was firmly resolved that pictures should not be used in places of worship under any circumstances.[3]

It is clear, however, that the Islamic disapproval of representational art, such as it was, was a purely negative influence and could not in itself account for the richness and diversity of Islamic art. For this we have to turn to the concern to express important internal realities, particularly the principle of *wahdat al-wuhjud*, the transcendent 'unity of being'. This perception of a transcendent unity is associated, in the Islamic view, with the perfection of the creation, and the whole volition of its art can be

Although Islamic art is highly conventionalised it is by no means a rigid system; there are countless variations on its basic themes: Central Asian tilework.

understood as an affirmation, or description, of this perfect order. This is the reason why virtually every aspect of Islamic art is characterised by a strong sense of orderliness, of balance and of symmetry.

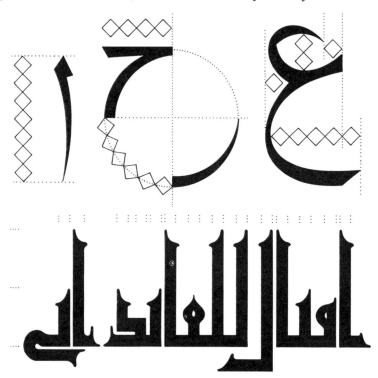

Islamic calligraphy is almost invariably laid out in an even and regular manner.

The emergence of Islam as a cultural force was soon reflected in its adoption of new modes of artistic expression, notably in a strong preference for decorative forms, and for flat rather than moulded surfaces. In fact Islam soon evolved a formulary of decorative art, with certain well-defined components, a scheme that was to endure, in countless variations, for hundreds of years to come. This canon of decorative ornament, which clearly satisfied something quite essential to the Islamic spirit, was very much the aesthetic equivalent of the common round of religious observances that gave shape and meaning to the life of the ordinary

The three components of the 'inspirational canon': calligraphy, widely used in Islamic art as a decorative element; ataurique, *or arabesque, stylised plant motifs; and purely geometric ornament.*

'In Islam icons are replaced by sacred writing, which is, as it were, the visible embodiment of the sacred word.'

Titus Burkhardt

239

believer. This decorative scheme, variations on which can be found in every part of the Islamic world, consists of three distinct categories, which are usually found in combination. The first, and most important, of these is calligraphy. The art of calligraphy was always very highly regarded in the Islamic world since it alone was able to give visible form to the revealed word of the Qu'ran. Many beautiful scripts were developed in the early Islamic period, and most have been widely used as a decorative element in architecture, textiles, ceramics etc. Islamic calligraphy, particularly when it was used as a design element, always had a measured and precise quality; its various styles are almost always presented in carefully constructed arrangements, and its letters are formed in a way that recalls the firmness of the pen rather than the flow of the brush.

Occasionally the exuberant foliage of arabesques is contained within the more rigid symmetries of pattern.

The second element of the Islamic decorative canon is that class of abstract plant designs that have become known in the west as arabesques. Plant forms were traditionally excluded from the ban on living things and could therefore be used with impunity as decorative features even in mosques.[4] As is the case with calligraphy, arabesque decoration is always laid out in an even and regular manner, in a way that gives the appearance that it is responding to its own internal logic, although it may occasionally be assembled into the more rigid symmetries of pure pattern.

The third conventional component of Islamic decoration is that aspect which most completely reflects the Platonic contribution to this art. The whole range of Islamic design is permeated with pattern and symmetry, but it is the yearning for the transcendent purity of form that is responsible for the proliferation of specifically geometric and abstract patterns and borders, which are often of great complexity. It was perfectly consistent with Islamic sentiments that, once established, this formalised approach to art should have been respectfully adhered to for centuries; typical also that these forms were felt to be appropriate for virtually any surface that

Even within the constraints of the highly formalised systems of Islamic geometric ornamentation there is scope for infinite variation.

was itself worthy of decoration, without regard for such mundane considerations as scale or function. For this reason one may find that secular architecture is decorated in the same manner as sacred, that similar patterns are found in the treatment of an illuminated Qu'ran as on a piece of textile or woodwork. This is a universal and an orderly style, one that is entirely appropriate to an Islam which saw itself as the universal religion, and which was untiring in its declaration of the unseen unity and order of creation.

It is quite typical of Islamic ornamentation that it should disregard the constraints of the medium and of scale. Similar kinds of pattern can be found in quite different locations. These examples are taken from the illuminated pages of a Qu'ran, but might as easily be decorating the walls of a mosque.

'At the same time as being rhythm and melody, arabesque implicitly retains its family relationship with the plant world, and its plant-like virtualities are ready to burst forth at any appropriate moment.'

Titus Burkhardt

241

Islamic geometrical ornament, as in this Egyptian mosaic panel, often presents a 'sample' of what is, in effect, an infinitely extendable pattern. There is often a conscious metaphor in such designs, as of providing a 'window' onto an ideal and eternal realm.

Although the different components of this decorative canon are quite distinct there are various ways in which they demonstrate a commonality of intention. To begin with there is in all three a sense of rhythmic continuity and a regularity of disposition; these are effects which combine to create the impression both of stillness and of a contained dynamism, like that of a frozen movement. Also, wherever they are found in an Islamic setting these decorative modes tend to emphasize the plane surface and to shy away from three dimensional or plastic effects; even where there is some depth to a particular design it will appear to refer to an imagined plane. There is more than a vestige here of the Pythagorean recommendation to avoid 'deepening the plane', and we can get an indication from this of the underlying objectives of this art, which is to direct the consciousness towards an inner perfection, and which intentionally avoids the possibility of snaring the mind in an imaginary world. The luxuriant intertwinings of arabesque plant forms (*ataurique*), which always seem determined to fill their allocated space in a regular and even manner, are not based on any actual plant, but rather reflect the inner rhythms of some ideal plant, or even of the growth patterns of vegetation in general. This exultation in the vitality of plant forms was, of course, always that much greater in the typically arid landscapes of most Islamic countries. There is a sense in which the patterns and symmetries that abound in Islamic art refer to all those more obvious manifestation of regularity in nature, to the observable symmetries of plants and crystals, but there is another important aspect of this art that is less immediately apparent; this is its a-centric tendency, its unwillingness to create too definite a focus, hence its attraction to the 'infinite' qualities of pattern. This

There is a deliberate a-centricity in much of Islamic ornament: Window lattice from Moorish Spain.

Decorative panel in Egyptian mosque, using marble and semi-precious stones.

feature has to be seen as an expression of the primary extension of the Islamic doctrine of unity, known as *al wahdah fi'l kathrab*, which translates as 'unity in multiplicity'. This conceives of the unity principle as an even and pervasive force throughout the creation, a concept that is, of course, entirely at variance with those religious attitudes in which the divine manifestation is 'centred', as in Christianity and Buddhism.

In fact the whole range of Islamic decorative art is charged with a potentiality, a numinosity even, that is not found in the ornament of any other culture. The elements of this art are uncentred, just as Islam itself is a universal religion. This is not to say that its role is that of a mere embellishment; on the contrary it has a unique and primary function in Islamic culture. The concern there is not to prettify an otherwise vacant space, but to display that divine ordering principle which, in the Islamic view, is at the very essence of being.

NOTES

1. Those who make these pictures will be punished on the Day of Judgement by being told: Make alive what you have created.' Transmitted by Bukhari. 'A house which contains images will not be entered by the angels.' Transmitted by Muslim.

2. In *De Idolatria*.

3. At the Council of Elvira, 306 AD.

4. In this Islam closely followed the Jewish interpretation of the second commandment which forbade the rendering of animals, but allowed the portrayal of plants and other objects.

The geometric 'roses' or 'stars' in Islamic decorative art are, according to Titus Burkhardt, 'The purest simile for the manifestation of the divine reality, al hakika, *which is the centre throughout, in each creature and in each cosmos, without any being or any thing being able to claim to being its sole reflection, creating an unending reflection of centres in each other':* Moroccan ceramic mosaic.

9

Vitality and fluidity in
Taoist art

Tao – Way of Change

> There was something formless yet complete that existed before Heaven and Earth. *Tao te Ching*

The Tao, a seamless web of unbroken movement and change, symbolised by the liquescent swirlings of a flotation pattern.

China has long been one of the great centres of civilisation and by the time of Christ its distinctive social institutions and artistic styles, with more than a thousand years of development behind them, were already highly evolved. By this time also China was thoroughly unified, both culturally and politically. This huge country had long possessed a single written language, a centralised government and a common system of morality. It was this cultural homogeneity, based on a sound rural economy, that enabled China to become the largest, most intensely populated area in the world, a position that it maintains to this day. In historical continuity it can only be compared to those civilisations with their origins in the

Mediterranean and Middle East, and possibly India, but in its own eyes China was *the* civilisation; the Chinese thought of their country as 'all that is under heaven'.

The traditional Chinese isolationist, or even xenophobic, attitude had its basis in geography. China is cut off from the rest of the Eurasian land mass by almost impenetrable natural barriers of mountains and deserts and for centuries its only experience of foreigners was of aggressive cultural inferiors who left an impression that was not dispelled by its first contacts with European expansionism in the late eighteenth century. Although it was to be a long time before China became even slightly interested in the outside world, the outside world, particularly the European powers, became very interested in China.

Quite apart from the more obvious attractions exerted by possibilities for trade and for religious conversion, China, with its advanced, though by this time somewhat decadent, culture, had all the fascination of the exotic. It had a most impressive artistic heritage, presented a highly developed system of government and morality and its values and expectations were based on a moral code that was entirely different from that of the Christian world. The obvious sophistication and aesthetic qualities of Chinese arts, crafts and textiles made an immediate impact on the westerners who first encountered them, but this was never accompanied by any genuine understanding of the philosophical basis of Chinese culture. The gap between the respective mental outlooks of China and the west was simply too great to be easily bridged. A great part of this difference was that between Christian monotheism and the essentially dualistic concepts that are inextricably woven into every aspect of Chinese thought.

These two lattice designs, one of which is symmetrical and formal, the other deliberately asymmetrical, are typical examples of Chinese domestic art. In a minor way they characterise the polarity of style in Chinese art in general, and this in turn reflects the dualistic attitudes that are a common feature of Chinese thought at all levels.

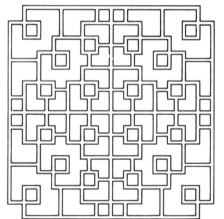 

This was a view of the world that was traditionally manifested on the social level in the 'binary' philosophical systems of Confucianism and Taoism. Confucianism maintained a rational and humane outlook, but was an essentially conservative creed; it was concerned above all else with the upholding of the status quo and, as the 'voice of authority' it had many of the more recognisable traits of conservatism everywhere.[1] Taoist attitudes, with which we are concerned here, never had any real equivalent in the west, at least not as in China where they were developed into a coherent body of thought with an institutionalised, or at least semi-institutionalised, place in society.

For a non-Chinese there are various difficulties in coming to a clear understanding of the Tao and of Taoism. The first of these, of course, lies in problems that arise from having to deal with unfamiliar concepts in translation from an unfamiliar system of thought. The Chinese language, particularly in its classical form, is resonant with subtle allusion and imagery, the flavours of which are apparently quite impossible to convey in western languages or, one might say, in western thought patterns. We encounter these difficulties with any of its texts, even with that most famous of all works in Chinese literature the *Tao te Ching*. This renowned Taoist canon, which has been described as succinct to the point of obscurity, has been translated in dozens of English versions, among which one can find passages that are given widely differing, and even contradictory, interpretations.

The ideograph for Tao. It combines the image of the head with that of the feet, conveying the impression both of a principle and of a progression, or forward movement.

The term 'Tao' itself has such a range of meanings, even in China, that it is generally reckoned to be untranslatable and is usually left alone. The word originally meant a road or a 'way', but like its English equivalent the term was extended to mean a sense of method, and by further extension a course of conduct. All Chinese systems of thought, in fact, have their Tao; for the Confucians the term implied an ideal order, or 'way' for human society, for Buddhists it was the path by which one arrived at a good or bad existence, but for the *Tao Chia*, the Taoists themselves, the Tao was something altogether more mysterious and profound. In their view it was a principle that was the supreme regulator of the universe, and, at the same time, one in which a particular code of conduct was implied. It was the 'absolute', but also the means of attaining a harmony between the visible world and the greater reality.

So the Tao, for its followers, was the way the universe worked; and their religion, or philosophy, insofar as it advocated any course of action at all, recommended a conformity to 'the spirit of the Tao'. But determining the precise nature of the Tao of the Taoists has never been an easy matter, for in attempting to come to grips with its strange beliefs one very soon encounters the aura of paradox and contrariness that is so much a part of its outlook. To try to comprehend the Tao too directly is, in its own terms, to try to approach the unapproachable; it is, in other words, genuine mysticism. According to one of its greatest sages the Tao is 'dark and elusive, difficult to describe'. But if the Tao is difficult to grasp, as it certainly appears to be, what can we say of Taoism? Again the picture is far from clear; there were at different times, and in different parts of China, many schools of thought and political and religious sects that were known as Taoists, and there are real difficulties in distinguishing their various aims and ideas, which seem to range from the most sublime of philosophies to the most vulgar of superstitions.

A magic diagram, typical of popular Taoism. This example, which is vaguely reminiscent of crackle-glaze effects, is intended to 'vitalise the brain'.

It is not at all easy for a Chinese, let alone an outsider, to come to terms with this apparently shapeless tendency which appears to have embraced so many disparate elements in the course of Chinese history. Taoism certainly has within it some powerful philosophical ideas, but it seems also to have carried baggage of many curious practices, including astrology, alchemy and an obsessional quest for immortality. It appears also to have had a strong element of political and social dissidence, and to have advocated extreme individualism, and yet its ideas have long exerted an

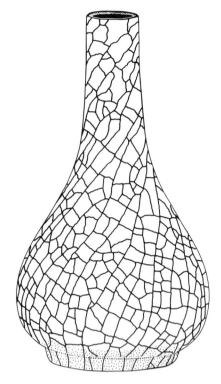

'Vital energy' as a decorative effect. The widespread use of crackle and liquescent glazes and marbling techniques in Chinese ceramics ultimately reflect the Taoist preoccupation with flux and energy.

influence on the whole of Chinese society. The subject of Taoism is permeated with paradox; Taoist texts themselves, often quirky and abstruse, seem to relish these disturbing qualities. Their counsel, too, can often appear confusing and perverse, but there is no denying its influence on the mainstream of Chinese culture, particularly on its art. Perhaps the best approach to the subject, and one that accords with its own spirit and method, that is to say by the use of paradox and negatives, is to describe what it is not. Whatever else it may have been Taoism was never orthodox. In China that role was always filled by the ethical system of Confucianism.

The rival philosophies of Confucianism and Taoism emerged, from a particularly critical period of Chinese history, at around the same time (the fourth century BC). Confucianism went on to become the dominant mode of political life in China; as a philosophy it was distinctly anthropocentric; its concerns were all to do with the orderly administration of society. It believed in the welfare and happiness of the whole of society, and held that this was best achieved by a firm and paternalistic form of government. It is worth noting that this was a somewhat revolutionary idea in its time when the normal conditions of existence were the misery of constantly warring feudal states. The Tao of the Confucians *(Ju Chia)* amounted to a proper way of life for social humanity, and in accordance with its perception of a moral order of the universe it developed a strict code of ethics and social proprieties.[2] This view of the world, needless to say, was all too rigid and stifling for the Taoists, who resented all forms of governmental restraint, and who were intensely sceptical of the Confucian values of permanence and social stability. These twinned systems of thought, with their polarised outlook, were to form the background of Chinese life for centuries, and in a sense they still do. It is important to realise, though rather difficult from a western viewpoint, that these highly distinctive philosophies were never at odds in any absolute sense, but were truly complementary. Confucianism, it is true, was ever the philosophy of the ruling elite, just as popular Taoism never lost its appeal for the masses, but in practice each was a counter to the excesses of the other.

The Taoists were forever ridiculing the pomposity of Confucian proprieties and were something of a thorn in the side of convention. For their part the Confucians regarded the Taoists as selfish individualists whose attitude contributed little to the general good. These differences in outlook ran very deep; the Taoists always felt that the Confucians had completely over-emphasized the importance of the role of man in the world, and that this in itself was a disastrous error. To them the universe was a place of eternal change, and they felt that all distinctions and laws, particularly those related to human conduct, were bound, sooner or later, to become inappropriate and to rigidify into hollow observance. It is certainly true that a great deal of Confucian 'knowledge' was concerned with such artificial matters as social rank and ritual. In order to preserve their own tranquillity of mind the Taoists, in contrast, advocated and practised a withdrawal from what they saw as the artificiality of human society. Their focus was on the order of nature rather than on society; they rebelled against conventional society and withdrew from it. Confucian literature contains many derogatory references to such Taoist hermits, 'those people who choose to live amongst rocks and holes in the ground', remarking that 'even if they were to be offered salaried employment they would not accept it'. They also describe the Taoists as 'railing against government, sneering at those in authority, belittling the importance of rank and emoluments and despising all those who hold official posts'. A lot of this sounds very familiar! One can sense the indignation of outraged authority carrying clearly across the centuries.[3]

The key difference between the teachings of these respective schools however is that between an esoteric and an exoteric approach, what the Taoists referred to as 'this' and 'that'. Confucian doctrines were of a 'this-worldly social-mindedness'[4] and its Tao was the idea of a social structure that accorded with the will of the higher powers of the universe. In contrast, the Tao of the Taoists was so mysterious that it could not be seen or heard, and could scarcely be spoken about! The very first line of the *Tao te Ching*, one of the most important of all Taoist canons, asserts that 'The way that can be told is not the constant Way'. And in another, *Chuang Tzu*, we are assured that 'The Tao cannot be heard, what is heard is not it. The Tao cannot be talked about, what is talked about is not it.' In spite of these injunctions however the Taoists did talk about their perception of the Tao, albeit in rather indirect and poetical terms.[5] From their various texts we can gather that this Tao is an all-pervasive, dynamic and creative force. It is what we might call nature ('the Way of Heaven') and true virtue consists only in following its example. The aspect of nature that impressed itself on the Taoists more than any other was that of the universality of change and transformation; all Taoist writings place great emphasis on this. The Tao is seen as an unending and infinitely creative process, existing by and through itself, but the Taoists were not oppressed by this realisation, nor did they advocate a passive response to it. On the contrary they advocated an identification with the force of the Tao. The Taoist sage was a wholly natural man. 'Those who do not shrink from the natural, nor wallow in the artificial, they are near to perfection.'[6] And again, 'It has been said that the natural abides within, the artificial without. Virtue abides in the natural.'[7]

Taoist philosophers, who were described as 'irresponsible hermits' or 'the madmen of Chhu' by the Confucians, were inclined to withdraw into the forests and mountains to meditate on the order of nature.

Painting by Hsia Kuei; collection of Akaboshi Tetsuma, Tokyo

The Taoists expressed a constant delight in the restless energy of nature. Detail from the scroll painting, 'Seven Junipers'.

Painting by Weng Cheng-Ming; Academy of Arts, Honolulu

There is a fascination with the movement of mists, clouds and water throughout Chinese painting. Illustrated examples from a painting manual.

'The natural' for the Taoists meant the conditions of absolute flux, change and transformation that they saw as the most conspicuous feature of the universe. Their view of nature was not at all that of a solid, material world, but one of a seamless continuum of events, and ultimately all their attitudes stem from this perception. They believed that the human mind, with its endless capacity for self-delusion, was entirely capable of formulating fixed concepts, extracting them, as it were, from the flow of events, but these had something of the nature of phantoms, and were too ephemeral to be relied upon. To them the observer was an integral part of this web of existence, and there was no way that he could extract himself from it. In the Taoist view the picture of the world that we are continually assembling for ourselves, however sophisticated, is nothing like as 'real' as we imagine, and the universe is in any case far too vast for our minds to comprehend. 'Those who study the Tao know that they cannot follow these changes to the ultimate end, nor search out their first beginnings; this is the place at which discussion has to stop.'[8]

With this degree of scepticism it is easy to understand how the Taoists would have been intensely critical of all Confucian attempts to maintain 'the best of all possible societies', but they occasionally referred to their own ideal society. This was one that existed only in the imagined past, in a sort of golden age of pristine nature. Such proposals as they were inclined to make with regard to the administration of society tended to refer to this remote, idyllic state. Such a society could not, of course, be recreated by the imposition of further laws of any kind, but rather by the forbearance of such means altogether. The best form of government, from this viewpoint, was the one that governed least; the state should, in any case, be ruled 'as one should cook small fish', that is to say, delicately. In their hearts the Taoists were antipathetic to all kinds of human society, and were more inclined to withdraw from it altogether, the better to contemplate the Tao in the wilds of nature. 'Those who follow the natural order flow in the current of the Tao. Those who follow men become involved in conventional society and with commonplace worldly knowledge.'

Taoism evolved into a subtle, coherent and impressive philosophy. If at times it is difficult for us to understand it is because its deepest principles, by its own account, cannot be readily grasped by the ordinary senses, or conveyed in words. The Taoists were not content to accept the 'world of appearances' at face value, as were the Confucians, so their cosmological speculations are far more profound and interesting. Their approach combines a deep mysticism with an intuitive and commonsensical understanding of the essentially dynamic nature of the universe. This resulted in a philosophy which is perhaps the most consistent of any of the world's great systems of thought. But although the Taoists were profoundly aware of the forces of change and transformation they were not themselves entirely immune to these forces; even their sublime philosophy was to degenerate. Although there were always adherents of the school of philosophical Taoism which became known as the *Tao Chia*, there also evolved a stream of Taoism which encompassed a whole range of popular cults and beliefs, the *Tao Chiao*. This latter movement, which involved every variety of superstition and magical practice, was eventually formed into a church, with its own pantheon of divinities and, ultimately, a papacy! But this side of Taoism, with its aims of subduing and conquering nature by trickery, and its quest for a literal immortality, is deservedly regarded as degenerate. One can explain this somewhat incongruous development

Mountains and mists were a favourite theme in Taoist-inspired art. The Taoists were conscious that the solid-seeming mountains were no less subject to the 'winds of Tao' than the mists in which they were enveloped. For them the order of nature was an order of constant change.

Painting by Mi Youren; Cleveland Museum of Art

to a certain extent as a 'separating out' of the components of Taoism, which originally combined the beliefs of various Quietist philosophical schools with far more ancient ideas of traditional shamans and magicians.

In China a distinction was always drawn between the philosophical school of Taoism and its more popular religious manifestations. Nevertheless there was a certain commonality between them; both revered the same founding figures and respected the same original texts, and both used the same terminology, though with quite different aims. So the influence of Taoism on Chinese life, though profound, was broad rather than specific. There is, for instance, little art that is avowedly Taoist, in the sense that there is a great body of Buddhist art in China. However its influence in this field is so great as to be virtually beyond determination, and this is true also of literature, poetry and calligraphy, indeed of most fields of artistic expression. In short it can be said that wherever in Chinese culture there is an emphasis on spontaneity and dynamism, or the movement of 'vital energy' in any of its manifestations, these reflect Taoist preoccupations, and are ultimately traceable to its intangible, mysterious and unconforming influence.

NOTES

1. Confucius is the conventional Latinisation of the name of the Chinese sage *Kung fu Tzu*, who lived in the fifth century BC. His ideas were set out in a series of conversations and discourses, the *Lun Yu*, that are generally known as the Analects.

2. There is a sense in which all Chinese philosophies are a study of the ways by which men can best be helped to live together in harmony; according to the Taoist philosopher Kuan Tzu, 'Order in a state is the supreme good: disorder the supreme evil.'

3. In this context it is hard to resist quoting Oscar Wilde on the occasion of the first translation of the Taoist classic *Chuang Tzu*, who he described as a 'very dangerous writer; and a publication of his work in English, two thousand years after his death, is obviously premature, and may cause a great deal of pain to many thoroughly respectable and industrious people.'

4. *Science and Civilisation in China* by Joseph Needham (See Bibliography).

5. This paradox is dealt with by the famous eighth-century poet Po Chu-i. 'Those who speak know nothing, those who know are silent. These words, I am told, were spoken by Lao-tzu. If we are to believe that Lao-tzu was himself one who knew, how comes it that he wrote a book of five thousand words?'

6. *Tao te Ching* (see Bibliography).

7. Ibid.

8. *Chuang Tzu* (see Bibliography).

Convoluted and eroded stones, as in this example from an old print, were much sought after, and can be seen as one of the more common expressions of popular Taoism. These objects were highly prized as garden ornaments and are essentially a metaphor for the principle of change, which can transform even the most obdurate of materials.

Ch'i – **The Vital Spirit**

> From heaven and earth to the ten thousand things, none of
> them can exist without ch'i.   *Pao P'u Tzu*

In ancient China ch'i, *or
'cloud energy', was seen as the
animating force of the entire
universe: Detail of a coffin lid
from the Han period.*

With the principle of *ch'i* we encounter another term that has been familiar
to the Chinese from antiquity, but which presents similar difficulties of
translation, and of conceptualisation, to that of Tao itself. This term, which
in literal translation comes out as 'cloud-energy', has its own ambiguities
and came to mean different things in the course of the development of
Chinese thought. Nevertheless as a general idea it maintained a certain
consistency. As a principle it is somewhat akin to the *mana* of primitive
peoples, and there are similarities also between it and the Brahman
concept of *prana*. According to Chuang Tzu, one of the most highly
venerated sages of Taoism, *ch'i* is the 'breath of the universe'. In a passage
from the text which bears his name *ch'i* is presented as an all-pervasive,
essential force; the following quotation also reveals the familiar Taoist
themes of the relativity of all attributes and the relentless workings of
change and transformation.

The calligraphic mark lung, *meaning dragon, symbolising the principle of
vital energy.*

Ch'i energy, which in the Taoist view gave life to nature and movement to water, was believed to be exhaled by the mountains, which is one of the reasons that Taoist sages, and the Immortals, were attracted to such regions.

Painting by Muqi; Nezu Institute of Fine Arts, Tokyo

The ten thousand things really are one.

What we think of as beautiful are spiritual and unearthly things.

What we think of as ugly are the foul and rotten things.

But the foul and rotten things may turn into spiritual and unearthly things.

And the spiritual and unearthly things may turn into foul and rotten things.

So, it is said, all things in the universe are pervaded by a single *ch'i.*[1]

Ch'i then, is the animating principle of the universe. In a cosmos which, in the Chinese view, was filled with fluid energies, it was the principal agent

The growth of plants was attributed to their inherent ch'i. *Taoist painters were particularly fascinated by the contorted shapes, and the powers of rejuvenation of old trees: Another detail from the 'Seven Junipers' scroll.*

Painting by Wen Cheng-Ming, Academy of Arts, Honolulu

of change. And, of course, there was no 'empty space' in this cosmology, any more than there is in that of modern physics; space is thoroughly imbued with energies of many kinds.

> The region between the sky and the earth how it resembles the bellows in a forge!
>
> Emptied, it is not exhausted,
>
> Moved, it produces more and more.[2]

The modes of transaction of *ch'i* energy were always a matter of particular interest to the Taoists; in fact an earlier school of philosophy, whose ideas contributed to the *Tao Chia* proper, described itself as the School of *Ch'i*. Health and vitality were felt to be closely related to the flow of *ch'i* through the body, it was identified with the life-breath that was received at birth and was the source of all confidence and vigour. The nurturing of this life-spirit became the objective of Taoist yoga, which seems to have involved the use of various breathing techniques. The aim of these practices was to 'accumulate *ch'i*' and there is a passage in the *Tao te Ching* which states: 'You cannot rule men, nor serve heaven, unless you have laid up a store' – a piece of advice that almost certainly refers to the practice of Chinese yoga, the 'store' in question being accumulated *ch'i*. There are many references in Taoist literature that refer to the importance of nurturing *ch'i*: 'Fear, pettiness, meanness – all those qualities that pollute the temple of the mind – are due to a shrinkage of the life-spirit. The valiant, the magnanimous, the strong of will are those whose *ch'i* pervades the whole body down to the very toes and finger-tips'.[3] Just as the state of well-being was dependent on the accumulation of *ch'i*, so also could it be lost by excessive behaviour, the 'perturbations' of anger, greed, desire, etc.

> The sages of old did not injure their souls by petty feelings about private matters.[4]

The circulation of *ch'i* was also important to Chinese medicine, whose traditional methods were inextricably involved with such philosophical concepts. The art of healing in China was, in great part, concerned with the careful management of these circulating energies; negative feelings were ascribed to a depletion of the 'vital spirit' and positive virtues accredited to an abundance of it.

> The vital spirit fills our whole frames, yet man cannot keep track of it. It goes, yet has not departed. It comes, yet is not here. It is muted, makes no sound that can be heard, yet of a sudden we find that it is there in the mind. It is dim and dark, showing no outward form, yet in a great stream it flowed into us at our birth.[5]

An appreciation of the central place that *ch'i* concepts occupy in Chinese thought is fairly important to a deeper understanding of the artistic intentions and objectives of a great deal of Chinese art and calligraphy, and also, because they were so influenced by China, those of Japan. There are many forms of expression in the arts of both of these cultures where the value of spontaneity, movement and vigour are a prominent feature; in these it is the 'vital spirit' that is being exposed to view. The customary method of invoking *ch'i* in the graphic arts is through the use of rapid and vigorous techniques. The *ch'i* energy that is latent

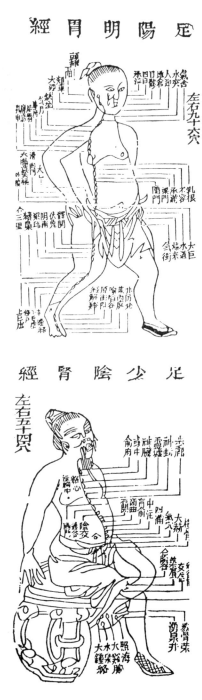

Diagrams of the organ meridian system. In China the art of healing was directed towards a careful management of ch'i *energy, which was believed to flow through the body in quite specific 'energy circuits'.*

Ch'i energy in brushwork. The forceful energy of Taoist-inspired calligraphy.

In paintings of this sort there is an identification between the ch'i energy that is expressed in the blossoming of an ageing plum bough and its dynamic treatment in broad brushwork.

Painting by Tami Bancho; British Museum

within the bough of an ancient plum tree, for instance, is brought out in energetic, *ch'i*-laden brush-strokes. Similarly, calligraphy that is executed in a rapid and confident manner can 'capture' and store the energy of *ch'i*. The art of landscape painting in China, where it has a long and impressive tradition, very often employs similar techniques; the objectives here are not, as in the European tradition, so much concerned with a formal description, or a romantic idealism, as with the distribution and resolution of 'subtle energies'. The landscape, to the Chinese, was permeated by inner currents of flowing *ch'i* energy, in much the same way that these were seen to circulate through the human body. The art of geomancy, of

the detection of these 'dragon arteries' was highly developed in China; landscape painting, and the painting of nature in general, was similarly concerned to evoke the energy currents that were seen to lie within all natural phenomena, both animate and inanimate.

It was through the arts of China that the west first came into contact, unknowingly, with Taoist principles, but the world view from which this art derived is, even yet, little recognised. Taoism, as we have seen, represents an evolved and coherent system of thought which has long exerted a deep influence on Chinese life, and many of its insights are as relevant now as they ever were. It may seem curious to us that an outlook could be so broad as to encompass social as well as aesthetic criteria, but with its non-conformist attitudes Taoism has always had its socio-political aspect. For the Taoists human society also has its 'dragon lines', pathways of subtle energy that take little or no account of the more formal structuring of society. In the Taoist view creative, and sometimes destructive, forces can be introduced into the body politic by way of these currents of inner energy, and, as with the rest of nature, it is these that agitate and disturb it, thereby ensuring its revitalisation; for *ch'i* is the 'breath of the dragon'.

NOTES

1. *Chuang Tzu*, translated by H.A. Giles (see Bibliography).
2. Ibid.
3. *Kuan Tzu*, quoted by Arthur Waley (see Bibliography).
4. *Lu Shih Ch'un Ch'iu,* quoted in Joseph Needham's *Science & Civilisation in China* (see Bibliography).
5. *Kuan Tzu.*

The flow of ch'i represented in a marbling design. A Celadon dish.

259

Chinese artists were fascinated by the action of water in all its settings, from mountain torrents and waterfalls to the broad sweeps of large rivers.

Fluidity and 'The Yielding'

The highest good is like that of water. *Tao te Ching VIII*

All people drink water, but I alone take it as my model. *Kuan Tzu*

The Chinese style, if one may be forgiven for dealing in such generalisations, stems ultimately from the unique continuity of its civilisation. The confidence and energy of this culture, with its prodigious artistic achievements, give it a primacy over all other countries of the Far East, for whom China was a constant source of cultural inspiration. Chinese art, like the art of all other major traditions, evolved its own aesthetic values and priorities of taste, and these have endowed it with its unmistakable characteristics. It is difficult to specify the precise qualities that go to make up this, or any other, style, but if there is one trait that is evident throughout Chinese art it is an inclination towards a certain *fluidity* of expression. This tendency, which is manifested in a whole variety of ways, confers on it a certain assured and undemonstrative quality, which is itself a reflection of deeper cultural attitudes.

One facet of the Chinese temperament that is so reflected is the quality of 'yieldingness', or *jeng*. Yieldingness, according to a well-known Chinese proverb, 'will overcome anything inferior to itself', a precept to which the whole course of Chinese history bears testimony. For it is a fact that

'Sketches of curious stones'. Such objects provided one of the most common images of the Tao. 'Nothing under heaven is softer or more yielding than water,' says the Tao te Ching, *'but when it attacks things hard and resistant there is not one of them that can prevail.'*

despite successive invasions and occupations, by alien and culturally inferior forces, China has always managed to absorb its conquerors and to re-establish the pattern of its civilisation.

The 'power of submission' is a constant theme of the *Tao te Ching,* whose philosophy has itself exerted the most profound influence on Chinese thought as a whole. This work constantly recommends 'the yielding' as a course of action, and it makes extensive use of the imagery of water and fluidity to convey the essence of its ideas. The following quotations are typical:

> What is of all things most yielding
> Can overcome that which is most hard.
> Being substanceless it can enter in even where there is no crevice.
> That is how I know the value of action which is actionless.

> Nothing under heaven is softer or more yielding than water
> But when it attacks things hard and resistant
> There is not one of them that can prevail.[1]

There are many other passages in a similar vein. The sort of ideas that are implicit in these metaphors were most fully worked out in the Taoist stream of Chinese thought, although there is little doubt that they became incorporated into the general approach to life in China, and that they came to play an important role in its art.

The characteristic fluidity of 'single-stroke' calligraphy.

In fact this 'fluid' modality finds an expression in innumerable ways; it is as apparent in the decorative motifs and traditions of calligraphy in China as it is in the gentle shapes and liquescent glazes of its ceramics. It was this tone also that became the dominant stylistic element in painting, particularly in its treatment of nature. Here one finds a constant fascination with the ever-changing, transitory aspects of natural phenomena, which are expressed in, among other things, a preoccupation with the restless activity of mists, clouds and rivers. Even vegetation and the substantial masses are portrayed as 'fluid' and yielding. In fact landscape painting in China was particularly and directly influenced by Taoist attitudes and ideas. As a creative activity it was perfectly consonant with the Taoist tendency to reject the artificialities of human society in favour of the Tao of nature. Nature was admired, not only for its physical beauty, but also for certain immaterial qualities; plants, streams and rocks were felt to be endowed with specific spiritual 'essences' or 'flavours', and in mountainous regions *ch'i* energy was exhaled in the form of clouds. In responding to these qualities and rendering them in the form of paintings or drawings the artist himself was yielding to the mysterious power of the Tao and sharing in the creative force of nature. The Taoists were also concerned with the 'improvement of vision', with the ultimate aim of seeing or experiencing the Tao directly. It was with this in mind that the painter Tao Ch'i declared that 'the substance of hills and streams embodies the inner laws of the universe'.

Painting in China, particularly of nature in the wild, was always regarded as the highest and most noble of the arts. Its greatest practitioners were usually amateurs, often they were scholars or high officials, and quite

Painting of a waterfall that clearly illustrates the Taoist perception of natural forces. This is not merely the passage of water as such, it is a stream of pure energy, or ch'i. *'The supreme Tao, how it floods in every direction! This way and that, there is no place where it does not go.*

Painting by Wang Wei;
Collection of Chishaku-in, Kyoto

262

frequently they remained anonymous. This again was in keeping with the spirit of the *Tao te Ching* which indicated that in order to develop his powers the true sage must 'put himself in the background' and 'remain outside'. Painting, moreover, was felt to be the most receptive medium for the expression of the essential, indivisible Tao, far superior to either speech or to the written word which, by their very nature could not 'express the absolute'. (*Chuang Tzu*)

Deeply eroded mountain ranges with swirling mists. The Taoists greatly admired such scenery because it so clearly exposed the workings of the principle of change.

Chinese painters were fascinated by the liveliness of nature; their paintings present few difficulties for the uninitiated since they are direct and representational, but the vision of nature from which their work drew its inspiration is an entirely different one from that which gave rise to European traditions of painting. Various schools of landscape painting arose in China, just as they did in the west, and they developed a succession of formal approaches to the subject, but the concern of these painters was not at all with the 'orderly distribution of elements' in the European sense. For the Chinese painter nature was above all else diverse, and this diversity was seen to derive from the forceful interaction of mysterious internal energies. As the painter Tao-Ch'i put it, 'Heaven cannot bind up the hills and streams to make them conform to one shape.'

Since natural scenery was so imbued with these energies, and so full of movement, it was natural that Chinese painters should have evolved techniques that were appropriate to their vision. Tao-Ch'i also declared that his aim in painting was 'to seek for life in the movement of the brush-tip'. It was this outlook, which concentrated on the vitality and fluidity of nature, that lay beneath the constant preoccupation of Chinese artists with water in one form or another; indeed landscape was felt to be hardly complete without its inclusion. This is shown in the very term for landscape painting in China, *shan shui,* which translates as 'mountain and water pictures'.

Chinese painters were intrigued by the action of water in every guise, in the mists that swirled around the peaks of mountains, in the torrents and waterfalls that poured down their sides, in the quiet power of the broader stretches of a river and in the ever-changing moods of the ocean. The

'Mountain torrent amongst rocks and pines'. A favourite theme of Chinese artists.

Painting by Siao Tchao; Museum of Boston

importance of the fluid element in this art is reflected in the degree of technical attention that it receives; the various modes of action of water, mists etc., are in general far more closely observed and better represented in Chinese painting than in other traditions. Many of the great Chinese painters wrote perceptive and scholarly treatises on art, and in these one can find the clearest expression of this fascination with the modes of fluidity; I include just two examples here, which are, it will be noted, widely separated in time.

> Water is a living thing. Its form should be tranquil and deep, it should be expansive, should be circling around, should have body; it should froth and splash and shoot; it should be alive with fresh springs, should have volume to reach a great distance; it should leap over waterfalls from the skies, should crash and hit the land below; it should be soft on a misty day

and resplendent on a sunny morning. These are the live movements of water. *Kuo Hsi (c. 1020-1090)*

The gathering and distribution of water and clouds express the continuity of hills and streams; the gestures of crouching and leaping up and turning of directions express their movements. Heaven binds the hills and streams by means of winds and clouds; the earth awakens them to movement by means of water and rocks. *Tao Ch'i (c. 1641-1717)*

To sum up then, there are strong associations in Chinese thought between the notions of fluidity and vitality, and between fluidity and the action of yielding. These matters, in fact, are regarded as being close to the essential reality of existence; even man, 'when he is born is soft and weak, but becomes hard and stiff in death'.[2] The preoccupation with fluid motifs in Chinese art conforms to the Taoist-inspired view of the universe as a place of absolute flux, movement and vitality, a view that has deeply influenced Chinese thought in general and which goes a long way to explain its common philosophy of adaptation to circumstance; it is rather difficult for us in the west to appreciate the extent to which this quality is regarded in China as a positive virtue.

For Taoists the ideal in conduct was that of accommodation; and for them it was entirely appropriate that this ideal should be expressed in a parable involving the fluid medium; I refer to one of the better-known stories of the *Chuang Tzu* anthology, 'Confucius at the Cataract'. In this the Master, who is a slightly ridiculous figure in Taoist literature, is alarmed to see an old man plunging into a raging torrent. He at once sends a disciple along the bank to try to rescue the old fellow but the sprightly ancient soon emerges from the water a little way off, completely unscathed. Intrigued by this Confucius closely questions the old man who is, needless to say, a Taoist sage, and hears how he has learned to accommodate himself to the swirling vortices of the rapids, and how, by this method, he has learned to deal with them on their own terms. 'Plunging in with the whirl, I come out with the swirl. I accommodate myself to the water, not the water to me.' The message is clear: rigidity of thought and behaviour are utterly inappropriate in a world that is so thoroughly permeated with the forces of change. In order to harmonise with the universal moving principle of the Tao, and to achieve fulfilment, man himself must be fluid and yielding in his conduct. In this, of course, Taoism is the very converse of every creed that recommends an adherence to rules of behaviour, social codes, divine or secular laws, or indeed artificial limitations of any kind.

In flow patterns such as this the Taoists found a model for their theories concerning the transmission of vital energies, including sexual energy.

NOTES

1. *Tao te Ching.* From the Waley translation, *The Way and its Power,* Chapters 43 and 78 respectively (see Bibliography).
2. Ibid. Chapter 76.

Part of a wave-like, continuous decoration from an early frieze.

In China landscape paintings are known as 'mountain and water pictures', and are frequently inspired by Taoist attitudes toward nature.

Painting by Kung Hsien

The Beauties of This Universe

The Chinese way of looking at life was not primarily through religion, or philosophy, or science, but through art.
George Rowley, Principles of Chinese Painting.

When, in the unsettled conditions of European art in the later part of the nineteenth century, various more adventurous painters sought inspiration outside the western tradition, it was the art of Japan that first attracted their attention. It is easy enough now for us to see those qualities in Japanese art that must have appealed to the Impressionists and their friends, but the adoption of certain of its modes at that time was a bold and imaginative step. There were good reasons why Japanese art rather than any other should have made such an impression at that particular time. First, of course, it was available: Japan had fairly recently been opened up to the outside world and there was a certain vogue for its artistic products. Also there was the fact that this art, though it clearly had an evolved and distinctive style of its own, was one that had itself been exposed to western influences. In other words this was an exotic art, but one that was in every sense accessible. In particular the unfamiliar composition and confident sense of colour of Japanese prints seemed new and exciting. Its stylistic conventions, though quite different from those of European art, raised no serious obstacles to aesthetic appreciation; in fact in many ways this art managed to project a curiously 'modern' outlook. Many important painters responded to the influence of Japanese art at this period and incorporated various aspects of it into their own work; there are paintings by Van Gogh, for instance, that are quite literal transcriptions of Hiroshige prints.

As it turned out however this influence was fairly short-lived, or at least its contribution was rapidly assimilated. In their relentless search for a new aesthetic identity, European painters soon went on to explore the arts of other, even more exotic, cultures – the tribal arts of Africa, the art of ancient Egypt etc – until each and every artistic tradition was, so to speak, brought within their trawl. This whole process came about, of course, as a result of the disturbance to the European artistic tradition caused by the introduction of the camera. As I have noted, it was not so much the invention of photography that provoked this disruption, as its popular acceptance and usage. The advent of the 'snapshot' camera had the effect of devaluing and vulgarising the skills of representation, towards which the main thrust of European art had previously been directed. There were, of course, wider perceptual implications to this innovation; in fact the camera was about to alter our whole way of looking at the world. If an eighteenth or nineteenth century Japanese print, or for that matter a tenth century Chinese painting, appears more modern to our eyes than their contemporary European equivalents this is at least partly because they, like the snapshot, were concerned with recording a fleeting moment of time.

The point of this digression is to highlight that process, which might be described as a cultural convergence, that occurred at the beginning of the modern period. There were fundamental differences of approach between Far Eastern and western methods of painting that sprang from differences of cultural perception. It was precisely because of the shaken confidence in the European tradition of fine art that the Impressionists were so receptive to Japanese and other artistic traditions. What is interesting here

No subject in nature was too humble for the Tao-inspired artist. The Great Tao was to be found in weeds, ants and even dung!

267

is that these changes in aesthetic attitudes were paralleled in other fields of cultural activity, notably in science. At the same time that European art was rejecting its old formal values and introducing new and more vital concepts, physics was shedding its deterministic views of the world in favour of revolutionary new ideas in which energy, rather than matter, occupied centre stage.

Painting by Chu Ta; collection of Kanichi Sumitomo, Oiso, Japan

In Taoism nature, and not man, is the measure of all things.

Chinese and Japanese art had long been concerned with the portrayal of the energy principle. The tenth-century painter Ching Hao, for instance, was expressing a conventional view of nature for his time when he declared that 'the different formations of mountains and streams are formulated by different combinations of the life-force (*ch'i*) and the formal force (*shih*)'. Fortunately we are greatly assisted in any attempt to come to an understanding of the aims of this art by the writings of the artists themselves, of which many still survive. In their various essays and treatises on art Chinese artists are very forthcoming about the motives underlying their particular concerns of style and technique, and they often express their attitudes in an extremely clear and coherent manner. It is perhaps not surprising that they should have been as fluent in their writing as in their painting; in China the painting of natural subjects, as distinct from official portraiture, had long been the province of gifted amateurs who tended to belong to a highly cultivated élite. For these artist-scholars painting and poetry served equally to reflect the ideals of a thoroughly evolved aesthetic philosophy; 'a poem is a formless painting, a painting a formless poem'.

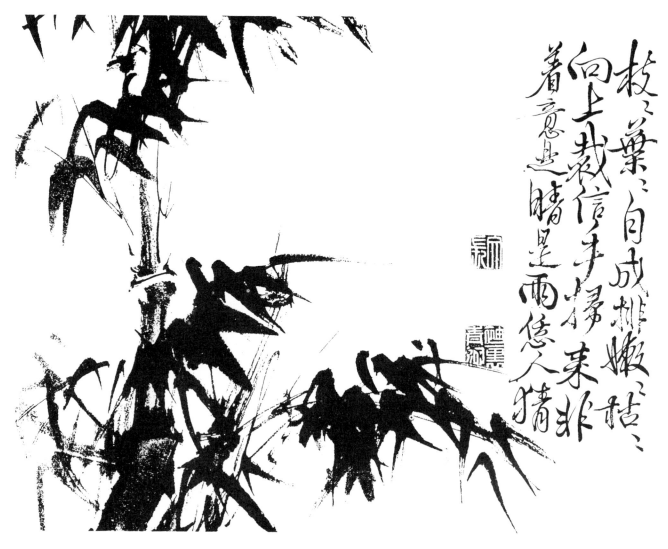

枝之葉之自成排嫩枯

向上裁信手揚来非

着意遮睛是雨恁人猜

Bamboo painting, which is always particularly expressive in Chinese art, occupied a category of its own and was closely related to the art of calligraphy.

Painting by Hsu Wei; Freer Gallery of Art, Washington DC

It was generally felt in these circles that a high degree of intellectual awareness, in addition to an artistic sensibility, was a virtual prerequisite for the real task of art, which was characterised as the need to penetrate to the inner realities, and to avoid the 'distraction' of external appearances. This is a theme that occurs again and again in the musings of Chinese landscapists; one can find some of the flavour of their artistic intentions in this extract from Ching Hao's 'Conversation on Method' where he recalls the time when he was first drawn to recapture the beauties of nature in painting.

> One day I went up to the Chengcheng Mountain to take a look. After a while I found myself under the shadow of some great rock formation opening up like a gate. The path was covered with moss and dripping dew and there was a variety of strange-looking rocks steeped in a vapoury atmosphere. I went straight ahead and found that there was a great growth of giant pines, some of whose trunks were of considerable girth. The bark was covered with green moss, and the scaly trunks rose straight up to a great height, reaching to the skies. Where a group of them formed a grove the air was pleasant with a sense of life and growth. Others stood aloof happily by themselves. Sometimes the twisting roots were exposed, and sometimes a

'The substance of hills and streams embodies the inner law of the universe.'

Tao Ch'i

'The different formations of mountains and streams are formulated by the combinations of life-force (ch'i)*, and formal force* (shih)*,' according to the painter* Ching Hao

Painting by Kuo-Hsi; Chinese collection

'All matter is formed of accumulated force. Thus even the undulations of hilltops and every rock and tree are possessed by a life-force inherent in them. They are multifarious, yet orderly, perhaps they exist in small numbers, but they are never dried and dead. Each has its own shape, and together they have a related unity. All things differ in shape and manner, yet all are governed by this life-force and possess the beauty of life'.

From *The Art of Painting* by Shen Tsung-ch'ien

tree overhung a torrent. They decked the banks and followed the river, breaking into cliff fissures and spreading out the green moss. I was pleasantly surprised and took my time enjoying it all. Next day I went again taking my painting brush with me. I must have done several thousand copies before I caught the spirit.

The following spring I met an old man at Stone Drum rocks. He asked me what I was doing and I told him. He asked me if I knew the techniques of painting and on realising that I did not, offered to teach me. He explained to me that there are six essentials in painting: first, spirit (*ch'i*), second, mood and atmosphere, third, thought, fourth, the scene itself, fifth the brush-work, and sixth the ink-work. I said 'Surely to paint is to render external appearances?' He replied 'I am sorry, you are mistaken. There is an external appearance which may not be mistaken for the true reality. Unless this is understood one will draw a mere likeness, but not capture the real essence. 'What do you mean likeness and reality?' 'A likeness,' replied the old man, 'is what you get when you portray a thing's form and miss the spirit; when the spirit is left out the form is dead.'[1]

The relegation of the criterion of 'external appearances' to fourth place is characteristically Taoist, as is the story of a chance meeting with a mysterious wise old man. Taoist-inspired painting and poetry was largely concerned with the interpretation of the ever-changing moods of nature, but its approach was invariably understated and indirect, using the power of suggestion and metaphor. Taoist painters were very fond of the dramatic yet restrained device of asymmetrical composition and the use of empty space; in this way their art, like the teachings of Taoist sages, gradually attunes the onlooker through particular inner rhythms of nature to the essence of the great Tao itself.

One of the most compelling and influential accounts of the purpose and objectives of landscape painting in China is to be found in a short, and rather enigmatic, essay by the artist Tsung Ping (375-443). In this he relates that when old age came upon him and he grew too feeble to climb mountains he re-experienced his former travels by painting the scenery of his memories on the walls of his rooms, and gazing at these pictures.

photo: British Museum (artist unknown)

A characteristic expression of the vigour and spontaneity of nature. Detail of a pine tree from an ink-painted handscroll.

A vertical height of three inches can represent a thousand fathoms, while a horizontal stretch of several feet can stand for the distance of several hundred miles. Thus it is that the onlooker is not hampered by its size, but is only concerned as to whether the shapes and forms are skilfully drawn. In this

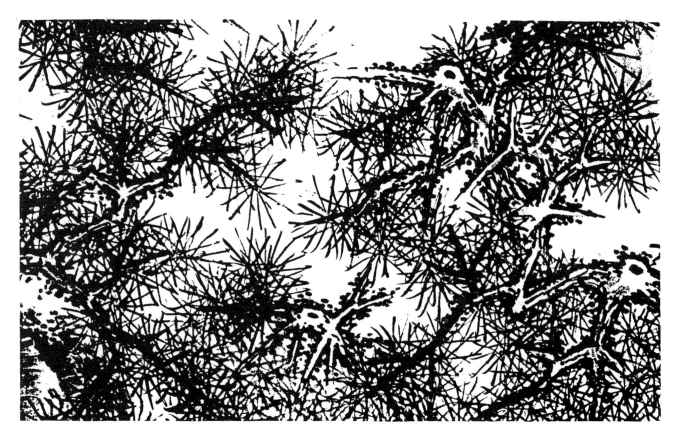

way, all fhe delicacies of the Sung and Hua mountains, and the beauties of this universe, can be recaptured in a painting. For that which meets the eye and calls forth response from the heart as the true form of things will, if the representation is skilful, meet the eye and call forth response from the heart of the onlookers. When this spiritual contact is established the true forms are realised and the spirit is recaptured. Is this not as good as seeing the mountains themselves? Moreover the spirit has no form of its own, but takes form in things. The inner law of things can be traced through light and darkness; if these things are skilfully represented they are truth itself.

Therefore in my leisured life, having put my mind in order, I wipe a wine cup or strum the lute and sit alone looking at a painting. Without leaving the crowded human habitations I roam and wander in the solitary wilds of nature. There the mountain peaks soar aloft, and the clouds and forest spread deep and far away. The sages and wise men are reflected from ages long ago, and all the interesting aspects of this life are absorbed into the mind. What more do I want? If I am enjoying myself and if I do that, what more can I ask?[2]

Tsung Ping was, of course a Taoist and, in the great tradition, spurned the allurements of office and wealth in favour of a life of contemplation of the Tao of nature. The essay from which this extract is drawn became important in itself, since it is generally taken to mark the ascendancy of the genre of landscape painting in China, a form that went on to become the most highly regarded mode of artistic expression.

'Steering through the eddies'. A Taoist metaphor for sage conduct.

'Great Tao is like a boat that drifts; it can go this way, it can go that.'

NOTES

1. *The Chinese theory of Art*. Lin Yutang (see Bibliography).
2. Ibid.

Afterword

•

Glossary

•

Select Bibliography

•

Index

•

Afterword

"Chaos provides a mechanism that allows for free will within a world governed by deterministic laws." James P. Crutchfield

I began this book by remarking on the imminent appearance on the scientific scene of an ultimate Theory of Everything, a TOE. I have also referred to the contemporaneous discoveries that have led science to detach itself from the idea that everything can necessarily be understood by taking it to pieces and examining the parts. The very fact that the term Theory of Everything is used in a jokey way is itself the best indication of the great changes of attitude within science. In a way there is nothing dramatic about these developments. In its recent history, science has consistently moved away from its original objective — the uncovering of absolute truths about the nature of the physical world — towards empirical concepts which are more inclined to offer hypothetical models of what the world might be like. The TOE, with its description of the basic constituents of the universe, will represent the culminating achievement of this approach. There is a sense however that these revelations, when they appear, will be no more than what we have come to expect of science. Rather more surprising perhaps are other important findings that have led scientists to an admission of an unsuspected indeterminacy at various levels of nature, to the realisation that it demonstrates an inherent and fundamental unpredictability, and that as a result it cannot be completely understood simply by analysing it from the bottom up, as it were.

Science, and its accompanying technology, have come to exert a profound influence on practically all cultural attitudes. Because of this, changes in the basic explanations of phenomena that emanate from within the scientific community are bound to continue to lead to changes in the world-views of the rest of us. The particular direction in which science appears to be heading, and the perceptual changes that this has necessitated, are matters that are so relevant to the general theme of this book that it is perhaps worth recapitulating the essentials. The traditional deterministic, reductionist views of science, the science of Descartes and Newton, were sustained by an underlying belief that ultimately everything could be perfectly and objectively described in mechanistic terms: moreover that, knowing these terms, one could then make accurate predictions. These methods were, and still are, extremely successful: more complex phenomena, such as the weather or human consciousness, are not anything like so amenable to this approach. Why is this? The atmosphere and the human brain, after all, only consist of agglomerations of particles and are subject to the same laws of physics as the planets in their regular orbits. How come it is so much more difficult to predict the behaviour of the former than that of the latter?

Clearly this question has a distinct bearing of one of the main topics of this book — the relative degree of order and disorder in the world. Perhaps the best head-on approach to the whole matter is by way of the question of Free Will. This thorny problem, which concerns the extent to which we are each the captain of our own destiny, has long been established as one of the most intractable of all metaphysical questions.

One of the more obvious shortcomings of a strictly deterministic interpretation of nature, whether it is religious or scientific in character, has always been that it reduces human behaviour to that of mere automata, which is clearly nonsense. Our consciousness is an active construction, and as a complex dynamic whole it will always represent far more than the sum of the influences that have contributed to it, considerable though these may be. Human consciousness, and therefore behaviour, is not only complex but is inherently unpredictable, and it is clear that many other complex systems, particularly those involving living organisms, share this characteristic. Until fairly recently this rather obvious fact has fitted awkwardly with the deterministic laws of physics. However new insights into non-linear dynamics have completely transformed this perception.

Indeterminacy, in the scientific sense, was first expressed through Heisenberg's Uncertainty Principle, a statistical law that deals with indeterminacy at the level of particle physics. When this principle became more widely known there was some speculation as to whether it might have any bearing on the long-standing problem of free will: in fact it does not. This is because the sort of statistical uncertainties that it describes are simply not apparent at higher levels. To put it crudely, if we were to notice a bus bearing down on us we would be well advised to jump out of the way rather than rely on Heisenberg's law. However, more recently there has appeared a whole new order of Indeterminacy, the now famous Chaos theories, whose concepts really do have a bearing on high level phenomena, and in particular on such complex systems as ourselves. We can summarise the general drift of these theories by saying that they show how a system can demonstrate complicated behaviour arising entirely as a consequence of simple, non-linear interactions of only a limited range of components. To use the analogy of the approaching bus again, we can imagine being saved from a disastrous deterministic event by the action of the driver applying his brakes. This is to say that a simple feedback operation might come into play, and feedback is a function that is highly characteristic of Chaos effects.

Quite apart from their intrinsic scientific value, the emergence of these new and wide-ranging indeterminacy theories is important for the reason that in offering a scientific explanation for much of the subtlety and richness of natural phenomena they bring science more into line with our own day-to-day experience of the world. Moreover they go a long way to explaining that most interesting question of all, namely the origin and nature of Purpose. This is to say that, by virtue of these insights, there is now a fair degree of understanding of just how the confused particulate madhouse that characterises existence at the fundamental level of matter connects to 'higher', self-determining and self-organising systems. These fascinating recent theories, then, offer a tantalising glimpse of new causative principles, but they also, or so it seems to me, make fresh conceptual demands. It is very likely that, following the lead of science, there will be a gradual relinquishing of our culturally-reinforced deterministic and reductionistic habits of thought; and probable that essentially linear concepts will, in time, be replaced by a more general notion of complementarity. Chaos and Complexity theories would seem to indicate that no phenomena can be ordered in any absolute sense, yet neither is there any condition that can be properly described as being completely disordered. Just as an apparent, or phenomenal, dualism was found to be implicated in quantum indeterminacy, so complementarity, in a broader sense, would seem to be intrinsic to these new concepts.

The new vision of the world that has been created for us by science, in which the ultimate constituents are little more than irreversible events occurring *in vacuo*, has robbed us of the notion of the universe as a piece of intricate celestial machinery and replaced this with the percept of a dynamic, self-creating, self-influencing cosmos. This view is of a world that is integrated in an absolute sense, but which is in a continuous state of 'coming into being'. Ultimately this self-creating unity is beyond description, yet as self-conscious entities ourselves we have to hold it to account, to delineate it, and to register our particular place in the seamless web of existence. One of the most obvious responses, and one that applies to the world of Man as well as to the world of Nature, is that of a fundamental yet complementary dualism. In early Chinese cosmogonies it was the Yellow Ancestor who initiated the world of being by separating Earth from Heaven, and thus disturbing the Primal Unity. With today's analysis of the material world as consisting of little more than 'organised energy', one might feel that this sort of basic explanation is as good as any for the mysterious and curiously complicated world in which we live.

D.W., Plas Tylwch, 1991.

Glossary: One, Two, Many . . .

The term 'monism', and to an even greater extent the terms 'dualism' and 'duality', are subject to a whole range of interpretations. The distinctions between these terms are important, indeed fundamental, to virtually every kind of religious or philosophical outlook. All advanced cultural attitudes have at their foundation some explanation or other concerning the forces or principles that are believed to have brought the world into being and which continue to sustain it. But the metaphysical question of whether one, or more than one, feature of the universe can be held to account for its complexity (and our knowledge of it), must still be considered an open one. This is to say that metaphysics has not 'advanced' in the sense that science and most other branches of knowledge have. Indeed the distinctions between dualistic and monistic (or monotheistic) doctrines are often rather more subtle than might first appear; many dualisms, for instance, are compatible with an interpretation of monism that sees the opposition between the one and the many as absolute. By contrast most monotheisms have dualistic aspects. The whole subject is beset by paradox. In fact most religions are dualistic to the extent that they affirm a separation between the sacred and the profane, and of course in most cases this distinction is emphasised by the separateness of the institutions of religious and secular life. It is a curious fact also that most major religious movements are divided into two main camps, e.g. the Hinayana and Mahayana vehicles of Buddhism, the Shaivite and Vishnavite tendencies in Hinduism, Sunnism and Shi'ism in Islam, and the East/West schism of Christianity which further divides into Catholicism and Protestantism. On a personal level we constantly encounter the dualism that holds between our awareness of ourselves as individuals and the 'outside' reality; this is to say that the process of acquiring sense data is itself bound to intervene to an unknowable extent between our minds and the material world. In the final analysis we have to admit that our words and thoughts may only really be relevant to the pluralism of the phenomenal worlds, and that they are less than adequate to deal with the greater reality beyond. But it is in the nature of human beings to attempt this; the glossary below, which lists various religious, philosophical and scientific interpretations of monism, dualism and related terms, deals with some of the more notable attempts to resolve this question.

Brahmanism

The non-dualism of classic Brahmanism culminates in the teachings of the Vedanta. Here we find the doctrine that matter is materialised energy which, in turn, is the phenomenal manifestation of an incorporeal, eternal essence that is the innermost self (*atman*) of all things. The *atman* both evolves the phenomenal realm of matter and simultaneously enters into it in the form of life-monads, or individual selves. In this view all things are but reflexes of *atman-brahman* in its eternal self which, in essence, is beyond all definition, name or form.

Buddhism

In Buddhist terms the involuntary state of mind common to all creatures causes them to mistake the true essence of reality, and this is the cause of all suffering. Buddhists view the apparent stability of empirical objects as merely the creation of our imagination, the ultimate reality consisting of separate, instantaneous bits of existence. This theory, of universal momentariness, implies that every duration of time consists of point-instants following one another; every extension in space of their arising in contiguity and simultaneously; every motion of their arising in contiguity and in sucession. Space, time and motion are imagined entities that have no real existence beyond that created by our imaginations from these point-instants; in other words phenomenality is regarded as without substance.

Cathars

A medieval Christian dualist heresy deriving ultimately from Gnosticism and Manichaeism (qq.v.); like them the Cathars held that matter was intrinsically evil, and that the highest

God was not the creator of this world. The movement, which was centred in southern France and Italy, was finally extirpated by an internal crusade and inquisition.

Chinese Dualism

Both of the great indigenous religious systems of China (Confucianism and Taoism) subscribe to the notion of a manifest phenomenal dualism that is derived from a primordial unity, a concept that has been described as a 'dualism that is really a monism'. Confucians and Taoists see the world, of people and nature respectively, as arising from a harmonious and organic interplay of the complementary principles of Yin-Yang (q.v.), and in fact this idea permeates Chinese thought in general.

Christianity, Dualistic tendencies in

Christian theology is dualistic insofar as it accepts a radical difference between good and evil (though it rejects a metaphysical duality). This dualism is permissive, in the sense that the devil is a creature of God and not an independent power. It is also dualistic in its concept of human beings; body is clearly distinguished from soul, and the latter is conceived to be destined for an existence quite independent of the former. In addition Christianity is dualistic in a soteriological sense; it posits a God who is separate from his creation, and especially human beings, and who has certain self-conscious purposes in regard to salvation which he is working out on the human race. Lastly there are those divisions, common to most advanced religions, between religious and social life (the Church and the world), and, of course, that between faith and knowledge.

Complementarity Principle

A principle of modern physics first enunciated by Bohr in the 1920s. It states that it is impossible to describe quantum-mechanical phenomena in as complete a manner as was assumed in classical deterministic physics. Essentially this is because the pairs of Conjugate Variables (q.v.) that must be known for an exact description in the latter are mutually exclusive in the former.

Conjugate Variables

In physics, these are pairs of variables that describe the behaviour of a quantum-mechanical system, either of which, but not both together, may be specified at precisely the same time. The most important of these comprise the position and momentum of a particle. See Complementarity, Indeterminacy.

Descartes

The classical exponent of dualism in the western philosophical tradition. In his view the created world is composed of two quite distinct kinds of substance: mind (*res cognitas*), and matter (*res extensa*); both are the creation of God who continuously exerts his will through each of them. His was a mechanistic philosophy which tended to view the world as an infinitely complex machine that operated in accordance with God's (fixed) laws. The major difficulty in Cartesian metaphysics is to explain how the mental and physical worlds might be related; Descartes' own suggestion was that they met in the pineal gland.

Dialectical Dualism

An eternal dialectic or tension between two opposed principles such as mind and matter (Descartes), love and hate (Empedocles), or, in Indian culture, *maya* (the illusory world of sense-experience) and *atman-brahman* (the essential identity of mind and ultimate reality).

Dualism

In very broad terms dualism represents the assumption of two formative principles, as distinct from both Monism and Monotheism (qq.v.), which assume one. In fact as a general statement the term admits of a considerable latitude in its interpretation. See below.

Dualism, Philosophical

The name given to any metaphysical theory that regards everything that is, material or immaterial, as having two aspects. Such a theory may belong to one or other of two general types: either that there are only two things, i.e. only two genuine substances however many 'things' there appear to be; or that, regardless of their ultimate number all existing things fall into one of two possible categories, such as mind and matter, or that they derive from two principles such as light and darkness. However, dualistic doctrines may easily be compatible with any form of monism that sees the opposition between the one and the many as absolute and which regard the multiplicity of phenomena as merely a fragmentation of the One.

Dualism, Religious

The distinction between monotheistic, dualistic and polytheistic religions is not always clear since both monotheisms and polytheisms may have dualistic aspects. In general however dualism may be characterised as either absolute or relative. In an absolute, or radical, dualism the two principles are held to exist from eternity (e.g. Manichaeism, Zoroastrianism – qq.v.); whereas in a relative, or mitigated, dualism one of the two principles may be derived from, or presuppose, the other (e.g. Cathars, Gnosticism – qq.v.). All religious dualisms, whether or not their two principles are co-eternal, have an ontological function; that is to say that these systems offer an account of opposed principles in being. Where the concept of a single creator figure is absent a dualistisc religion will also have a cosmogonic function, i.e. the interaction between the two principles will account for the origin and continuity of the universe. See also Dialectical, and Eschatological Dualism.

Eschatalogical Dualism

Concerned with the resolution of a perceived dualistic state of affairs in which, typically, evil will be eliminated at the end of history. Gnosticism, Manichaeism and Zoroastrianism (qq.v.) are of this kind.

Gnosticism

A body of thought that was actually pre-Christian in origin, but which became the basis of various heretical movements in the early Christian centuries. Gnosticism was syncretic, drawing on Buddhism and Zoroastrianism (qq.v.), with accretions from Judaism and Mithraism, the Greek philosophies of Stoicism and neo-platonism and the mythologies of Babylon and Egypt. Gnostics believed that the world was created not by the highest God, but rather by a subordinate power or *demiurge*. In their outlook they were greatly influenced by Persian dualism, which envisaged a continuous war between good and evil, spirit and matter; this concept was reinforced by Buddhist ideas that goodness might only be found through dissociation from the carnal world. The Gnostic stream of thought persisted as a heretical Christian dualist movement through Manichaeism (qq.v.), the Bogomils, the Paulicians and the Cathars (qq.v.), i.e. right up to the late Middle Ages. It also exerted a profound influence on Islamic thought, chiefly through the more mystically–inclined doctrines of Sufism.

Heraclitian Monism

Heraclitus was an early Greek philosopher who laid out his theories in a deeply prophetic style around 500 BC Highly individual and reclusive, his originality as a metaphysician lies in his conclusion that what is fundamental is not a substance of any kind, but a process. Despite his emphasis on the primacy of change, Heraclitus is a monist. 'All is one, the divided and the undivided, the begotten and the unbegotten, the mortal and the immortal, reason and eternity, father and son, God and justice'; 'Upward and downward are the same, the beginning and end are one', etc.

Indeterminacy (or Uncertainty) Principle

A principle of modern physics, first enunciated by Heisenberg in the 1920s, which states that no measurement can determine both the position of a particle and its momentum (or any other pair of Conjugate Variables [q.v.] such as time and energy) so accurately that the product of their errors is less than Planck's constant.

Islam

Islam considers itself to be the primordial religion because it is based on the doctrine of the transcendent unity of being. Dualism or duality, in this context, means the abolition of the very idea of God; by extension the created world, and matter itself, is not evil as it was to the Manichaeans and neo-Platonists.

Islamic Monism (*Tawhid*)

The basis of all the articles of belief in Islam. This monism however is subject to a wide degree of interpretation, from the simple assertion that Allah is the only being with a real or absolute existence, to more pantheistic notions that 'Allah is all'. On the other hand the concept of 'association', the worshipping of a 'companion' of Allah (i.e. polytheism) is anathema to all Muslims. See Monads.

Kind and Substance, Theories of

It is important when dealing with the terms monism and pluralism to distinguish between their intention as being theories either of *substance* or of *kinds*. The first of these concerns the question of the number of things in the world; the second the number of kinds of things in the world. It can be misleading to compound these two criteria and assert, for instance, that 'monism attempts to explain the universe from a single principle'; a philosopher can be a pluralist of one sort and a monist of another.

Mani and Manichaeism

Mani was born in 216 AD and he taught and was crucified within the realm of Zoroastrian Persia, but he was regarded by his contemporaries as the most important of heterodox Christians. His system blended later Zoroastrian beliefs in the eternal opposing duality of light and darkness with the Gnostic myth of a corrupted creation. However Mani always referred to himself as the Apostle of Jesus Christ. Within a century of his martyrdom Manichaean churches were established from Turkestan to Carthage and despite persecution the movement flourished up to the tenth century.

Mass-Energy Equivalence

This is the famous concept expressed by Einstein in the relation $E=mc^2$, where E is the energy, m the mass, and c the speed of light. This follows from relativity theory and has been strikingly illustrated by the release of energy in nuclear fission.

Mazdakism

Persian dualistic religion that rose to prominence in the late 5th century. Although no Mazdakite books survive it seems likely that this was a reform movement, placing an optimistic interpretation on Manichaean dualism. According to Mazdak doctrines there exist two original principles, good (or light) and evil (or darkness). Light acts by free will and design, Darkness blindly and by chance. By accident the two became mixed, producing the world.

Monads

The term used by Leibnitz to designate the ultimate elements in his metaphysical system. Monads, unlike atoms, were conceived of as non-spatial, qualitative entities within whose diverse content the whole universe is mirrored. The theory is pluralistic in that it assumes a multiplicity of ultimate elements. A somewhat similar metaphysical system, the so-called Ashirite monads, was adopted by Islam as the basis of their doctrine concerning the nature of the relationship between Allah and the world; however the Islamic perception of monads extends to include the notion of time. Time is granular, consisting of a series of time-atoms in the void.

Monism

A speculative theory of the universe which attempts to reduce it, with all its apparent diversity, to the unity of a single principle. In the face of the fundamental dualism of matter and mind however the monist must either make his ultimate principle material, in which case his monism becomes a version of idealism, or assert an ultimate principle in which the two sides are in equipoise. Materialistic monism found its most extreme and rigorous exponent in Parmenides (q.v.); in later Greek philosophy this form of monism found a more elaborate expression in the metaphysical speculations of the Stoics. Among modern classical philosophers Spinoza best represents that monism which preserves matter and mind in equipoise, as aspects of a single substance. See Kind and Substance, Theories of.

Monotheism

The doctrine that there is but one God. Although monotheism is not necessarily antagonistic to philosophical dualism it is necessarily at odds with every form of religious dualism or polytheism. Of the major world religions only Judaism, Christianity and Islam are, strictly speaking, monotheistic.

Neo-Platonism, Duality in

The aim of this school, which was founded in the third century BC by Plotinus, was to give expression to the supreme unity, the source of all existence and knowledge. To do this Plotinus raised the unity above that of Plato's 'ideal of the good', with the consequence that it became inaccessible to knowledge, i.e. the source cannot be identified without losing its self-contained unity. Matter is evil, but it is also illusory, a sort of overflow of the divine goodness. Neo-Platonism continued during the fourth and fifth centuries and was a powerful influence on Christian theology. See Platonic Dualism.

Neo-Pythagorism, Duality in

This was a school principally associated with the figure of Appollonius of Tyana (first century AD), according to whom God was wholly spiritual, while matter was the source of evil, from the contamination of which people must free themselves by ascetic practices.

Non-Dualism

A term generally applied to the monism of classical Brahmanism (particularly that of the Vedanta), and of later Buddhism. This is a transcendental monism however which is far removed from the monism of the western philosophical tradition. See Brahmanism, Buddhism.

Pantheism

A theory of the universe which identifies God with the totality of existence; however, whilst it is easy to state a broad contrast between pantheism and monotheism it is virtually impossible to determine a precise dividing line between them, since pantheism can be seen simply as an emphatic expression of monism. Among the Greek philosophies pantheism is most clearly exhibited in later Stoicism; it is the basis of Ibn-Arabi's mystical system, as it is of Spinoza's.

Parmenides

The founder of the Eleatic school of philosophy and generally recognised as the first logician. In his view only the world as a whole ('being') exists in its own right. 'Being' does not change, it is beyond time, never came into existence and will never pass away; change and motion are illusions of the senses. His conclusions are demonstrated in their most extreme form in the paradoxes of Zeno (q.v.).

Permanence and Change, The metaphysical problem of

See Heraclitus, Parmenides.

Persian Dualisms

See Mani and Manichaeism, Mazdakism, Zoroastrianism, Zurvanism.

Physics, Dualisms in

Two dualisms had to be overcome to arrive at the modern view of matter; one was the dualism of mass/energy, and the other of the wave/particle. The first of these was resolved as a consequence of relativity theory, the second as a result of quantum theory. See Complementarity Prinicple, Conjugate Variables, Indeterminacy Principle, Mass-Energy Equivalence.

Platonic Dualism

In the western religio-philosophic tradition the concept of a spirit or soul as being consistently immaterial goes back to Plato. Plato regarded ideas alone as being truly existent, but had difficulty in explaining the world of phenomena without introducing a second principle of non-being or 'necessity'. This so-called Platonic matter is the basis of phenomenal existence and the explanation of all its imperfections and evils. In Neo-Platonism (q.v.) the notion of 'emanation' is used to bridge the gap between matter and the supra-essential deity, a concept that carried Platonic dualism through to the Christian consciousness and which reinforced its tendency towards asceticism and other-worldliness.

Theodicy

A theory which attempts to reconcile the imperfections of the material world, which manifests both physical and moral evil, with the justice, reason and other attributes of God.

Yin-Yang

In Chinese thought, the two primogenial elements from which the universe evolved and which, through their continuing interaction, sustain the world of being. These 'two powers of nature' are conceived to be complementary and interdependent, and although they are held to represent such polarities as male/female, light/dark, positive/negative etc. are never seen as 'good' or 'bad', or as opposing principles in the Manichaean sense.

Zeno

The disciple of Parmenides (q.v.) who developed his master's theories with a series of arguments, in the form of paradoxes, against plurality and motion, e.g. that concerning the size of a world of many things which, he argues, must be both infinitely large and infinitely small: infinitely large because it consists of an infinite number of parts that occupy space; infinitely small since its ultimate components must be indivisible and thus without size.

Zoroastrianism

The ancient religion of Persia, which contained both monotheistic and dualistic features. On the one hand Zoroaster's teachings centre on *Ahura Mazda*, who alone is regarded as being worthy of worship, but this monotheistic aspect is modified by an ethical dualism; the Wise Lord has an opponent, *Ahriman*, who embodies the principle of evil. This dualism is Eschatological (q.v.) in that it is believed that *Ahura Mazda* will finally vanquish the spirit of evil, but it has to be said that in later Zoroastrianism the dichotomy between the light and the dark is more highly emphasised. Zoroastrianism undoubtedly influenced each of the major monotheisms of Judaism, Christianity and Islam.

Zurvanism

A modified form of Zoroastrianism that appeared in Persia in the third to seventh centuries AD. It was opposed to orthodox Zoroastrianism, which by that time had become thoroughly dualistic in its doctrines. Fatalistic and pessimistic, the Zurvanists held that every terrestial phenomenon has its counterpart in some celestial, transcendent and invisible phenomenon. They also believed that time alone, limitless, eternal and uncreated, was the source of all things.

Select Bibliography

The sources that I've drawn on in producing this book are so many and varied that a complete list of them would be as tedious a task to plough through as it would be to compile — even if, by now, I could remember them all. I have therefore limited this bibliography to the more useful and readable sources in each of the various categories touched on in the book.

Brain Asymmetry
Beaton, A. *Left Side, Right Side* (Batsford, London, 1985)
Gazzaniga, M.S. *The Split Brain in Man* (Scientific American, August 1967)
Kimura, D. *The Asymmetry of the Human Brain* (Scientific American, March 1973)
Springer, S.P. and Deutsh, D. *Left Brain, Right Brain* (Freeman, New York, 1981)

Chaos Theory
Crutchfield, J.P. and others *Chaos* (Scientific American, December 1986)
Gleik, J. *Chaos: Making a New Science* (Viking, New York, 1987)
Mandelbrot, B. *The Fractal Geometry of Nature* (Freeman, New York, 1977)

Chinese Art
Cahill, J. *Chinese Painting* (Skira, Lausanne, 1960)
Lin Yutang *The Chinese Theory of Art* (Panther, London, 1969)
Vandier-Nicolas, N. *Chinese Painting: An expression of a Civil*isation (Lund Humphries, London, 1969)

Chinese Thought
Fung Yu-Lan *A Short History of Chinese Philosophy* (Macmillan, New York, 1958)
Giles, H.A. (trans.) *Chuang Tzu* (George Allen & Unwin, London, 1961)
Hughes, E.R. *Chinese Philosophy in Classical Times* (Everyman, London, 1942)
Needham, J. *Science and Civilisation in China* (Cambridge University Press, Cambridge, 1956)
Waley, A. *The Way and its Power* (George Allen & Unwin, London, 1934)
Waley, A. *Three Ways in thought in Ancient China* (George Allen & Unwin, London, 1939)

Contemporary Cosmology
Hawking, S. *A Brief History of Time* (Bantam, London, 1988)
Horgan, J. *Universal Truths* (Scientific American, October 1990)
Novikov, I. *Black Holes and the Universe* (Cambridge University Press, Cambridge, 1990)
Pagels, H.R. *The Cosmic Code* (Penguin, London, 1982)
Schramm, D.N. and Steigman, G. *Particle Accelorators Test Cosmological Theory* (Scientific American, June 1988)
Silk, J. *The Big Bang* (Freeman, New York, 1980)
Weinberg, S. *The First Three Minutes* (Basic Books, New York, 1977)

Cosmology, History of
Koestler, A. *The Sleepwalkers* (Penguin, London, 1964)

Crystallography
Bragg, Sir W.L. and others *The Crystalline State* (Bell, London, 1933)
Burke, J.G. *Origins of the Science of Crystals* (U.C.L.A., Berkeley, 1966)
Burke, J.G. *Snowflakes and the Constitution of Crystalline Matter* (U.C.L.A., Berkeley, 1967)
Phillips, F.C. *An Introduction to Crystallography* (Longmans Green, London, 1963)

Dualistic Heresies
Moore, R.I. *The Origins of European Dissent* (Blackwells, London, 1977)
Runciman, Sir S. *The Medieval Manichee* (Cambridge University Press, Cambridge, 1947)

Greek Thought
Barnes, J. *Early Greek Philosophy* (Penguin Classics, London, 1987)
Barnes, J. *The Presocratic Philosophers* (London, 1982)
Burnet, J. *Early Greek Philosophy* (Adam & Charles Black, London, 1930)
Gorman, P. *Pythagoras, a Life* (Routledge & Kegan Paul, London, 1979)
Plato *The Laws, The Republic, Timaeus and Critias* (Penguin Classics)

Islamic Art
Burkhardt, T. *The Art of Islam* (World of Islam Festival Publishing, London, 1976)
Grabar, O. *The Formation of Islamic Art* (Yale University Press, New Haven & London, 1973)
Kuhnel, E. *The Arabesque* (Sammler, Graz, 1976)
Lings, M. *The Quranic Art of Calligraphy and Illumination* (World of Islam Festival Publishing, London, 1976)

Islamic Thought
Christopher, J.B. *The Islamic Tradition* (Harper & Row, New York & London, 1972)
Nasr, S.H. *Ideals and Realities of Islam* (George Allen & Unwin, London, 1966)
O'Leary, D. *How Greek Science passed to the Arabs* (Routledge & Kegan Paul, London, 1949)
Rosenthal, F. *The Classical Heritage in Islam* (University of California Press, Berkely, 1975)
Watt, W.M. *Islamic Philosophy and Theology* (Edinburgh University Press, Edinburgh, 1962)

Primitive Art
Boaz, F. *Primitive Art* (Dover Books, New York, 1955)
Campbell, J. *The Way of the Animal Powers* (Times Books, London, 1984)
Lommel, A. *Prehistoric and Primitive Man* (Paul Hamlyn, London, 1966)

Symmetry
Hargittan, I.(ed.) *Symmetry: Unifying Human Understanding* (Pergamon, New York, 1986)
Lockwood, E.H. and Macmillan, R.H. *Geometric Symmetry* (Cambridge University Press, 1978)
Washburn, D.K. and Crowe, D.W. *Symmetries of Culture* (University of Washington Press, Washington, 1988)

Index